SCIENCE ANNUAL

A Modern Science Anthology for the Family

2008

Published 2007 by World Almanac Education Group, Inc.

Funk & Wagnalls and F&W are registered trademarks of World Almanac Education Group, Inc.

This annual is also published under the title *The 2008 World Book Science Year* © 2007 World Book, Inc.

Library of Congress Control Number: 65-21776
ISBN–13: 978-0-8343-5301-5
ISBN–10: 0-8343-5301-6

Printed in the United States of America.

STAFF

EDITORIAL

Editor in Chief
Paul A. Kobasa

Associate Director, Supplementary Publications
Scott Thomas

Managing Editor, Supplementary Publications
Barbara A. Mayes

Senior Editor
Kristina A. Vaicikonis

Senior Researcher
Cheryl Graham

Editorial Assistant
Ethel Matthews

Indexing Services
David Pofelski, Manager
Aamir Burki, Associate
Manager

Permissions Editor
Janet Peterson

GRAPHIC DESIGN

Associate Director
Sandra M. Dyrlund

Associate Manager, Design
Brenda B. Tropinski

Associate Manager, Photography
Tom Evans

PRODUCTION

Director, Manufacturing and Pre-Press
Carma Fazio

Manufacturing Manager
Barbara Podczerwinski

Production Manager
Anne Fritzinger

MARKETING

Vice President
Patti Ginnis

Director, Direct Marketing
Mark R. Willy

Marketing Analyst
Zofia Kulik

CREATIVE MEDIA APPLICATIONS, INC.

Dan Oehlsen,
Lary Rosenblatt,
& Barbara Stewart

EDITORIAL

Managing Editor
Melissa White-Fournier

Editors
Matt Levine
Susan Madoff

Copyeditor
Laurie Lieb

Proofreader
Barbara Allen

GRAPHIC DESIGN

Senior Designers
Alan Barnett
Fabia Wargin

Production
Alicia Fox
Luis Leon
George Ramirez

Asker, James R., B.A.
Managing Editor, *Aviation Week & Space Technology* magazine. [*Astronomy* (Close-Up)]

Barker, David, B.S., M.S., Ph.D.
Project Manager, Publishers Resource Group. [*Conservation*]

Bernick, Jeanne, B.S.
Crops and Issues Editor, *Farm Journal Media.* [*Agriculture*]

Brett, Carlton E., M.S., Ph.D.
Professor, Department of Geology, University of Cincinnati. [*Fossil Studies*]

Chiras, Daniel, B.A., Ph.D.
Visiting Professor, Colorado College at Colorado Springs. [*Environmental Pollution*]

Cooper, Ilene, B.J., M.L.S.
Children's Books Editor, *Booklist.* [*Books About Science for Younger Readers*]

Clynes, Tom, B.A.
Free-Lance Science Writer. [**Science Studies,** *Renewable Energy; Energy*]

Despres, Renée, Ph.D.
Free-Lance Writer. [*Medical Research*]

Graff, Gordon, B.S., M.S., Ph.D.
Free-Lance Science Writer. [*Chemistry*]

Hay, William W., B.S., M.S., Ph.D.
Professor Emeritus, Geological Sciences, University of Colorado at Boulder. [*Geology*]

Haymer, David S., M.S., Ph.D.
Professor, Department of Cell and Molecular Biology, John A. Burns School of Medicine, University of Hawaii at Manoa. [*Genetics*]

Hester, Thomas R., B.A., Ph.D.
Professor Emeritus of Anthropology, University of Texas at Austin. [**Consultant—Special Report,** *The Ancient Maya: Deciphering New Clues; Archaeology*]

Johnson, Christina S., B.A., M.S.
Science Writer, California Sea Grant College Program, Scripps Institution of Oceanography. [*Oceanography*]

Johnson, John, Jr.
Science Writer, *Los Angeles Times.* [**Special Report,** *A Cosmic Assignment*]

Klein, Catherine J., Ph.D., R.D.
Senior Staff Scientist, Life Sciences Research Office. [**Consumer Science,** *Low-Calorie Alternatives for a Sweet Tooth; Nutrition*]

Knight, Robert, B.A., M.M.
Free-Lance Writer. [*Drugs*]

Konrad, Rachel, B.A.
Silicon Valley Correspondent, The Associated Press. [*Computers and Electronics*]

Kowal, Deborah, M.A., P.A.
Adjunct Assistant Professor, Emory University Rollins School of Public Health. [**Consumer Science,** *Antibacterial Cleansers; Public Health*]

Kris-Etherton, Penny K., Ph.D.
Professor of Nutritional Sciences, Pennsylvania State University. [**Consultant—Consumer Science,** *Chocolate*]

Lowenstern, Jacob B., A.B., M.S., Ph.D.
Research Ecologist, United States Geological Survey. [**Consultant—Special Report,** *Yellowstone*]

Lunine, Jonathan I., B.S., M.S., Ph.D.
Professor of Planetary Science and Physics, University of Arizona Lunar and Planetary Laboratory. [*Astronomy*]

March, Robert H., A.B., M.S., Ph.D.
Professor Emeritus of Physics and Liberal Studies, University of Wisconsin at Madison. [**Consultant—Special Report,** *A Cosmic Assignment; Physics*]

Marschall, Laurence A., B.S., Ph.D.
Professor of Physics, Gettysburg College. [*Books About Science*]

McDowell, Mindi, B.A., M.A.
Free-Lance Writer. [**Consumer Science,** *Voice over Internet Protocol*]

Milius, Susan, B.A.
Life Sciences Writer, *Science News.* [*Biology*]

Milo, Richard G., B.A., M.A., Ph.D.
Associate Professor of Anthropology, Chicago State University. [*Anthropology*]

Morring, Frank, Jr., B.A.
Senior Space Technology Editor, *Aviation Week & Space Technology.* [*Space Technology*]

Peres, Judy, B.A., M.S.L.
Specialist Reporter, *Chicago Tribune.* [**Special Report,** *Polio*]

Pielke, Roger, Jr., B.A., M.A., Ph.D.
Director, Center for Science and Technology Policy Research, University of Colorado at Boulder. [*Atmospheric Science* (Close-Up)]

Popson, Colleen, B.A., M.A.
Free-Lance Writer. [**Special Report,** *The Ancient Maya: Deciphering New Clues*]

Ratnieks, Francis L. W., B.Sc., M.Sc., Ph.D.
Professor of Apiculture, Department of Animal and Plant Sciences, University of Sheffield, U.K. [**Special Report,** *The Latest Buzz About Honey Bees*]

Smuskiewicz, Alfred J., B.S., M.S. Free-Lance Writer. [*Archaeology* (**Close-Up**); *Physics* (**Close-Up**)]

Snow, John T., B.S.E.E., M.S.E.E., Ph.D.
Dean, College of Geosciences, Professor of Meteorology, University of Oklahoma. [*Atmospheric Science*]

Snow, Theodore P., B.A., M.S., Ph.D.
Professor of Astrophysics, University of Colorado at Boulder. [*Astronomy*]

Tamarin, Robert H., B.S., Ph.D.
Dean of Sciences, University of Massachusetts Lowell. [**Special Report,** *Paradise Found; Ecology*]

Teich, Albert H., B.S., Ph.D.
Director, Science and Policy Programs, American Association for the Advancement of Science. [*Science and Society*]

Tsai, Irene, B.S., M.S., Ph.D.
Free-Lance Writer. [*Engineering*]

White-Fournier, Melissa
Free-Lance Writer. [*Consumer Science, Chocolate*]

WORLD BOOK ADVISERS

Mary Alice Anderson, B.S., M.A.
Lead Media Specialist, Winona Area Public Schools, Winona, Minnesota, United States

Ali Banuazizi, B.S., M.A., Ph.D.
Professor of Political Science and Codirector of Middle Eastern & Islamic Studies Program, Boston College, Chestnut Hill, Massachusetts, United States

David J. Bercuson, O.C., B.A., M.A., Ph.D. Professor of History and Director, Centre for Military and Strategic Studies, University of Calgary, Calgary, Alberta, Canada

Marianna Anderson Busch, B.A., Ph.D. Professor, Department of Chemistry and Biochemistry, Baylor University, Waco, Texas, United States

Anne Innis Dagg, B.A., M.A., Ph.D. Academic Adviser, Independent Studies, University of Waterloo, Waterloo, Ontario, Canada

Jesus Garcia, M.A., Ed.D. Professor of Curriculum and Instruction, University of Nevada, Las Vegas, Las Vegas, Nevada, United States

Marc B. Garnick, M.D. Professor of Medicine, Harvard Medical School, Harvard University; Physician, Beth Israel Deaconess Medical Center, Boston, Massachusetts, United States

Michael F. Graves, B.A., M.A., Ph.D. Professor Emeritus of Literacy Education, University of Minnesota, Twin Cities Campus, Minneapolis, Minnesota, United States

John T. Greene, B.A., M.A., Ph.D. Professor Emeritus of Religious Studies, Michigan State University, East Lansing, Michigan, United States

Alan E. Mann, B.A., M.A., Ph.D. Professor of Anthropology, Princeton University, Princeton, New Jersey, United States

Adrian Mitchell, B.A., M.A., Ph.D. Director, Postgraduate Programs, Faculty of Arts, University of Sydney, Sydney, New South Wales, Australia

Jay M. Pasachoff, A.B., A.M., Ph.D. Field Memorial Professor of Astronomy and Director, Hopkins Observatory of Williams College, Williamstown, Massachusetts, United States

Michael Plante, B.A., M.A., Ph.D. Jessie J. Poesch Professor of Art History, Newcomb Art Department, Tulane University, New Orleans, Louisiana, United States

Robert B. Prigo, B.S., M.S., Ph.D. Director of Teacher Education and Professor of Physics, Middlebury College, Middlebury, Vermont, United States

Michael Seidel, B.A., M.A., Ph.D. Jesse and George Siegel Professor of Humanities, Columbia University, New York City, New York, United States

Whitney Smith, A.B., A.M., Ph.D. Director, The Flag Research Center, Winchester, Massachusetts, United States

Ivan Soll, A.B., Ph.D. Professor of Philosophy, University of Wisconsin-Madison, Madison, Wisconsin, United States

Scott L. Waugh, B.A., Ph.D. Executive Vice Chancellor and Provost, University of California, Los Angeles, United States

5

CONTENTS

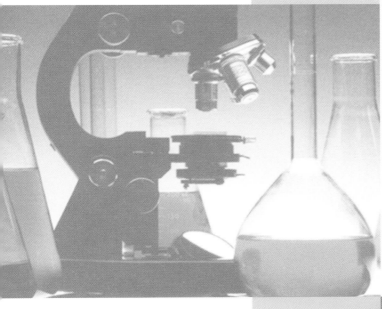

The discovery of the 3.5-million-year-old remains of a child and the establishment of the world's largest marine reserve were among the developments that made the year eventful in science and technology. These two pages present highlights of the stories chosen by the editors of *Science Year* as the most memorable or important of the year, along with page references for the complete articles.

POLIO BATTLE RAGES ON

The poliovirus continues to evade attempts to eradicate it, despite the efforts of the Global Polio Eradication Initiative to achieve a world free of poliovirus by 2008. Nevertheless, public health officials have made great strides in reducing the number of cases of the disease. By 2006, polio remained endemic in only four countries. In the Special Reports section, see **POLIO: FIGHTING A PERSISTENT FOE**, page 86.

SECRETS LOCKED IN MARTIAN POLES

New findings about the amount of water locked in an ice cap at the Martian South Pole were revealed in April 2007. Astronomers analyzing data from the European Mars Express Orbiter believe the information is essential to determining how much water may once have flowed on Mars and whether such an amount was sufficient to support life on the Red Planet. In the Science News Update section, see **ASTRONOMY**, page 164.

DNA FOUND IN 38,000-YEAR-OLD BONES

An analysis of DNA from a 38,000-year-old fossilized bone belonging to a Neandertal, reported in November 2006, revealed that Neandertals were a different species than *Homo sapiens*. In the Science News Updates Section, see **GENETICS**, page 217.

HONEY BEE TROUBLES

Researchers mapped the complete honey bee genome in 2006, gaining a deeper understanding of how these sophisticated insects communicate. But a mysterious condition called colony collapse disorder threatened the survival of honey bees, as well as the future of agricultural industries that depend on them. In the Special Reports section, see **THE LATEST BUZZ ABOUT HONEY BEES**, page 42; in the Science News Update section, see **AGRICULTURE**, page 150.

CONSENSUS ON CLIMATE CHANGE

The Intergovernmental Panel on Climate Change released a controversial report in February 2007 that points to human activity as the cause of global warming. The report describes the effects of global climate change on weather patterns and the impact such change will have on society, particularly the world's poorest nations. In the Science News Update section, see **ATMOSPHERIC SCIENCE**, page 170, and the Close-Up **FINDINGS OF THE INTERGOVERNMENTAL PANEL ON CLIMATE CHANGE**, page 173.

NEW PACIFIC PARADISE

In June 2006, United States president George W. Bush declared more than 13,000 square kilometers (5,000 square miles) of coral reefs northwest of Hawaii a national marine reserve. Conservationists consider the Northwestern Hawaiian Islands Marine National Monument, which contains more than 7,000 species, a major step toward protecting the fragile ecological balance in the Pacific Ocean. In the Special Reports section, see **PARADISE FOUND**, page 56.

A LINK TO OUR PAST

The 3.5-million-year-old remains discovered in Ethiopia in 2006 represent the most complete fossilized skeleton ever found of a child who lived so long ago. Anthropologists have learned that the child belonged to the same species as the famous australopithecene known as Lucy, an early human ancestor. In the Science News Update section, see **ANTHROPOLOGY**, page 152.

CANCER PREVENTION FOR WOMEN

A new vaccine designed to keep women from contracting certain types of cervical cancer was approved by the U.S. Food and Drug Administration in June 2006. Calls to make the vaccine mandatory stirred debate throughout the United States. In the Science News Update section, see **DRUGS**, page 200.

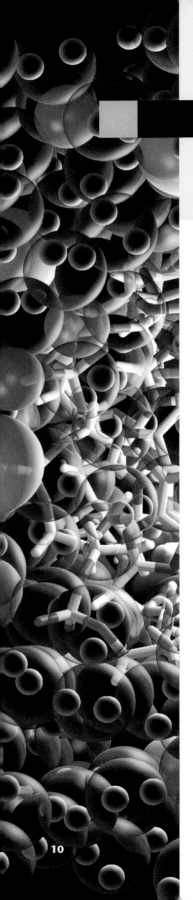

SPECIAL REPORTS

These feature articles take an in-depth look at significant and timely subjects in science and technology.

The Ancient Maya: Deciphering New Clues

By Colleen Popson

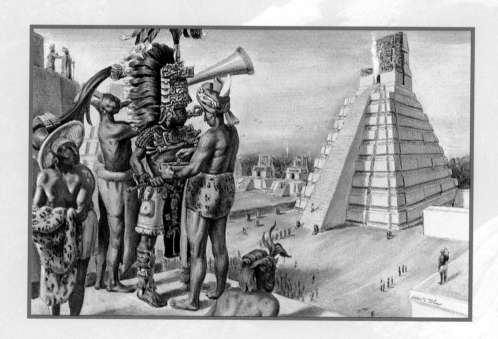

An ancient Maya site sought by archaeologists for more than 40 years; a buried pyramid with a breathtaking mural and a stone block with intriguing writing; details of a deadly struggle between two Maya superpowers unveiled by a hurricane; hints that women may have played a greater role in Maya politics than previously thought; the role of warfare in the collapse of the Maya; these are among the discoveries that in 2007 had archaeologists rethinking long-held beliefs about a people who created a magnificent civilization in what are now southeastern Mexico and Central America. These findings are also filling in missing chapters in Maya history, giving archaeologists a new, more complex understanding of these sophisticated, resourceful, and innovative people.

The author:
Colleen Popson, a freelance writer, has been associate editor and Washington correspondent at *Archaeology* magazine.

Traditionally, ancient Maya history is divided into three periods: the Preclassic Period (2000 B.C. to A.D. 250), Classic Period (250 to 900), and Postclassic Period (900 to the mid-1500's). During the late Preclassic Period, farmers lived in small villages and gathered food from surrounding forests to supplement their harvest. The Maya built their first large ceremonial centers (large pyramids) between 600 and 400 B.C. Between 400 B.C. and A.D. 250, several large Maya settlements dotted the lowlands.

The Classic Period is considered the height of the ancient Maya civilization. During this period, the Maya founded their greatest cities and made remarkable achievements in the arts and sciences. Among these developments were one of the first advanced forms of writing in the Western Hemisphere, two complicated and highly accurate calendars, and a mathematical system that included the concept of zero—a concept unknown to Europeans until the 1400's. During the Classic Period, the Maya also perfected the practice of erecting *stelae,* large stone slabs or monuments carved to record important dates and significant events or ceremonies in the lives of the Maya rulers and their families.

During the Postclassic Period, the Maya abandoned some of their cities in the lowlands of Honduras, Mexico, Belize, and northern Guatemala—now the *department* (state) of El Petén. This had been the heart of ancient Maya civilization during the Classic Period. Some Maya moved north to build new cities in the lowlands of northern Yucatán, in what is now Mexico, while others moved to the southern Guatemalan highlands. Important changes took place in Maya political and economic systems during the Postclassic Period. For example, sea trade became much more common, resulting in prosperity for Maya coastal cities.

Archaeologists have been fascinated by the ancient Maya ever since discovering their ruined cities in the mid-1800's. During the first several decades of Maya archaeology, scientists focused on exploration and discovery, showering attention on sites with major architecture and monuments. In the first half of the 1900's, many of the important cities of the Classic Period in Guatemala, Mexico, Belize, and Honduras were thoroughly explored. These cities were dominated by large, impressive architecture, particularly pyramids and temples set atop high mounds. Excavations of tombs within the cities' temples and palaces revealed stunning jade jewelry, intricately painted ceramic vessels, offerings of food and drink, and large objects made of *obsidian* (dark, glassy rock) and *flint* (hard, gray or brown, grainy rock) that had been chipped and carved into abstract or symbolic shapes sometimes resembling kings or *deities* (gods and goddesses). Such symbols largely reflected the lives and activities of the

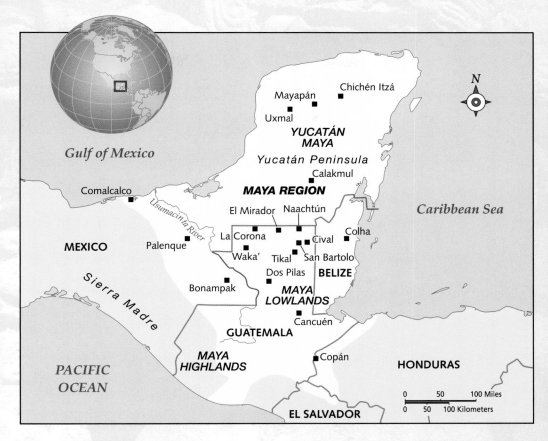

The areas in North America and Central America inhabited by the ancient Maya included present-day Belize and parts of Mexico, Guatemala, Honduras, and El Salvador.

ruling classes and gave little attention to less elite populations or those in rural areas away from the ceremonial centers.

In the 1960's and 1970's, *Mayanists* (archaeologists who study the ancient Maya) began to take a broader view of Maya society. At Tikal, almost the entire settlement was mapped, well beyond the central pyramids and temples. At Barton Ramie (Belize), archaeologists excavated rural settlements, paying particular attention to the kinds of *artifacts* (anything made by human skill or work, especially a tool or weapon) used in farming. By the late 1980's and into the early 2000's, archaeologists focused their research on dissecting the day-to-day life of the ancient Maya and how their civilization worked. These scientists also continued to study the mysteries that had not been answered in earlier Maya research.

Hunt for a mysterious city

In the mid-1960's, about two dozen carefully carved Maya sculptures appeared on the *antiquities* market, (market for very old objects, often of great value), having been looted and transported illegally to the United States. The site from which they were taken was unknown, but

The ruins of the Maya city of Palenque, located in the Mexican state of Chiapas, continue to provide archaeologists with a wealth of information about Maya culture. A World Heritage Site, Palenque reached its pinnacle during the Late Classic Period (from A.D. 600 to 900).

some scholars suggested it was in Guatemala's El Petén lowlands. It became known as Site Q (*Q* stands for *que*, Spanish for *what*), and its location became a major mystery in Maya studies.

In 1997, a team of archaeologists that included Ian Graham of the Harvard University Peabody Museum in Cambridge, Massachusetts, and David Stuart, now at the University of Texas at Austin, explored a cluster of ruins in Guatemala called La Corona. There they found an inscription that mentioned a king named Chak Kutz (Red Turkey). This same ruler was also mentioned in an inscription on a Site Q object from A.D. 690 that had been purchased on the antiquities market in 1965. The finding suggested that La Corona was Site Q. However, Maya kings from one site often appear in inscriptions at other sites, so doubts remained.

In 2005, scientists from Yale University in New Haven, Connecticut, and Southern Methodist University (SMU) in Dallas followed up on Graham's work at La Corona. On their last day of exploration, while exploring a looter's tunnel, Yale anthropologist Marcello A. Canuto found a small chamber with a stone panel of *hieroglyphs* (picture writing).

About 140 hieroglyphs on the stone panel record a date in A.D. 677 for the founding of a shrine dedicated to the god K'uhul Winik Ub'. The carving matched—in style, subject, and time period—inscriptions from the Site Q artifacts, thus proving that La Corona was Site Q.

The not-so-dark ages

Recent discoveries at the site of San Bartolo in Guatemala provide evidence that some regions of the ancient Maya civilization developed much earlier than archaeologists had believed. San Bartolo is located in the northeast corner of Guatemala, north of the well-known Maya site of Tikal. Archaeologist William Saturno of the University of New Hampshire in Durham has recorded at least 100 structures, including a ball court (a feature typical of many Maya and other Mesoamerican sites) and a palace. Dominating the site is a large central plaza with several temple-pyramids, the tallest rising 30 meters (100 feet). The site appears to have been occupied from about 800 B.C. (Middle Preclassic) through the Late Preclassic Period (about 400 B.C. to A.D. 250). One of the site's most important structures, the Las Pinturas temple-pyramid, was constructed during this time. The building consists of a series of layers or overlying structures—a new structure built over the previous one—a style typical of Maya pyramids.

A stone panel of carvings and hieroglyphs tells the story of the Maya king, Taj Chan Ahk, appointing an official to take charge of one of the king's city states. The panel was discovered inside a Cancuen palace in northern Guatemala in 2004 by Arthur A. Demarest and his team of archaeologists from Vanderbilt University.

Visitors to the National Anthropology Museum of Mexico in Mexico City study a Maya stone carving that was found in the Pyramid of the Moon, ruins built by the Teotihuacán culture near present-day Mexico City. The discovery of such a major Maya artifact in a Teotihuacán structure suggests cross-cultural exchange between the two civilizations.

Among the ruins at San Bartolo were panels containing intricate glyphs. What made these glyphs unique when compared with Classic ruins found at sites such as Tikal and Palenque (Mexico) was that *radiocarbon dating* of organic material associated with these glyphs dated them to the Preclassic. (Radiocarbon dating is a method of determining the age of ancient objects.)

San Bartolo is not the only site to indicate that the Preclassic Period of Maya history was quite sophisticated. Evidence from huge centers within Guatemala, like Nakbe and El Mirador, shows that the Maya were highly organized from an early date. The architectural

An artist's reproduction of the mural at San Bartolo depicts a figure that may represent the Maya corn god performing a ritual, flanked by kneeling worshipers. The discovery of the ancient mural in Guatemala was made by William Saturno now at the University of New Hampshire. Saturno and a team of archaeologists associated with the National Geographic Society said they believe the mural is the earliest intact Maya wall painting. Only a section of the mural, about 1.8 meters (6 feet) wide and more than 0.6 meters (2 feet) high—apparently uncovered by looters—is visible. Saturno speculates that the complete mural may be 10 times larger.

Saturno positions a broken piece of the mural (right).

Saturno and his team dated the mural to about A.D. 100 by comparing it with other murals found in nearby Tikal. Saturno discovered the mural while seeking shade in a tunnel dug by looters. The tunnel led to an ancient, ruined pyramid over which a newer pyramid had been built (left). The exposed section of the mural found by Saturno lay in a small chamber filled with rubble. The Maya apparently covered the painting with mud, which helped preserve it.

construction at El Mirador, in particular, is more substantial than anything built subsequently. The premier building, El Tigre, is six times the size of Temple IV at Tikal, which dates from the Classic Period. At Cival, in Guatemala, 2,000-year-old human-sized masks and an intricately carved portrait were found by archaeologist Francisco Estrada-Belli of Vanderbilt University in Nashville in 2004. The Preclassic portrait, showing a Maya king, is the oldest Maya portrait of a king to date. In addition, Preclassic finds have not been limited to artistic works. Even at rural sites, major Maya endeavors were begun during the Late Preclassic. For example, at the site of Colha in northern Belize, locally available flint was used to mass produce stone tools during the Late Preclassic. The Late Preclassic craft specialists also made adzes (axlike tools) and hoes for export. During the Classic period at Colha, workshops were dedicated to the production of weaponry, such as spear points.

Women's work

Before the mid-1990's and the early 2000's, the excavations and exploration of Maya ruins revealed very little about the roles that women played in Maya civilization. The history of women was limited to the documentation of their relationships as wives and mothers of ruling kings. But in 2004, David Lee, a Canadian archaeologist, and an SMU graduate student discovered a royal burial chamber at Waka' (today known as El Perú), 60 kilometers (37 miles) to the west of Tikal in Guatemala. Within the chamber were the remains of a woman, along with a stingray spine in the pelvic region of her skeleton that suggest a type of bloodletting that was reserved for Maya rulers. Maya rulers offered blood to the gods to appease them or gain favor for their city. The evidence of bloodletting suggests that the skeleton is that of a queen who once ruled the ancient Maya. Hieroglyphs depicted on a monument also mention a queen, giving greater credibility to the idea that the Maya were ruled by both men and women.

A year later, in 2005, archaeologists discovered a stela at the site of Naachten, also in Guatemala. The stela is unusual because it depicts women; however, the age of the stela makes it even more significant. This stela, dated to about A.D. 300, is the oldest stone-carved portrait of a Maya woman. It is believed that the woman was a queen or served in another high-ranking position. The scientists at Naachten are also evaluating the idea that perhaps the stela depicts an important deity of Maya mythology.

In 1996, Diane E. Wilson, then a graduate student at the University of Texas at Austin, reported on remains indicating that Maya women may also have performed work that was usually done by men. In 1980, the bones of a woman had been found during an excavation of a house and workshop. Wilson later studied these bones in detail. The skeleton showed notable enlargements in the bones of the arms and hands. Archaeologists have linked this type of enlargement to *flint-knapping* (chipping flint to shape it into tools and weapons)—traditionally, a role held by men. However, based on the evidence of the skeleton found at Colha, it appears that the Maya woman was also a flint-knapper.

Superpower struggles

The Maya area witnessed the rise and fall of a number of major cities, often accompanied by conflict and bloodshed. In the early years of Maya studies, scholars assumed that the Maya centers were empty ceremonial sites headed by peaceful priests and stargazing rulers. As more sites were discovered and studied, however, this view began to change. Only a portion of Maya written history exists because the Spanish destroyed many records during their conquest and occupation of Mesoamerica (from the late 1500's to the 1820's). Nonetheless, from the remaining stelae and *codices* (ancient, handwritten books),

A Maya mural depicts a scene at the royal court at Bonampak, Mexico, where the king (center) is presented with prisoners captured in battle. Defeated rulers and other important prisoners of war were sacrificed to the gods in religious ceremonies. The restored mural was painted toward the end of the Classic Period, around A.D. 790, as rival cities in the Maya civilization began to fight each other.

Archaeologist Arthur Demarest (above left) and ancient-writing specialist Federico Fahsen, both of Vanderbilt University in Nashville, Tennessee, discuss hieroglyphics found on stairs uncovered in 2002 by a hurricane (red) at an ancient Maya site called Dos Pilas in Guatemala. The hieroglyphics tell the often-bloody story of a city caught in the middle of a protracted war between two superpowers, Tikal and Calakmul, in the A.D. 600's. Before the 2002 hurricane, only 8 of the stairway's 10 steps had been found.

extensive, detailed dynastic histories have been pieced together for many Classic Period cities—exposing a world filled with warfare, prisoner capture, sacrifice, and short-lived alliances.

Many archaeologists argued that warfare appeared to be more prevalent than once thought. Defensive structures, such as the ditch and parapet fortification around the site of Becan (Mexico); depictions of captives, the most famous of which are those in the murals at Bonampak; and evidence of the destruction and abandonment of some sites all pointed to a more competitive, hostile culture than was previously imagined.

Conflict was not limited to small-scale fighting. Evidence of the struggle between the superpower cities Tikal (Guatemala) and Calakmul (north of Tikal in Mexico) was revealed on 10 steps of an ancient 18-step stairway in Dos Pilas (south of both cities). In 2002, a hurricane that struck the area, removing debris, revealed 10 more steps on what was originally thought to be an 8-step stairway. Frederico Fahsen, a researcher from Vanderbilt University, deciphered glyphs inscribed on the newly uncovered steps. The steps detail events in the life of Balaj Chan K'awiil, the king of Dos Pilas about 1,500 years ago. The steps also show that Dos Pilas was a pawn used in the power struggle between Tikal and Calakmul. From A.D. 600 to 800, these cities, using battle and marital alliances, vied for rule over smaller kingdoms of the southern and central lowlands.

Initially, Dos Pilas was loyal to Tikal, where Balaj Chan K'awiil's brother ruled. Almost 25 years into his rule, Calakmul attacked and seized Dos Pilas. Balaj Chan K'awiil was captured but was allowed to keep his land and throne with the condition that he would do the bidding of Calakmul. Fulfilling his part of the bargain, Balaj Chan K'awiil launched a 10-year war against Tikal. The war ended with

A mural from Las Pinturas at San Bartolo dates to the Preclassic Period of Maya history (from A.D. 100 to 200). In this portion of the mural, which is 9 meters (30 feet) long, the maize god is crowning himself. Much of Maya art depicts aspects of divine rule.

Dos Pilas as the victor, and Balaj Chan K'awiil's brother was sacrificed along with other Tikal nobles. Continuing its conquests, Dos Pilas became a major regional power under Calakmul. Later, Tikal rose up again and attacked Calakmul. Following this crushing blow, the Maya lowlands broke up into numerous regional rivalries.

Hieroglyphs and monuments found at Caracol in southern Belize indicate similar warring between Caracol and Tikal. Many scholars believe that regional warfare was a catalyst in the collapse of the ancient Maya.

A collapse or cycles of change?

The archaeological record shows that between A.D. 750 and 900, the Maya stopped building in their major cities and ceased carving stone monuments; the population dropped off significantly. But identifying the reasons for this change has been a great challenge for Mayanists. Theories abound, from environmental stress to warfare to drought to disease to internal revolt. Most archaeologists now attribute this change to some combination of events, as was the case in the collapse of other ancient civilizations.

Although warfare, climate, and environmental interaction provide logical reasons for the so-called Maya collapse, do they account for all factors that would explain this phenomenon? There is not just one story that fits Tikal, Copan, Calakmul, and Caracol. Each region experienced the collapse differently, and before assigning a single cause, many scholars are calling for more information, admitting they simply do not know enough.

What archaeologists are really looking at when they study the past is change, and collapse would certainly show up in the archaeological record. In studying any type of cultural change, it is important to understand what came next. We have to define *change* and how it is recognized. After all, scientists know that more than 6 million native Maya speakers still inhabit Mexico and Central America; they represent many different groups with established beliefs and traditions that stretch back to before the Spanish Conquest in the 1500's.

Archaeologists also know that Maya civilization continued to flourish throughout the northern part of the modern Yucatán peninsula for hundreds of years following the so-called collapse of major sites in the southern lowlands. Some major centers, like Lamanai in northern Belize, did not experience a collapse and appears to have prospered in the Late Postclassic and early Historic periods. It is thought that a change of economic organization and focus arose during this period. The appearance of nonnative goods in greater numbers during this period suggests a widespread coastal trading network. Also, distinct cultural influences from Central Mexico and Oaxaca appear in the art and architecture of sites, predominantly in mural painting, ceramic figurines, and incense burners in both Classic and Postclassic times and suggest the trading of goods and culture.

Further, based on periods of abandonment at sites such as Cival (A.D. 100) and El Mirador (A.D. 150), it is apparent that a few major sites of the Preclassic Period may have experienced their own—as yet unexplained—collapse from around A.D. 100 to 200. But even with this period of decline, it is clear that the complexity, the artwork, the political organization, and the religion that have come to define Maya civilization appeared during the early Preclassic Period, earlier than originally thought. A better understanding of this long cultural history is helping scholars put the sequence of Maya civilization in clearer perspective. It was not simply a culture that rose to greatness and then disappeared; rather, it has gone through many phases over some 2,500 years and continues to do so.

Even with recent discoveries, researchers have only scratched the surface. The story of the ancient Maya constitutes a complicated, compelling chapter of human nature, interaction, and development—one that becomes clearer and richer with each satellite photograph analyzed, each sherd of pottery cleaned, and each glyph deciphered.

■ FOR ADDITIONAL INFORMATION

Books and periodicals

Foster, Lynn V. *Handbook to Life in the Ancient Maya World*. Oxford University Press, 2005.

Masson, Marilyn A. and Friedel, David. *Ancient Maya Political Economies*. AltaMira Press, 2002.

Tarpy, Cliff. "Place of the Standing Stones: Unearthing a King from the Dawn of the Maya." *National Geographic* May 2004, 66–79.

Web sites

Mundo Maya Web site— http://www.mayadiscovery.com/ing/

National Geographic Magazine: Descent Into the Maya Underworld Website— http://magma.nationalgeographic.com/ngm/0411/sights_n_sounds/media2.html/

Nova Online Lost King of the Maya Web site— http://www.pbs.org/wgbh/nova/maya/

Science Museum of Minnesota: Maya Adventure Web site— http://www.smm.org/sln/ma/

A COSMIC ASSIGNMENT

By John Johnson, Jr.

Students join
the hunt for
the mysterious
high-energy
cosmic ray.

TERMS AND CONCEPTS

Atmospheric fluorescence: Sparks of faint bluish light in the upper atmosphere given off when cosmic ray particles interact with nitrogen.

Cerenkov radiation: Light emitted when a particle passes through a transparent substance at a speed greater than that at which light moves in that medium.

Cloud chamber: An instrument that makes the paths of cosmic rays and other electrically charged particles visible.

Cosmic rays: Electrically charged, high-energy subatomic particles that travel through space.

Electronvolt: A tiny unit of energy; 50,000 electronvolts are needed to accelerate electrons enough to light up a color TV screen.

Extensive air shower: The avalanche of infinitesimal particles set off by a cosmic ray when it enters Earth's atmosphere.

Muon: A pion that is composed of quarks.

Photon: A unit particle of light.

Pion: A subatomic particle that exists for only a few billionths of a second before decaying into an electron.

Primary: A cosmic ray at high altitude.

Quark: One of a group of particles, each with a charge less than that of an electron, regarded as fundamental constituents of matter.

Supernova: A star that suddenly becomes extremely bright and then gradually fades.

The author:

John Johnson, Jr. is a staff writer who specializes in science for the *Los Angeles Times.*

The solution to one of the scientific world's great mysteries may come not from the winner of a Nobel Prize in the sophisticated laboratory of a great research institution, but from high school students in Los Angeles, Seattle, or Lincoln, Nebraska. In all of these places, and dozens more around North America, students are operating cosmic ray detectors and collecting data. Whether or not they succeed in corralling the next record-breaking particle, the experiments are already providing students with something they rarely get in high school—hands-on scientific experience with consequences.

"Most high school students have a Hollywood idea of science," said R. Jeffrey Wilkes, a physicist from the University of Washington in Seattle, who helped start the North American Large-area Time-coincidence Array (NALTA). "They think it's done by geeks who sit down at the computer and type out a few things and something magical comes out." NALTA is showing students that science does not belong only to professionals with advanced degrees, nor is it all about unraveling impenetrable equations. "I tell them science is not a big book of answers to memorize," Wilkes said, "but a big pile of questions."

Fly's Eye mystery

Physicist Pierre Sokolsky was in his office at the University of Utah in Salt Lake City in October 1991 when a student walked in with the latest data from the university's Fly's Eye cosmic ray observatory. *Cosmic rays* are electrically charged, high-energy subatomic particles that travel through space. Astronomers think that cosmic rays fill galaxies and cross immense stretches of space between galaxies. For a decade, the Fly's Eye telescopes on the Dugway Proving Grounds in the shadow of Camelback Mountain had been recording high-energy cosmic rays and the billiard-ball reactions they set off in Earth's atmosphere. Now Sokolsky's student, Hungye Dai, was puzzling over an odd result. It seemed the Fly's Eye detectors had snared the most powerful cosmic ray ever measured—300 million times more powerful than the most energetic particle that the Tevatron particle accelerator at the United States Department of Energy's Fermilab in Illinois was capable of producing.

If the measurement was correct, it was evidence that some new and unimaginably powerful force was at work in the cosmos. But Sokolsky was not impressed. "You know, you always expect to see stuff like that, and it's usually just junk," he said later. "Go away and look at it some more," he told Dai. Both Dai and Sokolsky studied the results further, and the more they looked, the more their skepticism melted away. The next year, they stunned the physics world with the announcement of their discovery.

For nearly two decades, the event recorded by Fly's Eye and a second set of similarly surprising observations by a Japanese group have gone unexplained. Now, with the help of NALTA, scientists hope to witness more of these events—and learn more about high-energy cosmic rays.

Nature and types of cosmic rays

The science of understanding the cosmos is divided into two categories. Observing electromagnetic radiation—from radio waves to visible light to gamma rays—is called *astronomy*. Studying bits of matter that stream down to Earth in uncounted numbers is called *cosmic ray physics*. Cosmic rays, in fact, are the only known matter that reaches Earth from outside the solar system. A cosmic ray particle can spend millions of years wandering around interstellar space before arriving on Earth. The nearest source of cosmic rays, however, is our own sun.

Scientists estimate that each second about 200 cosmic ray particles, with the energy of several million *electronvolts* (tiny units of energy), strike every square yard on Earth. The reason people do not notice them is that cosmic ray particles are refugees from the quantum world, meaning they cannot be seen by the naked eye. Cosmic rays are mostly charged particles, such as electrons (negatively charged particles) or protons (positively charged particles). Others are the nuclei of atoms,

A team of high school students and teachers retrieves cosmic ray detectors from a shutdown research project in New Mexico for use by the California High School Cosmic Ray Observatory program, one of the programs sponsored by the North American Large-area Time-coincidence Array (NALTA). The California team installed 140 of the detectors—nicknamed *shmoos* for a cartoon character—at 70 schools.

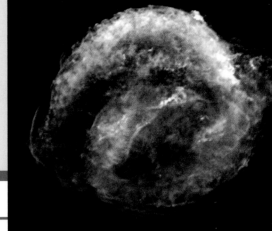
Supernova

TYPES OF PRIMARY COSMIC RAYS

Type	Source
Solar energetic particles (SEP's)	Produced by the sun during solar flares and other eruptions on its surface. Most consist of protons and other atomic nuclei with relatively low energies.
Galactic cosmic rays (GCR's)	Come from outside the solar system. Most are atomic nuclei with a positive charge because all electrons have been stripped away during high-speed galactic travel. May get their energy from supernovae.
Anomalous component (ACP's)	Unusual cosmic rays that develop from electrically neutral atoms that become ions (positively charged) near the sun. Carried far into space by the solar wind, the ions pick up additional energy from collisions with interstellar gases and then flow back toward the sun.
Ultrahigh-energy (UHE) extragalactic	Highly mysterious rays that almost certainly come from outside our Milky Way Galaxy, though their origin and source of energy are unknown. Have much more energy than galactic cosmic rays. Few of these reach Earth, so a very large area detector is required to observe them.

Solar flare

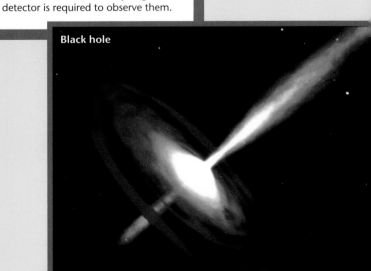
Black hole

particularly of hydrogen, but they can also consist of heavier nuclei, such as those from iron atoms.

There are two types of cosmic rays. A high-altitude ray is known as a *primary*. As the atmosphere gets denser, below about 15,000 meters (50,000 feet), a primary ray starts slamming into molecules. Each collision produces about a thousand *secondaries*, or *pions*, subatomic particles that exist for only a few billionths of a second before decaying into electrons and *muons*. (Pions themselves are composed of *quarks*, one of the two fundamental constituents of matter.)

More collisions continue, producing thousands more particles. By the time this avalanche of infinitesimal particles—called an *extensive air shower*—reaches the ground, the initial cosmic ray has created a "whole zoo of elementary particles," according to Sokolsky. Each air shower can cover as much as 25 square kilometers (10 square miles).

The energy in a cosmic ray can range over 17 orders of magnitude. To understand how large that range is, consider that the difference between a single dollar in your pocket and the entire national debt of the United States—about $8.7 trillion—is just 13 orders of magnitude.

Most of the lowest-energy rays come from within the Milky Way Galaxy. They consist of *solar energetic particles* and *galactic cosmic rays*. They travel serpentine routes through space at nearly the speed of light, being bounced around and deflected by the magnetic fields of stars and even the Milky Way's weak magnetic field. These rays constantly rain down all over Earth.

The most energetic rays, called ultrahigh-energy cosmic rays, are rarer. Fewer than one particle each week with energies above 10^{18} electron-volts strikes each square kilometer (0.4 square miles) on Earth. Fewer than one particle per century with energies above 10^{20} electron volts lands on each square kilometer. Although a single electron volt is a tiny amount of energy, particles traveling at these higher energies pack the punch of a baseball thrown at 160 kilometers (100 miles) per hour.

While no one is certain where these rays come from, it is believed that they must come from outside our galaxy because they contain enough energy to escape the magnetic fields that would otherwise keep them within their home galaxies. University of Chicago physicist James Cronin has called ultrahigh-energy cosmic rays "messengers from the extreme universe."

Why scientists study cosmic rays

The reason people do not notice these tiny daggers from beyond is that the atmosphere protects us from the most harmful effects of cosmic rays. Astronauts and airline pilots, however, are exposed to more of the most energetic particles than earthbound human beings. A 2005 study in the journal *Archives of Ophthalmology* found that airline pilots were

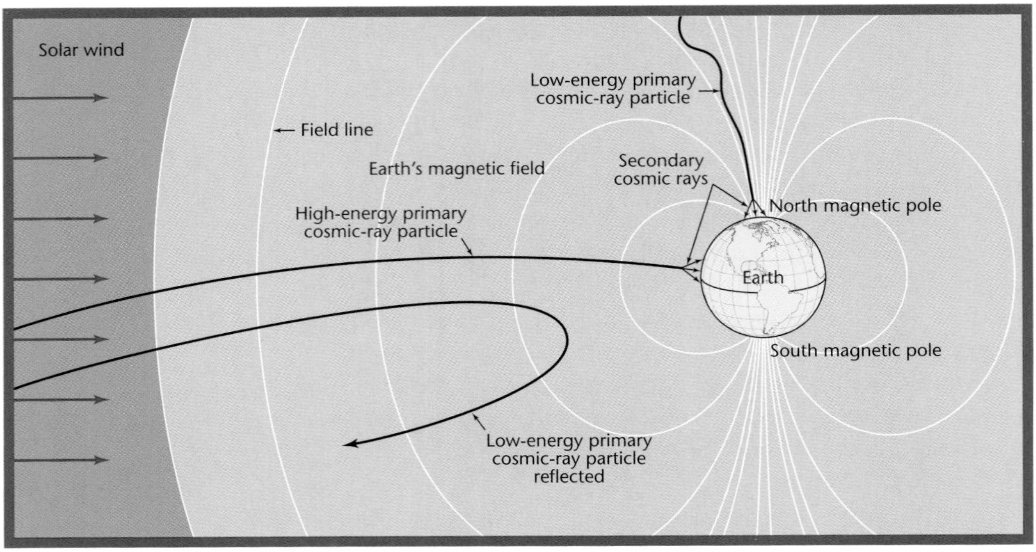

Solar wind

← Field line

Earth's magnetic field

Low-energy primary cosmic-ray particle

Secondary cosmic rays

High-energy primary cosmic-ray particle

North magnetic pole

Earth

South magnetic pole

Low-energy primary cosmic-ray particle reflected

To reach Earth's atmosphere, particles called *primary cosmic rays* or primaries must penetrate the planet's magnetic field. Low-energy primaries cannot travel far across the magnetic field's lines without being reflected. They can only approach Earth along the field lines near the poles. Some high-energy primaries can cut across the field lines. Primaries collide with atomic nuclei in the atmosphere, producing showers of *secondary cosmic rays.*

particularly vulnerable to certain types of *cataracts*. (A cataract is a clouding of the lens of the eye.) Other studies have shown an increased incidence of certain cancers and mutations in genes of the blood cells.

The health dangers are so worrisome that, according to some astrobiologists, the greatest challenge confronting the National Aeronautics and Space Administration (NASA) as it plans a mission to Mars is not building a spacecraft capable of getting there and back, but designing one that can prevent cosmic rays from harming the crew during the long journey. One of the greatest hurdles facing potential moon colonists is building shelters with walls several feet thick to block incoming cosmic rays.

Another reason scientists continue to be fascinated with cosmic rays, particularly the highest-energy rays, is that no one can explain why they exist. Few people love mysteries as much as physicists, and the mystery of ultrahigh-energy cosmic rays is a particularly juicy one.

There is no known physical process that could produce rays with the energies recorded by the Fly's Eye experiment. A *supernova* (a star that suddenly becomes extremely bright and then gradually fades) on the verge of blowing itself to bits would not be capable of packing particles with that much power. Even quasars, the most energetic objects known to exist in the universe, would have difficulty supercharging a particle to the energies measured by Fly's Eye. The existence of these high-energy particles could mean that our understanding of the way the universe works is seriously flawed.

Of course, there is another possibility—Sokolsky and his colleagues could be wrong. Measuring cosmic ray air showers is not a perfect science. Clouds, for instance, can affect the instruments. Sokolsky considered that possibility and rejected it. "I see no reason to retract that event," he said. "I don't believe there was an instrument error."

If the Fly's Eye results were unique, Sokolsky might have had a hard time justifying this view. But two years after the Fly's Eye event, the Japanese experiment, called the Akeno Giant Air Shower Array (AGASA), came up with similarly astounding results, recording several cosmic ray showers above 10^{19} electronvolts.

Physicists have invoked some unusual ideas to explain these findings, including a reformulation of the theory of special relativity, proposed in 1905 by German-born American physicist Albert Einstein. That theory,

HOW COSMIC RAYS REACH EARTH

Cosmic rays entering Earth's atmosphere collide with gas molecules, producing an avalanche of secondary particles called an extensive air shower. The first of these secondary particles, called *pions,* exist for only a few billionths of a second before decaying into a variety of subatomic particles, including negatively charged electrons and muons. Heavier muons reach the surface, passing through people at the rate of 100 per minute, and may even penetrate thousands of meters (feet) below the surface.

How cosmic rays get to earth

An astronaut working outside the International Space Station and other space travelers are exposed to high-energy cosmic rays, a form of radiation. Such rays pose a serious health threat to astronauts on an extended voyage to Mars or long stay on the moon.

which explains the behavior of matter, energy, time, and space, is one of the foundations of modern physics. "It could be something exotic, like defects in space-time," Sokolsky said. "If that's the origin, that would really be exciting."

But there's another problem. There's nothing in our region of space that could produce rays as energetic as those found by Fly's Eye and AGASA, and so they must come from outside our galaxy. However, according to the laws of physics, highly energetic cosmic rays should not come from any more than 150 million *light-years* from our solar system. (A light-year is the distance light can travel in one year—9.46 trillion kilometers [5.88 trillion miles].)

The belief that the highest-energy rays cannot come from great distances is based on research done in 1966 by physicists Kenneth Greisen of Cornell University in Ithaca, New York; and Georgiy Zatsepin and Vadim Kuzmin, both working at the MSU Skobeltsyn Institute of Nuclear Physics in Moscow. These scientists predicted that cosmic rays with extremely high energies would interact with particles left over from the big bang, the cataclysmic event that brought the universe into existence. These particles, mostly *photons,* make up what is called the cosmic microwave background. (Photons are the elementary particles that make up light.) This background radiation fills interstellar space with the distant echo of the big bang.

After bumping into enough of these particles, a cosmic ray's energy would drop enough so that when it finally reached Earth, it would carry much less force. This theory is called the GZK (Greisen-Zatsepin-Kuzmin) limit. According to the mathematical model, no ultrahigh-energy ray from distances beyond about 50 *megaparsecs* (about 3 million light-years) should reach Earth. The fact that Fly's Eye and AGASA recorded rays higher than this limit is known as the GZK paradox.

Scientists have tried to trace back these highest-energy rays to certain areas of the sky. One area of interest is the Beta Lachramae Galaxy. Some astronomers speculate that this galaxy could have a supermassive black hole at its center, with jets aimed at Earth that shoot out energy like a Roman candle, with majestic cones of fire coming out both ends. Other candidates are several galaxies near the Big Dipper. "There are hints," said Sokolsky. "But so far the experiments have been too small."

How scientists study cosmic rays

Studying cosmic rays is both a science and an art. Because they travel so fast and rain down on Earth from all directions, finding and cataloging the elusive ultrahigh-energy rays is like searching for a needle in a planet-sized haystack. Particle scientists use high-altitude balloons and spacecraft to measure primary cosmic rays before they enter Earth's atmosphere. But most of what scientists know about cosmic rays comes from ground detectors that capture the air showers.

Several kinds of detectors are commonly used, and the best modern detectors have backup systems to cross-check the results. One type is a specially fitted fluorescent telescope that measures light in the ultraviolet range. Such instruments spot the telltale interaction of particles with nitrogen in the upper atmosphere, which causes sparks of faint bluish light. This light is known as *atmospheric fluorescence*. The Fly's Eye experiment in Utah uses this type of detector. Scientists measure the light to figure out how many particles are in a single shower. Then they add up the particles in the shower to work their way back up to the original particle that started the chain reaction.

Another type of detector uses a basin of purified water to trap the particles. The particles passing through the water also emit *Cerenkov radiation* in the form of photons. Cerenkov radiation, named for the Russian scientist who first studied it, is light emitted when a particle passes through a transparent substance at a speed greater than that at which light moves in that medium. (In all transparent media, light moves slower than it does in a vacuum.) The photons bounce off the walls of the detector's holding tank and enter a measuring device called a *photomultiplier*. As its name implies, this device multiplies the light flashes into an electronic signal that can be measured. From this signal, analysts arrive at an approximation of the power of the original cosmic ray.

The simplest device, called a *scintillator detector,* consists of a piece of specially treated plastic sheeting. Held in sunlight, the plastic has a faint purplish glow. Cosmic ray particles passing through it excite the atoms in the plastic, which again give off photons. This device has a photomultiplier behind the plastic sheet.

The Japanese experiment, located 120 kilometers (75 miles) west of Tokyo, used 111 of these detectors—each in a specially designed hut—covering a total of about 100 square kilometers (40 square miles). Although AGASA recorded several of the highest-energy rays, Japanese scientists got no closer than their American counterparts to figuring out what was going on.

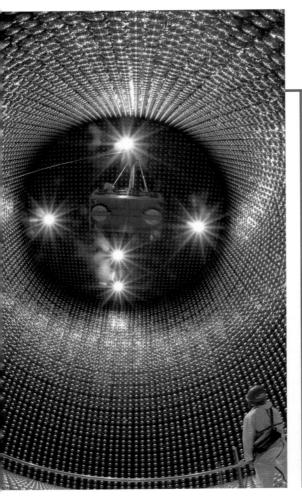

DETECTING COSMIC RAYS

A technician works on the large Super-Kamiokande neutrino detector (left) at the University of Tokyo's Institute for Cosmic Ray Research. The underground detector—a cylinder 41 meters (135 feet) tall filled with 45,000 metric tons (50,000 tons) of ultraclean water—is lined with 11,200 light sensors. When muons from air showers pass through the water, they activate the sensors. The arrow of light (below) was created when a muon entered the cylinder at the bottom of the image (red) and exited through the detector's side wall (green).

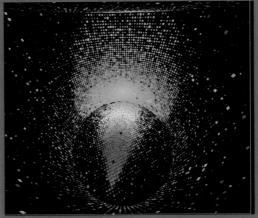

The Pierre Auger Observatory, under construction at the foot of the Andes Mountains in Argentina, will give scientists two methods of detecting and studying cosmic rays. The facility will include 24 specialized telescopes housed in 6 buildings (above) for use in tracking the development of air showers. It will also include 1,600 water tanks (right) spread over 3,000 square kilometers (1,200 square miles) to record secondary rays hitting Earth. Using the differences in the arrival times at various tanks, scientists will be able to determine the direction from which the parent primary rays came.

On Nov. 10, 2005, scientists presented the first observations from a new detector array—at least 10 times more sensitive than either Fly's Eye or AGASA—located at the barren foot of the Andes Mountains in Argentina. The Pierre Auger Observatory is named for the French physicist who figured out that cosmic ray air showers were the product of a single event. First proposed in 1992, the observatory is the vision of 250 scientists from 15 countries. When the facility is completed in late 2007 or early 2008, it will have 1,600 surface detectors. The observatory uses both water-tank detectors and fluorescent telescopes to measure the ultraviolet light of the air showers. Each tank of ultrapure water is 3.7 meters (12 feet) wide and holds 11,400 liters (3,000 gallons). The tanks are located about 1.6 kilometers (1 mile) apart. Scientists estimate that a giant air shower could hit 40 of the tanks.

CHICOS IN ACTION

High school students make a cosmic leap forward.

CHICOS cosmic ray detectors (right) at the Chaminade Middle School in Chatsworth, California, are painted in school colors. The detectors are monitored round-the-clock by classroom computers.

A student (left) at James Monroe High School in Los Angeles views an area map showing the location of operational and planned CHICOS computers. The project includes 180 detectors distributed over 400 square kilometers (150 square miles) (below).

California HIgh school Cosmic ray ObServatory
C H I C O S

Twenty-four telescopes—six in each of four buildings—are spread along the perimeter of the experiment.

Auger's advantage over its predecessors is not just increased sensitivity. Because it covers such a wide area—a landscape of 3,000 square kilometers (1,200 square miles)—it is much more likely to sense any ultrahigh-energy rays that strike the area. Due to its size, Auger should record dozens of high-energy events every year. The detectors are so sensitive that they should be able to reconstruct the direction from which the original cosmic ray came to within one degree. "If we don't see anything interesting, the mystery deepens," Sokolsky said.

NALTA

The Pierre Auger Observatory, with its technological wizardry and high ambition, has a good chance to catch the next ultrahigh-energy cosmic ray, but in science, nothing is certain. In cosmic ray detection, covering the maximum area possible is just as important as the sophistication of the measuring instruments.

With that need in mind, particle physicists realized a huge grid of detector sites already existed in North America—schools. The hunt for high-energy cosmic rays could cover not just hundreds of square kilometers, but thousands. In 2001, at an international physics conference in Aspen, Colorado, a group of physicists met to talk about the plan. "We had the idea of using relatively simple experiments that would allow high school students to participate in frontier science," said Wilkes, the University of Washington physicist who helped start the program. "That's when we formed NALTA."

NALTA now embraces 11 different array experiments. Hundreds of schools and thousands of students have participated. Teachers have found creative ways to obtain detectors cheaply. Robert McKeown, a physics professor at the California Institute of Technology (Caltech) in Pasadena, and the driving force behind the Los Angeles-area NALTA experiment, obtained 180 scintillators from a shut-down experiment in New Mexico. His team of teachers and students has installed 140 of them—they are nicknamed *shmoos* after a legless and armless cartoon character—at 70 schools. Most are middle schools and high schools, but a few elementary schools also are involved in the project. Altogether, the Los Angeles experiment, called the California High School Cosmic Ray Observatory (CHICOS), covers about 400 square kilometers (150 square miles).

At South Pasadena High School, cables connect detectors on the roof with a computer in teacher Dean Papadakis's physics classroom. When a detector records a hit above a certain energy level, a discriminator circuit pulses. This information is transmitted each night to computers at Caltech for analysis.

CHICOS students and teachers (top) work together to deploy and monitor cosmic ray detectors. A student and teacher (right) prepare a detector that will become part of the CHICOS array.

"Sometimes I hook up speakers to the computer so the students can hear a beep when a cosmic ray comes through," Papadakis said. He also uses small *cloud chambers* filled with dry ice and alcohol so students can see the tracks left by rays. (A cloud chamber is an instrument that makes the paths of cosmic rays visible.) "To actually see a real ray is neat," said senior Katherine Siew. Student Sampson Hill liked the cosmic ray experiment because it "showed how things really work. It's different from reading schoolbooks. You get to see it happening."

Students interested in participating in CHICOS attend a three- to five-day orientation program each summer on the Caltech campus. Just being on campus "does wonders for your self-esteem," said Hill. He hopes to attend Caltech.

"We've had some of the students apply to Caltech," McKeown said. "Others have gone to MIT [Massachusetts Institute of Technology in Cambridge] and other places after being associated with the project." Even students who do not go on to elite universities have benefited from the project. At a time when national policymakers worry about lagging U.S. performance in science education, McKeown said that CHICOS is helping to close the gap. "There's plenty of evidence that students in Los Angeles know something about cosmic rays, and they wouldn't have without this project," McKeown said. CHICOS has produced one scientific paper. Titled "Search for Correlated High Energy Cosmic Ray Events with CHICOS," the paper was published in 2005 in the *Journal of Physics G: Nuclear and Particle Physics*.

Not all the NALTA experiments are as professionally managed, or as smoothly operating, as CHICOS. For example, some NALTA teams have had difficulty linking up their various sites so they can track incoming rays simultaneously. CHICOS coordinates its detectors with the aid of global positioning system (GPS) satellites. To Wilkes, the most important goal is exposing students to high-end physics in a way that does not either bore or intimidate them. "I like to point out to students that they are more likely to get a Ph.D. in physics than to become an NBA basketball player," Wilkes said.

In the meantime, none of the NALTA institutions has—so far—uncovered the next ultrahigh-energy cosmic ray. "We've seen high energy events," McKeown said, but nothing has arisen that could not be explained by normal, well-understood physical processes. "Everybody is holding their breath," Wilkes said.

■ FOR ADDITIONAL INFORMATION

Books and periodicals
Close, Frank, and others. *The Particle Explosion*. Oxford University Press, 1987.
Sokolsky, Pierre. *Introduction to Ultrahigh Energy Cosmic Ray Physics*.
    Westview Press, 2005.

Websites
CHICOS: California High School Cosmic Ray Observatory—
    http://www.chicos.caltech.edu/brochure2005/index.html
High Resolution Fly's Eye: Physics @ the U—http://www.cosmic-ray.org/
Pierre Auger Observatory: Studying the Universe's Highest Energy Particles—
    http://www.auger.org/
SLAC: Stanford Linear Accelerator Center: Virtual Visitor Center—
    http://www2.slac.stanford.edu/vvc/cosmicrays/crslac.html

The Latest Buzz About Honey Bees

The world's most interesting animal lives in your backyard.

By Francis L. W. Ratnieks

The honey bee is, arguably, the world's most remarkable animal. Consider some of the amazing things these insects do.

- The "waggle dance" used by forager worker bees to direct nest mates to food sources or nest sites is the most complicated animal signal scientists have ever discovered. Yet this dance is only one of dozens of signals workers use to coordinate the life of a colony.

- Unlike nearly all other animals, honey bee workers reproduce indirectly—that is, they spend their short lives rearing their sisters and brothers—rather than directly—rearing their own daughters and sons.

- Honey bee colonies are so productive and run so smoothly that industrial engineers use them as inspiration for devising more efficient computer systems or workplaces for human workers. However, bee colonies—unlike human corporations—have no bosses.

- In addition to producing honey and wax, honey bees are the world's most important pollinator. They pollinate $14 billion worth of crops in the United States alone each year, including almonds, apples, cherries, kiwi fruit, melons, peaches, pears, raspberries, soybeans, and strawberries.

A worker honey bee with a bulging pollen basket (left) moves in to collect more pollen and nectar from a flower. Honey bees use their pollen baskets—smooth areas surrounded by long, curved hairs on their hind legs—to carry pollen to their nest. The nectar is transported inside the bee, in the honey stomach. Honey bees also collect water to cool the nest. A worker with its long tongue extended (above) loads up with water.

The author:
Francis L. W. Ratnieks is a Professor of Apiculture in the Department of Animal and Plant Sciences at the University of Sheffield in the United Kingdom.

TERMS AND CONCEPTS

Eusocial: Used to describe organisms that live in social groups where some individuals reproduce and some do not. The nonbreeding members care for the young of the breeding individuals and work on behalf of the group. In eusocial insects like honey bees, the breeding individual is called the "queen" and the nonbreeding individuals are called "workers."

Forage: To hunt or search for food.

Larva: *plural: larvae;* The early form of an insect from the time it leaves the egg until it becomes a pupa (the stage before the insect becomes an adult). Larva look somewhat like worms.

Natural selection: Natural selection is a process in nature by which the organisms best suited to their environment are the ones most likely to leave offspring. The theory of natural selection was first explained in detail in the 1850's by the British naturalist Charles R. Darwin. He believed all plants and animals had evolved—that is, developed by changing over many generations—from a few common ancestors by means of natural selection.

Nectar: A sweet liquid found in many flowers, which attracts insects and birds that carry out pollination. Bees gather nectar and make it into honey.

Pollination: The act or process of carrying pollen from the anthers (produces pollen) to the stigmas (the part of a flower that receives pollen) of flowers for fertilization, as by insects or the wind.

Sterile: Used to describe organisms that are unable to reproduce.

The Austrian biologist Karl von Frisch, who decoded the waggle dance and discovered that bees have color vision, called the honey bee "a magic well." He said, "The more you draw from it, the more there is to draw." Even though people have studied honey bees for thousands of years, scientists make new discoveries about these insects every year.

One group of scientists in Australia recently learned how these expert navigators calculate distance—by decoding waggle dances to determine how far the bees themselves thought they had flown. Studies of honey bee communication have revealed new insights into the ways these insects recruit additional *foragers* (gatherers) to collect food from other locations where flowers are abundant, as well as the way they make a group decision about where best to build a new nest. In 2006, an international team of scientists announced that they had analyzed the honey bee *genome* (the complete set of genes in a cell). This information has already shed new light on honey bee evolution and promises new insights into how the bees maintain their remarkably sophisticated society. Finally, my own research team has discovered that worker bees devote their lives to rearing brothers and sisters rather than laying their own eggs only partly because they have evolved to act in the best interest of their family. We found that workers also "police" each other, killing eggs laid by other workers.

Meanwhile, in 2007, honey bee populations throughout the world faced a number of threats, including disease, loss of habitat, and pesticides used in agriculture. In addition, a mysterious condition, which became known as colony collapse disorder (CCD), caused thousands of hives in the United States and other countries to die out unexpectedly during the winter of 2006-2007.

Bees are actually hairy vegetarian wasps. Over time, a species of wasp took to feeding on nectar and pollen, rather than on nectar and insect prey, and gave rise to the first bee species. How did this change in diet occur? No one knows for sure, but pollen would have been available on the same flowers from which the insects collected nectar. The oldest known bee is a 100-million-year-old fossil found in the Asian country of Myanmar (formerly, Burma). The bee way of life was successful, probably because flowers were becoming abundant on Earth at that time. Today, there are about 17,000 bee species. Flowers, in turn, benefited from the bees. Scientists believe that over millions of years, bees helped create the wide variety of flowers in the world today by moving pollen—needed for the development of seeds—from one plant to another of the same type. In doing so, they increased genetic *diversity* (variation) within species, which leads to the development of new species over time.

THE ANATOMY OF A HONEY BEE

The honey bee, like all insects, has a body that is divided into three sections: the head, the *thorax* (chest), and the abdomen.

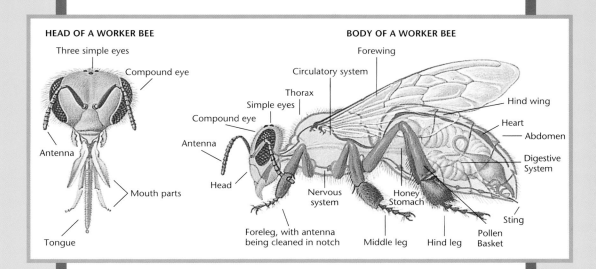

HEAD OF A WORKER BEE

Three simple eyes
Compound eye
Antenna
Mouth parts
Tongue

BODY OF A WORKER BEE

Forewing
Circulatory system
Thorax
Simple eyes
Compound eye
Antenna
Head
Hind wing
Heart
Abdomen
Digestive System
Nervous system
Foreleg, with antenna being cleaned in notch
Honey Stomach
Middle leg
Hind leg
Sting
Pollen Basket

On the head of the bee (above left) are five eyes—three small ones that form a triangle on top of its head, and a large *compound eye* on each side of its head. Each compound eye has thousands of lenses crowded closely together. Within its mouth, the bee uses its tongue to suck water, nectar, and honey. The bee's antennae—slender, jointed feelers attached to the front of the bee's head—are used for the senses of touch, taste and smell. The insect's *honey stomach*, (above right) in which it carries nectar, is in the abdomen. Most bees depend on their stingers as their only means of defense. Glands attached to the stinger produce a *venom* (poison) made up of complex chemical substances.

Worker   Queen   Drone

Drones (above right) are male bees and they mate with the queen. The queen (center) is the only female that mates and produces young within a hive. Worker bees (above left) are female and are unable to mate, but they care for the young within the hive or forage for food outside it.

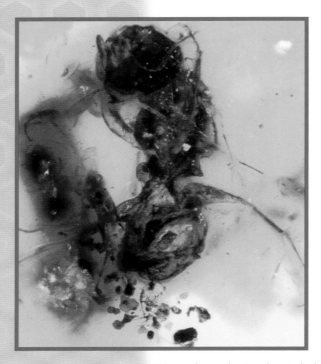

This 100 million-year-old bee was preserved in *amber* (a hard yellow or yellowish-brown gum, the resin of fossil pine trees) in Myanmar in Southeast Asia. Its discovery was reported in 2006 by George O. Poinar of Oregon State University in Corvallis and Bryan Nicholas Danforth of Cornell University in Ithaca, New York. The fossil is the oldest-known bee and has characteristics of both bees and wasps, which may provide the evidence of an evolutionary link between the two insects.

Most bees are solitary creatures. A female builds a small nest in the soil or in a crevice and rears a few larvae on pollen and nectar. But some bees, including honey bees, are *eusocial*—that is, they live in a colony with a queen and workers. The discovery of a fossilized worker bee from a species of stingless bee—a close relative of the honey bees and bumble bees—indicates that eusociality in bees evolved at least 65 million years ago. Eusocial bees live in complex societies consisting of a mother queen, whose main job is to lay eggs, and her offspring. Nearly all the tens of thousands of members of a honey bee colony are females that do not reproduce but tend the offspring of the queen. These so-called worker bees also construct the wax combs and defend the hive or nest and forage for food. Honey bee colonies also include a few thousand males, called drones, in the spring and summer.

In ancient times, honey was the most important sweetener for food and for making alcoholic drinks. At first, people got honey by raiding wild honey bee nests in hollow trees. It was only natural that beekeeping—hives are actually nest cavities provided by a beekeeper—would develop as a way to have a steady, reliable source of this enjoyable food. Carvings in Egyptian tombs dating to at least 4,000 years ago show hives made of clay tubes. Bees were so valued for their honey and for their wax, which was used to make candles, that ancient people often named their children after them. *Deborah* and *Melissa* mean *bee* in Hebrew and Greek, respectively.

Apis mellifera, the western honey bee, is native to Europe, Africa, and the Middle East. European settlers introduced *A. mellifera* to North and South America and Australia, the three continents without native honey bees.

Asia, the continent where honey bees originated, has eight other species. Four are quite similar to *A. mellifera*. One species, *Apis cerana*, is even kept in hives. However, *A. mellifera* produces more honey than any other honey bee or bee species and has become the world's most important bee species for beekeeping.

Although beeswax and honey enrich our lives today, neither is essential. But in farming, the pollination services of honey bees are essential.

A beekeeper is shown checking a comb while bees swarm around his head. In 2007, beekeepers in the United States and other countries, worried about colony collapse disorder which has affected bee colonies in more than 22 states in the United States. Scientists continued to investigate the cause of the disorder and anticipate its ultimate impact on agriculture.

Many plants cannot self-pollinate and require pollen from another plant of the same species. In most grasses and many trees, wind transports the pollen. But in most flowering plants, animals, especially bees, do this. Most flowers reward the pollinating animal with nectar.

Crops requiring pollination, such as melons and apple or almond trees, are grown in large areas requiring many pollinators during bloom. *A. mellifera*, which forages on many different species, can pollinate most flowers and is the world's single most important pollinator species.

Economic importance is one reason why scientists study honey bees. But if honey bees produced no honey or wax and did not pollinate crops, scientists would still study them because they are excellent model systems for answering many basic questions in biology. One indication of the honey bee's importance in biology is that it became only the fourth insect whose genome has been sequenced. Honey bee biologist Gene Robinson of the University of Illinois at Urbana-Champaign, one of the leaders of the sequencing team, stressed that this large investment of time and money was justified by the honey bee's importance in pollination and as a model system for studying social biology. The honey bee genome will provide key information for many studies in which genetic data are relevant.

One early insight of the genome project is that *A. mellifera* originated in Africa—after its ancestor had spread there from Asia—and then spread into Europe. Another intriguing result is that the honey bee has a greater number of genes involved in *olfaction* (taste and smell) than does the fruit fly, *Drosophila*, another insect species whose genome has been sequenced. This makes sense given the importance of olfaction to honey bees in communicating by *pheromones* (chemicals used for communication), detecting robber bees from other hives by their different odors, and learning the scents of flowers. But unraveling how the different genes involved in olfaction function, and how the olfaction system evolved, will require decades of work.

Eusocial insects: an evolutionary puzzle

For many years, bees seemed to challenge the theory of *natural selection,* the basis of modern biology. Natural selection, first explained in detail in the 1850's by the British naturalist Charles Darwin, is a process in nature which causes evolution. Individual organisms of the same species vary slightly—they are not all exactly the same. Those best suited to their environment will leave more offspring. If this variation is *heritable* (can be passed on to offspring), then the next generation can be slightly different to the previous generation in ways that increase survival and reproduction. But worker insects have zero or little reproduction. Instead, they work to rear the queen's offspring. How could such *altruism* (selfless behavior) evolve if the altruistic worker has no offspring? The problem was solved in 1964 by British biologist William Hamilton. Hamilton's work is the most important contribution to the theory of natural selection since Darwin and has greatly aided our understanding of honey bees and other eusocial insects. The essence of Hamilton's contribution was to point out that workers could pass on copies of their genes indirectly, by rearing relatives, such as brothers and sisters, rather than directly, by rearing sons and daughters. His theory also showed the importance of kinship and altruism in social behavior. For example, one organism is more likely to help another if the two are close relatives.

Worker and queen honey bees are both female, but they differ greatly. The queen has enlarged ovaries and can lay 2,000 eggs per day. Her daughter workers do everything else—forage, feed larvae, build combs, and defend the nest. But workers are not sterile. Although they cannot mate, they can lay unfertilized eggs that develop into males if reared. However, less than 0.1 percent of the workers in a colony with a queen lay eggs, and only 0.1 percent of the males are workers' sons.

The rarity of workers' sons seems to go against Hamilton's theory. Why rear less-related brothers (the queen's sons) rather than more-related sons? While working on my doctorate at Cornell University in Ithaca, New York, in the late 1980's, I theorized that Hamilton's theory makes sense if we consider other workers. Because a queen mates with about 10 males, the workers are mainly half sisters. As a result, workers are more related to the queen's sons than they are to other workers' sons and so have a strong incentive to stop each other from reproducing. My name for this theory was worker policing. Although the theory made sense, there was no direct evidence for worker policing.

KARL VON FRISCH (1886–1982)

Austrian biologist Karl von Frisch believed that "every single species challenges us with all, or nearly all, the mysteries of life." Von Frisch was a zoologist who studied the behavior of bees. His early research showed that bees are sensitive to different types of light, can see colors, and differentiate floral scents from one another. In 1923, he developed a theory that honey bees use different types of movement to alert each other about where to find food. He called the bees' behavior the "waggle dance." Although some scientists have been skeptical that the waggle dance actually communicates information, research carried out by other scientists has conclusively shown that dance-following bees obtain information from the dance itself and not just from odors of flowers on the dancing bee's body.

Von Frisch's commitment to understanding the behavior of bees was rewarded in 1973, when he received the Nobel Prize in Physiology or Medicine. In the decades since von Frisch's death in 1982, he has been proved correct as the honey bee continues to be a "magic well," with a never ending series of novel and important discoveries being made by scientists studying this remarkable animal.

Years later, I was able to perform an experiment that led to the discovery of the first proof of worker policing—in the honey bee. By transferring eggs laid by workers in a colony without a queen (in queenless colonies many workers lay eggs) into a colony with a queen, my colleague Kirk Visscher, now at the University of California at Riverside, and I showed that workers kill worker-laid eggs by eating them. Since then, research in my laboratory and in others has shown that worker policing occurs widely in bees, wasps, and ants.

In November 2006, Tom Wenseleers, now at the University of Leuven in Belgium, and I published research showing that effective policing deters worker reproduction. By comparing 10 species (9 wasps and the honey bee), we showed that fewer workers lay eggs when policing is more effective. In the honey bee and in some wasps, policing kills nearly all worker-laid eggs, while in some wasps only half are killed. If most worker-laid eggs are killed, it is better for the workers to work, so that their colony rears more of their brothers and sisters, rather than lay eggs.

Dancing bees talk to researchers

The waggle dance is performed in the nest by forager honey bees. The dance communicates the distance and direction of the flower patch the foragers have visited to unemployed foragers. Dances are made on the vertical wax combs. The distance to the flowers is encoded in the

OPTICAL FLOW

Optical flow is the perceived movement of the environment by the eye. Mandyan Srinivasan of Australian National University in Canberra trained foragers to go to a feeder at the end of a narrow horizontal tunnel 6 meters (19.6 feet) long with a mesh roof (left). The walls had a black and white pattern of horizontal stripes or squares. The squares provide greater optical flow to a flying bee. Srinivasan and his researchers then decoded waggle dances, which told them how far a bee thought she had flown.

When bees flew both 35 meters (115 feet) to the tunnel and 6 meters (20 feet) down a tunnel with a checkerboard black and white pattern that gave great optical flow, they thought they had flown approximately 200 meters (656 feet). But when the tunnel had horizontal stripes, giving less optical flow, they thought that they had flown less than 50 meters (164 feet).

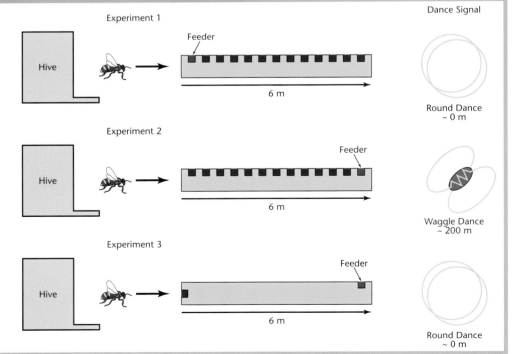

speed of the dance. The dancer indicates direction by the angle of her body relative to the vertical comb.

To calibrate the distance component of the waggle dance, von Frisch gave foragers syrup feeders at known distances from the hive, marked the foragers with paint dots so individuals could be recognized, and observed their dances in a glass-walled observation hive. This procedure can be used in reverse, decoding dances to determine where workers are foraging. Madeleine Beekman, now at the University of Sydney in Australia, and I decoded dances made by a colony at my laboratory in Sheffield, England. In August, the bees flew west an average distance of 5 kilometers (3 miles) but as far away as 14 kilometers (8.7 miles). In May, the average distance was only 1 kilometer (.62 miles). Why the difference? It comes down to economics. People will commute long distances to well-paying jobs, and so will bees. In May, flowers are abundant, and there is no need to fly far for nectar. In August, however, flowers are generally scarce, but west of Sheffield, huge patches of heather are in bloom. So in August, long-range commuting is more profitable.

An ingenious experiment led by Mandyan Srinivasan of Australian National University in Canberra decoded waggle dances to determine how flying workers measure distance. Von Frisch studied this behavior and concluded that bees measure distance by the energy they expend to reach their destination. However, Srinivasan's work shows that *optical flow* is used. Optical flow is the perceived movement of the environment by the eye. For example, astronauts in the space shuttle experience less optical flow than cyclists, even though they travel farther because the environment does not pass by the eye as quickly in space as it does on the road.

Srinivasan trained foragers to a feeder at the end of a narrow horizontal tunnel 6 meters (19.6 feet) long with a mesh roof. The walls had a black and white pattern of horizontal stripes or squares. The squares provided greater optical flow to a flying bee. By decoding waggle dances, the researchers could tell how far a bee thought she had flown. Bees that flew down the tunnel with squares thought they had flown farther than those that flew down the tunnel with stripes. Getting the bees to fly closer to the ground than they normally do, and especially by having squares instead of stripes, increased optical flow. Optical flow is probably used by other species to measure distance. But only honey bees (and people) can tell a researcher how far they think they have gone.

How useful is the waggle dance in foraging?

Most eusocial insects communicate the location of food to nest mates, but the ways in which they do this vary. Whereas honey bees use waggle dances, many ants use trails of pheromones or follow an experienced forager. How useful is the waggle dance? Research carried out by Gilly Sherman and Kirk Visscher of the University of California at

THE WAGGLE DANCE OF HONEY BEES

Honey bees use the waggle dance to communicate to unemployed foragers the distance and direction of flowers that the foragers have visited.

The angle of the dancing forager's body to the vertical (below right) gives the angle of the flowers relative to the sun (below left). The waggles (movements back and forth) communicate the food's distance. A forager uses the waggle dance to communicate the location of a food source to unemployed foragers (bottom left and right).

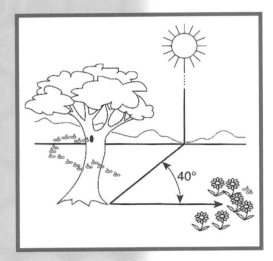

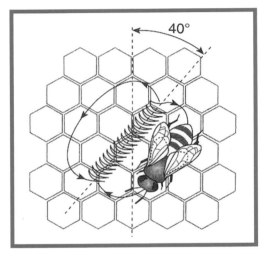

Riverside compared the foraging success of colonies with and without waggle dance communication by weighing hives. (Most weight change is due to changes in honey stores and so is a good measure of nectar foraging.) The obvious way to do this experiment would be to compare hives with and without dancing. But it is impossible to stop bees dancing. What is possible, however, is to cause bees to perform uninformative dances by putting a hive on its side. Lacking the vertical frame of reference, waggle dances are disoriented. But if a horizontal observation hive is given a directional light source, the bees orient their dances to this, instead of to gravity. By comparing horizontal observation hives with and without a directional light source, the researchers showed that dance information increases foraging success. But the advantage did not occur all year. Further research is needed to determine the circumstances under which dances help. Probably, flowers are often so abundant that workers can find good patches on their own. But at certain times, good patches are rare, making communication worthwhile. Honey bees can forage as far as 14 kilometers (8.7 miles), but no one bee could scout this enormous area. Communication enables a colony to share the knowledge of food sources among thousands of foragers.

Being self-organized

Keeping a large organization running smoothly is a major challenge. Amazingly enough, an insect colony is organized without specialized managers—it is "self-organized." In self-organization, individual workers react to their local environment and colony-level organization emerges. For example, if workers foraging at more profitable locations are more likely to recruit nest mates, then the colony's foragers will focus on the better locations, even though no one is in charge or knows where all the food patches are or how good they are.

Tom Seeley of Cornell University has investigated self-organization in honey bee foraging. By training foragers from an observation hive to two syrup feeders, he showed that more concentrated syrup led to more waggle dancing. In turn, more dancing led more foragers to the better feeder. The relationship was simple—twice as many dances led to twice as many recruits. Self-organization is also used in balancing the numbers of nectar foragers and nectar receivers, who unload the foragers and store the nectar in cells. Seeley found that foragers experiencing long delays in being unloaded are more likely to make a type of dance known as the tremble dance. This special dance causes more bees to work as receivers. If a colony has too few receivers, more are recruited. If it has enough, no more are recruited.

Computer simulations and experiments on the nectar collection and storage system by myself; Carl Anderson, now at QBit Technology in Maryland; and Adam Hart, now at the University of Gloucestershire in

This honey bee worker has a varroa mite on its back. The varroa mite is a major parasite of honey bees. First discovered in the early 1900's in Asia, it was later introduced to the United States in the late 1980's. If left untreated, the varroa mite can destroy entire colonies in as little as seven months. Treatment for varroa mites includes plastic strips containing chemicals that are toxic to the mites. However, new generations of mites have shown adaptations that make them resistant to the poison, leading scientists to explore new strategies to control or even eliminate this parasite.

England, solved a confusing element of the tremble dance. Nectar foragers sometimes stop unloading to one receiver and begin unloading to a second. Why? It is like a supermarket shopper checking out some purchases at one register and the rest at another. The simulations showed that the total time wasted is small—if a forager stops unloading to a receiver, then this receiver can unload another forager. By unloading to several receivers, the forager gets several estimates of the amount of time foragers must wait to unload and, therefore, has more information to determine whether the system is out of balance and new receivers are needed.

Threats to honey bees

The honey bee is our best insect friend, whose pollination efforts are vital to modern agriculture. Because intensive farming makes it harder for wild pollinators to survive, growers move beehives onto farms during bloom to ensure adequate pollination. The world's largest pollination event takes place in the Central Valley of California every February when 1 million hives are placed in the almond groves.

Despite the importance of honey bees to agriculture, the number of U.S. hives has fallen from 5.9 million in 1947 to 2.4 million in 2005 because beekeeping has become less profitable. Honey is traded worldwide, and U.S. beekeepers must compete with beekeepers in such countries as China and Mexico where lower salaries make beekeeping more profitable. Managing hives in the United States also has become more difficult and costly due to the arrival of several additional honey bee pests and diseases in the past few decades. These include chalkbrood (a fungus that kills honey bee larvae), tracheal mite (a mite living on adult honey bees), small hive beetle (a beetle that lives in the hive on stored food and brood), and—the most serious—*Varroa* mite (a mite living on pupal and adult honey bees). For many years, *Varroa* could be treated quickly and for only a few dollars per hive per year using strips of plastic impregnated with a chemical highly toxic to *Varroa* mites but not to bees or people. However, *Varroa* mites have evolved resistance to the chemicals used. *Varroa* mites were originally found on the Asian hive bee *Apis cerana*, where they bred only on drone pupae (stage before adulthood) and did little harm. The movement of bees by beekeepers has allowed *Varroa* to infect *A. mellifera* and spread worldwide. *Varroa* is more harmful to *A. mellifera* as it can breed on worker pupae as well.

In early 2007, beekeepers in California and many other states discovered that many hives had died out unexpectedly during the winter. The cause is currently unknown but may well be a disease; one possibility is a virus that shortens the lifespan of worker bees, causing the colony to die out during the winter when replacement worker bees are not being reared. Research in the United Kingdom by Stephen Martin of the University of Sheffield and Brenda Ball a bee pathologist at Rothamsted Research in Harpenden, England, had previously shown that the presence of *Varroa* mites caused new viral transmission pathways that, in turn led to the collapse of the colony.

It is clear to me that Karl von Frisch's "magic well" is far from empty. Researchers continue to make exciting discoveries about the remarkable honey bee.

▌ FOR ADDITIONAL INFORMATION

Books and periodicals

Buchmann, Stephen L., and Repplier, Banning. *Letters from the Hive: An Intimate History of Bees, Honey, and Humankind.* Bantam Books, 2005.

Ellis, Hattie. Sweetness and Light: *The Mysterious History of the Honeybee.* Harmony Books, 2004.

The Honeybee Genome Sequencing Consortium. "Insights into Social Insects from the Genome of the Honeybee *Apis mellifera.*" Nature, October 2006, 931-949.

Horn, Tammy. *Bees in America: How the Honey Bee Shaped a Nation.* University Press of Kentucky, 2005.

Wenseleers, Tom, and Ratnieks, Francis L. W. "Enforced altruism in insect societies." *Nature,* November 2006, 50.

Web sites

Mid-Atlantic Apiculture Research and Extension Consortium—http://maarec.cas.psu.edu/

PBS Online/wNetStation—http://www.pbs.org/wnet/nature/alienempire/multimedia/hive.html

Texas A & M University, Department of Entomology—http://honeybee.tamu.edu/

U. S. Department of Agriculture, Agricultural Research Service— http://www.ars.usda.gov/is/video/vnr/ccd.htm

PARADISE FOUND

THE WORLD'S LARGEST MARINE SANCTUARY IS CREATED NEAR HAWAII.

BY ROBERT H. TAMARIN

To the west and slightly north of the eight main Hawaiian Islands is an area of the Pacific Ocean called Papahānaumokuākea. The name is a combination of two Hawaiian words that symbolize Mother Earth and Father Sky. On June 15, 2006, United States President George W. Bush signed a proclamation that turned this ocean region into the world's largest marine reserve—the Papahānaumokuākea Marine National Monument, also known as the Northwestern Hawaiian Islands Marine National Monument.

This area is composed of volcanic islands, aquatic environments, coral reefs, and *atolls* (ring-shaped coral reefs and small islands that enclose a lagoon), creating an archipelago about 1,900 kilometers (1,200 miles) long. It contains some of the healthiest coral reefs on Earth, and a number of rare and endangered species live within its boundaries. The monument encompasses more area than all the U.S. national parks combined, and if it were a state, it would be the fifth largest.

Ten major islands and atolls make up the monument. The islands are small and only sparsely vegetated. Fanning out from the islands are more than 13,000 square kilometers (5,000 square miles) of coral reefs. More than 7,000 animal species live in the monument. About 25 percent of these are *endemic*—found only within the Hawaiian Islands. Many species here are at great risk of extinction due to overfishing and the introduction of invasive alien species. The monument is home to approximately 1,200 remaining Hawaiian monk seals—the most endangered seal in U.S. waters. In addition, monument waters are an important habitat for such other marine mammals as spotted dolphins and humpback whales. The islands themselves are a nesting place for albatross, boobies, and frigate birds, which are among more than 14 million migratory seabirds that pass through the region each year. The sandy beaches are vital to green sea turtles, another endangered species. Within five years, all fishing will be prohibited within the monument's boundaries, and visitors will need permits to enter the area.

In addition to its animal inhabitants, Papahānaumokuākea is important to native Hawaiian traditions. As a result, the monument is available to native Hawaiians for traditional activities, including spiritual celebrations and subsistence fishing. Polynesian artifacts and remnants of dwellings have been discovered on several of the islands.

Beneath the watery surface of the monument lie the hulks of more than 60 known shipwrecks. These wrecks are the focus of archaeological research and cleanup efforts. The monument includes the Midway World War II Memorial, a facility for research, education, and ecotourism.

The creation of the monument represents a major step forward in preserving the ecological and cultural heritage of this Pacific Ocean region. When President Bush signed the proclamation establishing the monument, he noted that it was "more than 100 times larger than Yosemite National Park. ... This is a big deal."

The masked booby *(Sula dactyltra)* is one of the many birds that fish the seas in the Northwestern Hawaiian Islands Marine National Monument and nest on Lisianski Island. Like most Pacific seabirds, the masked booby is threatened by overfishing and nest raiding by such predators as rats and *feral* (wild) cats. However, the monument provides a protected haven that prevents intrusion by human activities. In addition, all areas of the monument are free of rats and cats.

The 20- to 30-centimeter (8- to 12-inch) spines of the red pencil urchin make it one of the easiest marine invertebrates to recognize among the coral reefs of the monument. As they move through the coral, the urchins feed on algae. In the past, people used the long red spines to write on slate boards. Today, urchins, like thousands of other marine species in the monument, are protected.

The author:
Robert H. Tamarin is Dean of Sciences at the University of Massachusetts in Lowell.

A bluefin trevally (top), a type of tuna that grows to about 1 meter (3 feet) long, prowls the shallow waters of a coral garden in search of prey. The abundance of small fish among the coral reefs and government restrictions on commercial fishing make the waters of the monument ideal hunting grounds for large fish.

The islands, atolls, and coral reefs that make up the monument are located to the northwest of Nihau, the most western of the major Hawaiian Islands. The marine monument, which covers 356,880 square kilometers (137,792 square miles), is home to 7,000 animal species, a quarter of which are native to the monument.

The Hawaiian monk seal (top)—known to the ancient Hawaiians as *Ilio-holo-i-ka-uaua* (dog that runs in rough waters)—is native to the area covered by the monument. About 90 percent of the seals reside for life on the island where they were born. Researchers are gathering data on the populations of these highly endangered animals in an attempt to stem their slide into extinction.

The green sea turtle (above left), once found in tropical and semitropical seas around the world, is another endangered animal. Protected in U.S. territory, the turtle is hunted elsewhere. From May to August, French Frigate Shoals, an atoll in the center of the monument, provides a nesting place for 90 percent of Hawaii's green sea turtles. The descendant of a land animal, the green sea turtle has survived as a marine creature for at least 150 million years.

Gray sharks (below) prowl the reef near Necker Island. Such protected habitats as the monument are important for sharks, which continue to be widely hunted for food. Thanks to the security afforded by the monument, sharks live in large numbers there, a rarity in many other parts of the world. Sharks are important parts of the monument's reef ecosystems because they eat weak and diseased fish, removing them from the population.

The reefs of the Northwestern Hawaiian Islands Marine National Monument provide an ideal habitat for the milletseed butterfly fish, which is native to Hawaii. The coral protects the fish from prey, and the area's abundance of *zooplankton* (microscopic organisms) provides the butterfly fish with an ample food supply.

More than 7,500 great frigate birds nest throughout the monument. Native Hawaiians call the bird *iwa*—which means *thief* in the Hawaiian language—because the bird obtains some of its food by "robbing" other seabirds of their catch.

The reefs of the monument provide a habitat for a huge variety of fish, including species that are unique to the park's Rapture Reef, a part of French Frigate Shoals.

Researchers handle a 4.5-meter (15-foot) tiger shark (right) shortly after the shark damaged the boat's hull and bit off a chunk of its rail. Tiger sharks often troll the waters of the monument in June and July to feed on young albatrosses that crash while testing their wings.

A researcher (above) surveys a section of a reef to analyze habitats, recording types and numbers of algae, coral, crabs, fish, and other reef residents.

Fish and Wildlife Service technicians on French Frigate Shoals band the leg of a Laysan albatross (left). The albatross can spend up to five years at sea. In recent years, scientists have noted a drop in albatross populations and have discovered that many of the birds are killed by getting caught on the fishing lines and hooks of commercial fishers. By identifying the birds, scientists can track the condition of the population within the monument.

French naturalist Jean-Michel Cousteau observes Laysan albatrosses tending their eggs (above) on Eastern Island at Midway Atoll. The Laysan albatross, which has a wingspan 1.8 meters (6 feet) across, can live up to 40 years. The monument provides crucial protection for this bird's nesting habitats. Almost 2 million birds stop off annually at Midway Atoll, which is home to 71 percent of the world's Laysan albatross population.

Laysan albatross chicks (left) face many threats to their survival. In some unprotected areas of Hawaii, Laysan albatrosses and their nests are threatened by dogs. One study revealed that at least 30 birds were killed in dog attacks on a single day. Midway Atoll provides a protected space away from dogs and other predators.

The wreck of the Japanese fishing vessel *Kaiyo Maru* lies beached on Laysan Island. The ship went aground in 1969. The waters of the monument contain the remains of at least 60 ships and aircraft, many of them from World War II (1939–1945).

Hans Van Tilburg (right), a maritime archaeologist, examines a *windlass* at the site of a wreck off Pearl and Hermes Atoll. A windlass is a winch, often turned by a crank, that is used to raise the anchor of a ship.

Site 45 (above) on Little Nihoa, on the monument's southeastern border, is one of numerous sites left by the native Hawaiians who lived on the island from 1000 to 1700. This site may represent the remains of a dwelling. Little Nihoa, which is about 1 square kilometer (0.38 square mile) in area, has more than 80 such sites. The preservation of these sites, which include burial caves, religious areas, and agricultural terraces, provides a link to Hawaii's cultural past.

Monument employees sail a Polynesian voyaging canoe, the *Hokule`a* (left), on a voyage throughout the Northwestern Hawaiian Islands in 2004. During the trip, voyagers held teleconferences with schools around the United States, giving students a close look at the habitats that the national monument is designed to preserve.

The Spanish dancer *(Hexabranchus sanguineus)* is a sea slug found around Laysan Island in the monument. The Spanish dancer is a *hermaphrodite* (each individual has both male and female reproductive organs), so an individual Spanish dancer can both lay and fertilize eggs, though it cannot fertilize its own eggs.

The stocky hawkfish *(Cirrhitus pinnulatus)* inhabits the coral reefs of Midway Island. The largest species of hawkfish, the stocky hawkfish can grow to 31 centimeters (1 foot) in length.

As the oceans become more polluted and marine habitats are destroyed, there are fewer and fewer places where divers can explore healthy reefs and their ecosystems. The Northwestern Hawaiian Islands Marine National Monument offers a sanctuary where corals and other marine life can thrive without being disturbed by humankind.

Like a ring of fire, Grand Prismatic Spring stretches 114 meters (375 feet) across the Yellowstone landscape. Its brilliant colors are created by microscopic life forms that thrive in hot temperatures.

A Place Where Earth Speaks

Yellowstone's spectacular sights are evidence of powerful geologic forces operating deep within Earth.

By Barbara A. Mayes

Yellowstone National Park is one of nature's grandest playgrounds. In lively displays, geysers blast thick columns of water and steam high into the sky. Scalding hot springs, their surfaces a swirl of brilliant blue, green, and yellow, simmer and splash. Giant pools of mud bubble madly like cooking pots, while steam and hot gases hiss from deep cracks in the ground.

Yellowstone National Park lies in the Rocky Mountains in northwest Wyoming and neighboring sections of Idaho and Montana. The park was named for the yellow cliffs found along the Yellowstone River, which runs through the park. Yellowstone has at least 10,000 geysers, hot springs, and steam vents—more than any other area of the world—including some of the world's largest and most powerful. Such spectacular sights draw millions of visitors to the park each year.

These thermal features also offer a window into the Earth's interior. Yellowstone's history is an amazing tale of cataclysmic volcanic eruptions, massive earthquakes, and a gigantic column of rock—heated to such a high temperature that it has the consistency of putty—lurking only a few miles beneath the park's majestic surface. For Earth scientists, Yellowstone provides a unique geologic laboratory for learning how the processes taking place far below the surface shape the world around us.

Yellowstone National Park, the first national park in the United States, covers the northwest corner of Wyoming and small sections of Montana and Idaho. The huge volcanic crater (outlined in red) in the center of the park, created by a massive eruption about 640,000 years ago, provides dramatic evidence of the powerful geologic forces operating below the surface.

Yellowstone is such a remarkable place that the first reports of the area were met with deep skepticism or outright disbelief. In 1807, a fur trapper named John Colter was probably the first person other than the American Indians to visit the Yellowstone area. In 1810, Colter reported on the marvels he had seen. Unfortunately, his report and those of other trappers and traders who followed him were considered tall tales.

In the early 1870's, however, two United States government expeditions were officially dispatched to investigate the reports. One of the parties included a photographer. The photographs of Yellowstone and its wonders created a sensation, firing public interest. Ferdinand V. Hayden, a geologist, proposed to the United States Congress that Yellowstone be set aside as a preserve, just like

The author:

Barbara A. Mayes is the managing editor of *Science Year.*

Yosemite in California. The proposal was fueled by the desire of influential railroad owners who wanted the preserve to be a magnet for tourism and provide them with more passengers on their newly laid rail lines. Preserving Yellowstone was also the goal of more public-minded supporters. By setting aside the lands as a preserve, the government could ensure that no individual would own Yellowstone's treasures. This would prevent prospecting and mining for metals and minerals and widespread land clearing for farming and timber production. In 1872, President Ulysses S. Grant signed legislation that made Yellowstone the first national park in the United States, "dedicated and set apart as a public park or pleasuring ground for the benefit and enjoyment of the people."

The drama beneath the surface

Modern Earth scientists are fascinated by the unique geologic drama taking place right beneath the park. This drama has two main players: earthquakes and volcanoes. More earthquakes occur in Yellowstone each year than in any other part of the Rocky Mountains. In fact, Yellowstone's network of *seismometers* (instruments that record the direction, intensity, and duration of earthquakes) registers about 1,000 quakes a year—an average of one every eight hours during the last 25 years. Yellowstone has so many earthquakes because it is riddled with *faults* (deep cracks). These faults extend as far as 10 kilometers (6 miles) into the crust and up to 87 kilometers (54 miles) in length. Most of the tremors caused by the earth-

Yellowstone's approximately 10,000 thermal features, including the mudpot (above) and Steamboat Geyser (top)—the world's largest geyser—are powered by heat released by an underground chamber of partially melted rock as well as an abundant supply of groundwater. The balance between the heat and water determines the features' surface appearance. The underground channels and reservoirs of a geyser contain more water that circulates more freely than those of a mudpot.

YELLOWSTONE HOT SPOTS

The Yellowstone volcano is fueled by a gigantic, relatively stationary plume of magma, called a hot spot, that acts like a blowtorch on the crust above. Many scientists believe that the line of increasingly younger volcanoes running from northern Nevada across southern Idaho to Yellowstone (right) tracks the movement of the North American Plate over the hot spot during the past 16 million years. A three-dimensional image of the Yellowstone plume (red, below), created by measuring the speed of *seismic waves* (vibrations caused by earthquakes) moving through Earth, indicates that the plume rises from at least 640 kilometers (400 miles) deep in the mantle.

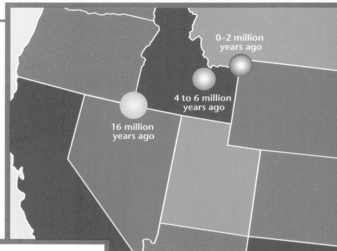

Source: National Park Service

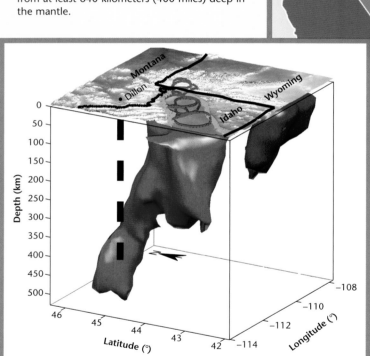

Source: Yuan, H., and Dueker, K. "P-wave Tomogram of the Yellowstone Plume." 2005.

quakes are so tiny that only the seismometers can detect them. Others are strong enough to bounce dishes out of a cabin's cupboards.

Some quakes have been deadly. In 1959, Yellowstone was rocked by an earthquake centered about 10 kilometers (6 miles) west of the park, near Hebgen Lake in Montana. The quake shook tons of rock from a mountainside, causing a landslide that killed 28 people. After the quake, geologists found that, in many places, the ground was tilted upward by 6 meters (20 feet) or more. Geologists believe that such earthquakes have hit the Yellowstone region every few hundred to every few thousand years.

The other chief player in Yellowstone's geologic drama is *volcanism* (volcanic activity). Yellowstone's many geysers and steam vents and the presence of volcanic rock led the park's early explorers to suspect there was "something volcanic" about the region. In 1959, geologist F. R. Boyd, then a graduate student at Harvard University in Cambridge, Massachusetts, discovered that much of the volcanic rock beneath Yellowstone's landscape was the result of the most devastating and violent type of volcanic eruption that can occur. Such eruptions violently expel large amounts of hot ash and dust. In the late 1960's, after years of analyzing rock samples and mapping layers of volcanic rock, geologists Richard L. Christiansen and H. Richard Blank of the United States Geological Survey (USGS) came to a startling conclusion: Such devastating eruptions had occurred not once, but three times in Yellowstone's history.

One reason geologists have been so interested in Yellowstone's volcanic nature is that, geologically speaking, it is an odd place for a large volcano to exist. Most volcanoes form where *tectonic plates* (huge segments of Earth's crust on which the continents and oceans ride) collide or separate. The Yellowstone area, however, is nowhere near the edge of a plate. Scientists now know that Yellowstone's volcanism is a special type, fueled by a phenomenon called a *hot spot*.

Blowtorches on the crust

Hot spots are gigantic, relatively stationary plumes of extremely hot, puttylike rock arising within the *mantle*. This layer of soft, stretchable rock lies between Earth's molten core and its rigid outer crust. Hot spots act like immense blowtorches on the crust above, melting it and fueling volcanoes.

The theory of hot spots was proposed in 1963 by Canadian geologist J. Tuzo Wilson to explain the formation of the Hawaiian Islands. This chain of volcanic islands sits in the middle of the Pacific Plate. Wilson suggested that the islands formed in assembly-line fashion when the seafloor moved over a fixed source of upwelling *magma* (molten rock) from the mantle—in other words, a hot spot. Since then, geologists have found evidence of many more hot spots around the world—more than 100 have been active within the past 10 million years.

In 1972, W. Jason Morgan, a geophysicist at Princeton University in New Jersey, suggested that the volcanism at Yellowstone, which sits in the middle of the North American Plate, was also caused by a hot spot. Morgan based his idea on the discovery that a line of volcanoes similar to those that have erupted at Yellowstone runs from northern Nevada across southern Idaho to Yellowstone. Many geologists believe these volcanoes, which grow progressively younger as they get closer to Yellowstone, reflect the movement of the North American Plate during the past 16 million years. As the plate has crept southwestward at the rate of about 4 centimeters (1.5 inches) per year, the hot spot it passes over has created this trail of volcanoes. For the past 2 million years, the Yellowstone region has been sitting directly above the hot spot.

Additional evidence for a hot spot beneath Yellowstone came from studies of *seismic waves* (shock waves caused by earthquakes). Because seismic waves move through different types of rock at different speeds—

for example, they move more slowly through molten rock than through solid rock—scientists can use them to piece together a picture of Earth's crust and upper mantle.

Geologists first set up a seismic network in Yellowstone in the early 1960's. By the early 1970's, studies of waves generated during Yellowstone's many earthquakes had provided strong evidence that a huge magma chamber about 80 kilometers (50 miles) across at its maximum lies perhaps 8 kilometers (5 miles) beneath Yellowstone. These studies also revealed that the chamber is at the top of a column of superhot, puttylike rock that rises from at least 640 kilometers (400 miles) deep in the mantle.

The hot spot under Yellowstone has, over millions of years, shaped and reshaped the region's landscape. During the past 2.5 million years, Yellowstone has experienced hundreds of eruptions. Some lasted only a few days; others continued for months. At other times, there were no eruptions for hundreds of thousands of years.

Yellowstone's monumental blowouts

Studies in 1992 by Christiansen, Blank, and geochemist John D. Obradovich of the USGS have shown that the first of the three major eruptions that rocked Yellowstone occurred about 2 million years ago.

The first blast was the largest. That eruption expelled 6,000 times as much magma as the amount spewed by Mount St. Helens in 1980. As the volcano erupted, the roof of the magma chamber collapsed and the ground fell inward, forming a *caldera* (huge crater) that covered the central and southwestern parts of the park and extended to Island Park, west of Yellowstone.

The second massive eruption was nearly as devastating as the first. The caldera from this eruption, which was smaller than the first caldera, centered on the Island Park area.

Over the next 600,000 years, the magma chamber grew by displacing the rock around it. Finally, about 640,000 years ago, the volcano blew again. This time it blasted more than 1,042 cubic kilometers (250 cubic miles) of ash into the air. Carried by winds high in the atmosphere, the ash blanketed an area from California to Louisiana and from Texas to Saskatchewan, Canada. Deposits of volcanic ash from this tremendous eruption remain today in parts of the Great Plains. The last eruption left a caldera approximately 76 kilometers long (47 miles) and 45 kilometers (28 miles) wide. The magma chamber under the caldera remained active during the next several thousand years.

Until about 70,000 years ago, lava continued to erupt intermittently from the volcano. In the layers of rock lining the walls of the Grand Canyon of the Yellowstone River and in many other places in Yellowstone, geologists have found lava flows and volcanic ash that were deposited after the most recent caldera-forming eruption. The lava flows filled in

FORMATION OF YELLOWSTONE CALDERA

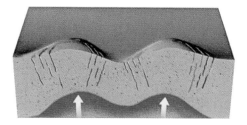

Yellowstone has been rocked by three "supereruptions" in the past 2.5 million years. The latest, which occurred 640,000 years ago, was the climax of a process that began 1.2 million years ago, when a huge magma chamber (red) formed over the hot spot. As the chamber grew, the expansion forced the ground above it upward, forming two large domes with deep cracks along the sides.

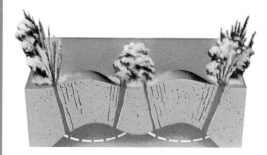

When the cracks reached the magma chamber, the volcano erupted. The blast blew more than 833.6 cubic kilometers (250 cubic miles) of ash and pumice into the air—at least 1,000 times as much as the amount of volcanic material produced by the 1980 eruption of Mount St. Helens in Washington.

As ash and other volcanic material blasted from the magma chamber, the draining chamber collapsed violently, creating a *caldera* (crater) 76 kilometers (47 miles) long and 45 kilometers (28 miles) wide. The floor of the caldera formed a new ceiling over the magma chamber.

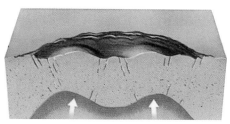

Until about 70,000 years ago, lava continued to erupt from the volcano. As many as 80 lava flows—some as much as 120 meters (400 feet) thick—filled in much of the crater and created the plateaus that cover most of Yellowstone today. The magma chamber refilled, and two new domes formed.

Source: United States Geological Survey

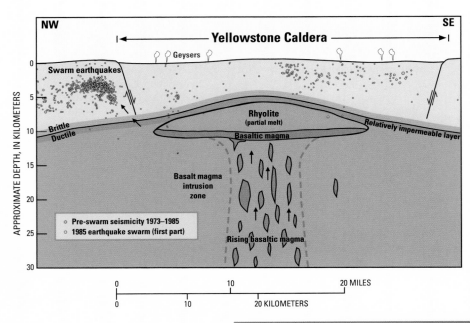

BENEATH THE SURFACE

The magma chamber that lies about 8 kilometers (5 miles) beneath Yellowstone (above) is about 80 kilometers (50 miles) in diameter. As magma and hot groundwater move through and around the chamber, the ground above it rises or falls. An image showing ground movement (right) in Yellowstone, made by a satellite-mounted radar system from 1996 to 2000, reveals how different parts of the park rose by various amounts during that time. The greatest rise—about 80 millimeters (3.1 inches)—occurred in the center of the bull's-eye to the northwest of Yellowstone Lake. The image was created by comparing two satellite images taken four years apart.

much of the caldera, obscuring its edges and creating the broad plateaus that cover most of Yellowstone today. Visitors to the park can see the tops of the lava flows on the Pitchstone, Madison, and Central plateaus.

Then, for thousands of years, glaciers covered most of Yellowstone. Their slow, grinding movements stripped rock from some areas and pushed mounds of rock elsewhere. The last glaciers disappeared about 10,000 years ago. As they melted, they filled Yellowstone Lake, and runoff from the lake drained northward, helping to deepen the Grand Canyon of the Yellowstone.

A natural plumbing system

Even today, there is plenty of action beneath the park's scenic terrain. Over time, the caldera moves up and down. Currently, it is moving up. From 1923 to 1975, the caldera rose about 72 centimeters (28.5 inches). To geologists, the rising crust is evidence of the powerful, Earth-shaping forces operating just below the surface. Other evidence can be found in the park's spectacular geysers, hot springs, and other thermal displays.

In addition to an immense heat source, Yellowstone has two other elements needed to produce thermal displays—water and deep fractures through which it can circulate. All the water that fills Yellowstone's hot springs and gushes from its geysers comes from rain or snow. Rain and snow falling in the area seep down through a network of interconnected cracks and fissures in the volcanic rock. As the water descends, it is heated by solid rock that has, in turn, been heated by magma. The heated water, now lighter, rises through cracks and porous rocks toward the surface. Scientists believe that the water at Yellowstone seeps down at least 2,400 meters (8,000 feet) and perhaps even 3,000 meters (10,000 feet). The journey down and back up to the surface may take hundreds or even thousands of years.

Scientists believe that the underground "plumbing systems" of many of Yellowstone's thermal features are basically similar, with variations depending on the balance of water and heat. The systems consist of main channels and reservoirs, at most 9 to 12 meters (30 to 40 feet) below the ground, surrounded by smaller channels that bring in hot water from below and cooler water from closer to the surface.

Columns of rock at Sheepeater Cliff represent the interior of a rising flow of thick lava that erupted from Yellowstone's magma chamber from 640,000 to 320,000 years ago. As the lava began to cool, it contracted, causing vertical cracks to appear. As the lava became solid rock, the cracks grew larger, dividing the rock into hexagonal columns. Over time, the soil covering the rock eroded, exposing the columns.

A *fumarole* (a hole in Earth's surface through which steam and gas rise), for example, develops from boiling groundwater below the surface. Steam—which occupies many times the volume of liquid water—and gas rise from the groundwater, forcing their way to the surface.

A mudpot forms where fumarolic steam condenses at the surface, partly aided by cool, shallow groundwater. The plumbing system of a mudpot contains slightly more water than that of a fumarole. Gases in the steam form acids that turn the local rock to clay. Particles of clay collect around the vent or opening of the underground channel. Because only a small amount of water trickles from the vent, the clay forms a gurgling pool of hot mud. Sometimes the bubbling mud is colored by minerals in the clay, forming paint pots.

Hot springs and geysers form when a plumbing system has abundant water. A hot spring has a wide, straight main channel through which hot water circulates freely. As a result, the water is never trapped and turned to steam. A geyser, which periodically erupts hot water and steam, has a channel that is constricted. As a result, water trapped at the bottom of the channel is heated far above the temperature at which it would boil at the surface. At first, the pressure of the water above acts like the lid on a pressure cooker, preventing this superheated water from turning to steam. Gradually, however, bubbles of steam begin to form. When they reach the surface, they push the water above them out of the geyser vent. This makes the column of water in the channel lighter, reducing the pressure on the superheated water at the bottom. As steam bubbles push more water out of the geyser, more water changes to steam. When the water pressure in the column falls low enough, water at the bottom of the column flashes to steam. The geyser erupts as the steam blasts its way out of the channel, carrying the rest of the water with it in an exuberant display.

If the balance between water and heat changes, a thermal feature itself may change. For example, a geyser sometimes erupts so powerfully that it enlarges its main channel. As a result, water in the channel can circulate freely and the geyser becomes a hot spring. In fact, scientists believe that most of the large hot springs in Yellowstone were probably geysers at one time. Similarly, if a hot spring plugs up with mineral deposits, it may become a geyser.

Fickle geysers

Some geysers, like Old Faithful, erupt regularly every hour or so. Others are unpredictable. Several factors may affect a geyser's schedule. For example, people sometimes play a part in altering a geyser's schedule. Although the park is peppered with warnings, careless visitors still toss rocks, coins, and litter into the geysers. These quickly become covered with mineral deposits and grow larger. As a result, they may choke off the

DANGEROUS NEIGHBORS

Old Faithful (right), Yellowstone's most famous geyser, and the park's other thermal features may be as damaging to plant life as they are spectacular to see. A patch of dead pine trees with white bases, called bobby soxers (below), illustrates the dangers of living near a hot spring. Minerals from runoff water were taken in by the roots and carried up into the trunks, killing the trees. As the minerals hardened, the trees became partially *petrified* (turned to stone).

channels feeding a geyser. Minute Geyser in the Norris Geyser Basin probably stopped erupting because of such human thoughtlessness.

Earthquakes are the chief cause of changes in geysers' schedules, however. Yellowstone's constant small earthquakes help to keep the channels clear by shaking loose mineral deposits that accumulate in the plumbing systems. Sometimes the quakes open new channels; other times they narrow or close channels.

Large quakes have a more dramatic effect. The Hebgen Lake earthquake in 1959, for example, made the geysers go wild. Some small geysers, including Sapphire Geyser, had major eruptions. Other geysers that had been quiet for years rumbled back to life and continued to erupt for days. Still others, including Old Faithful, began to erupt more frequently. In addition, the water in many hot springs got hotter.

Life among the thermal features

Such fickle behavior makes life precarious for lodgepole pines in the park. If a geyser begins to erupt more vigorously or a new geyser begins to spout, nearby trees may die almost instantly in a scalding shower of steam. Shifts in the runoff of water from hot springs can also claim victims. Yellowstone's geyser basins are pockmarked with patches of dead pines awash in the hot water. The white cuffs at the bases of these trees—called bobby soxers by some researchers—

Yellowstone's underground furnace makes the park's geyser basins and streams especially hospitable to the park's animal population during the coldest months. Some birds that normally migrate to a warmer climate for the winter, such as the trumpeter swan (above), live year-round in the ice-free Yellowstone River. A spike elk (right) crosses the steam-covered surface of a large hot spring known as Boiling River. When food is scarce, elk and bison may graze on beds of microscopic organisms that thrive in the springs' high temperatures.

tell the story. Mineral-rich water from the hot springs was taken in by the trees' roots and carried up into the trunks. As the minerals hardened, the trees became partially petrified.

Other park inhabitants find the hot springs and geysers a more congenial environment. Brilliant ribbons of color in hot springs are caused chiefly by *thermophiles*—life forms that exist and thrive in high temperatures. Thermophiles are chiefly *archaea* (microscopic organisms similar to bacteria but chemically different) and bacteria. The kind—and color—of thermophiles growing in the hot springs depend on the temperature of the water. For example, yellow thermophiles are usually found in water with temperatures as high as 75 °C (167 °F). Orange thermophiles find their niche in cooler water with a temperature of 10 to 13 °C (50 to 56 °F). Many hot springs contain thermophiles of various colors, indicating that many temperature variations can be found in just one pool. Some of the thermophiles in Yellowstone hot springs can be found

A bison digs through the snow near a hot spring to find food. In winter, bison and other large grazing animals often forage near geysers and hot springs, where the relatively warm soil may support plant life during even the coldest months.

Yellowstone National Park Ranger Gary Nelson explores thermal vents at Mary Bay at Yellowstone Lake. Underwater investigations of the lake have revealed a fascinating repository of archaeological, geological, and biological treasures.

nowhere else. Scientists study them to investigate how organisms can flourish in what seems to be a hostile environment.

Other organisms find the thermophiles a ready food source. Several types of tiny flies that live in or on the hot springs eat the thermophiles. The flies, in turn, provide food for mites, spiders, and insects. Much larger animals rely on the thermophiles as well. During the winter, when food is scarce, bison and elk may graze on beds created by photosynthetic thermophiles, which use sunlight for energy.

Some animals use Yellowstone as a winter spa. In the geyser basins and streams, they find warmth and food even in the middle of winter.

For example, rare trumpeter swans live year-round in the ice-free Yellowstone River, despite air temperatures that often plunge to –40 °C (–40 °F). In the warm water of the Firehole River, trout grow to record size.

What lies ahead?

Ironically, Yellowstone's unique array of geysers, hot springs, and mudpots may be the signposts of the park's ultimate destruction. Will the Yellowstone volcano erupt again? Geologists have only history to guide them. Yellowstone's last major eruption was about 70,000 years ago. Should this sleeping giant awaken with the kind of explosive eruptions it has produced in the past, much of western North America could be devastated. Certainly, a major eruption like the last one would be an event beyond the size and scale of anything human beings have experienced since the beginning of recorded history.

In the meantime, scientists continue to explore—and monitor—the geologic drama unfolding at Yellowstone. In 2001, the USGS, the University of Utah in Salt Lake City, and Yellowstone National Park established the Yellowstone Volcano Observatory (YVO) to provide long-term monitoring of volcanic, hydrothermal, and earthquake activity at and below the surface of the park. Monitored around the clock, the observatory was established not because scientists fear an imminent threat from volcanic eruptions, but rather as a facility for studying a geologically active system. According to Jacob B. Lowenstern, USGS scientist-in-charge of YVO, the observatory is "a natural evolution of our collective work over the years to track and study Yellowstone's unrest. … We hope to use YVO to share even more of what we are learning with the public, park visitors, and nearby residents, and to be in a better position to provide warning of any future hazardous activity."

■ FOR ADDITIONAL INFORMATION

Books and periodicals

Geiger, Beth. "Yellowstone: A Supervolcano." *National Geographic Explorer!* March 2006, pp. 4-11.

Smith, Robert B. *Windows into the Earth: The Geologic Story of Yellowstone and Grand Teton National Parks.* Oxford University Press, 2000.

Web sites

National Park Service: Yellowstone National Park Web site—http://www.nps.gov/yell/

Steam Explosions, Earthquakes, and Volcanic Eruptions—What's in Yellowstone's Future?—http://pubs.usgs.gov/fs/2005/3024/

Yellowstone Volcano Observatory Web site—http://volcanoes.usgs.gov/yvo

Polio:
Fighting a persistent foe

By Judy Peres

A crippling disease that nearly disappeared in the 1900's continues to find new victims in the 2000's.

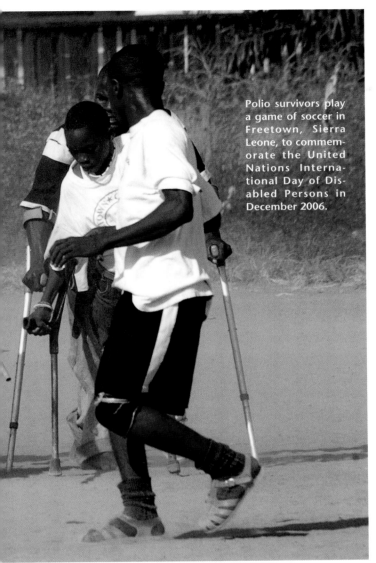

Polio survivors play a game of soccer in Freetown, Sierra Leone, to commemorate the United Nations International Day of Disabled Persons in December 2006.

In the early 1950's, parents in the United States lived in terror. On the hottest days of summer, they kept their children away from beaches and swimming pools and warned them against sipping from water fountains. They feared the children would contract a highly infectious disease that could paralyze its victims in just a few hours and for which there was no cure. That disease was *poliomyelitis*, commonly called polio. In 1952—the height of the last major polio epidemic in the United States—the disease claimed 3,145 lives and left 21,269 people with mild to disabling paralysis. By 2007, however, at least two generations of Americans were unfamiliar with polio and its devastating effects.

Thanks to highly effective vaccines, polio has become all but extinct in the United States and most other developed countries. No more than a handful of cases occur in these countries each year, usually either caused by the polio vaccine itself or brought in by new immigrants from regions where polio is still prevalent. In some parts of the developing world, however, polio continues to cripple and kill despite the efforts of officials and volunteers who have made the disease the target of the world's largest international health project. In 2003 and 2004, a resurgence of polio in Africa and Asia slowed these efforts. Nevertheless, new strategies continue to reduce the rate of infection. These strategies have included better methods for tracking the virus around the world and a new vaccine that specifically targets the virus responsible for the paralyzing form of polio. In 1988, when the global *eradication* (elimination) program was launched, the paralyzing form of the disease struck an estimated 1,000 children worldwide each day. By 2007, that rate had dropped to four or five. Although most efforts around the world focus on wiping out the virus, researchers are also studying the long-term effects of polio. A condition called post-polio syndrome, first recognized in the mid-1980's, can strike polio survivors years, or even decades, after the original attack.

The author:

Judy Peres is a specialist writer for the *Chicago Tribune.*

The poliovirus

Polio is caused by a *virus* (a microscopic organism that lives in a cell of another living thing). The virus enters the body through the mouth and then infects the digestive system. Human beings are the only natural host of the virus. Technically, polio can be caused by any one of three *enteroviruses* (viruses that infect the *gastrointestinal tract,* where digestion takes place). These polioviruses are called Type 1, Type 2, and Type 3. No country has reported a case of Type 2 since 1999, and so scientists believe that strain has been wiped out. Most efforts by researchers and public health officials have focused on Type 1, the strain that causes most cases of paralytic polio.

Once inside the body, the poliovirus starts multiplying in the throat. Within a week, it spreads to the gastrointestinal tract, where it can live for a number of weeks, multiplying all the while. From there, it is absorbed into the bloodstream and *lymphatic system* (network that returns fluid from body tissues to the bloodstream), which can distribute the virus throughout the body. If the virus reaches the *central nervous system* (the brain and spinal cord), it can invade nerve cells and multiply so rapidly that it damages or kills the cells. Paralysis results when a large number of cells are destroyed. Fortunately, most people who become infected by the poliovirus develop only flulike symptoms or no symptoms at all. Scientists estimate that 1 in 200 infected individuals—and perhaps as few as 1 in 1,000—become paralyzed.

Spread of the disease

Although the poliovirus most often infects young children, adults and adolescents can also contract the disease. Pregnant women, the elderly, and people with a weakened *immune system* appear to be at an especially high risk. (The immune system comprises the cells, molecules, and tissues that help defend the body against diseases and other harmful invaders.) Crowded living conditions and poor hygiene make it easier for the virus to spread. Ironically, it was the development of modern plumbing in the early 1900's that allowed for the outbreak of polio epidemics in Western countries. Before then, the poliovirus was *endemic* (constantly present somewhere in the population), and most children developed protective *antibodies* (molecules that destroy disease-causing microorganisms). Modern sanitation interrupted the spread of the virus, leaving large groups of people with no *immunity* (resistance to disease). As a result, in 1916 alone, there were 27,000 cases in the United States and 6,000 deaths.

The poliovirus is transmitted mainly through contaminated *fecal material*—solid waste from the body. Typically, infected people who fail to wash their hands properly after using the bathroom pass the virus to others. Less commonly, the virus can be spread indirectly,

WORLDWIDE REDUCTION OF POLIO

Since 1988, the number of worldwide polio cases has fallen by more than 99 percent, the result of the Global Polio Eradication Initiative.

According to the World Health Organization (WHO), it appears that there were more cases of polio in 1981 than 1980, but this is not necessarily the case. Many countries worldwide put measures in place in 1981 to ensure official reporting of polio. Thus, a number of polio cases in 1980 remained uncounted. Variations in the data from 2000 to 2001 were caused by changes in uniform reporting for all countries.

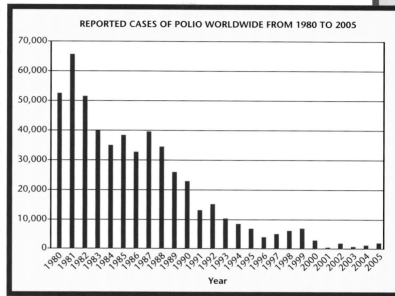

REPORTED CASES OF POLIO WORLDWIDE FROM 1980 TO 2005

Source: World Health Organization.

Polio is *endemic* (regularly found) in only Afghanistan, India, Nigeria, and Pakistan. People in countries where polio is nonendemic became infected with polio because of exposure to the virus through travel or contact with infected migrants from countries in which the disease was endemic.

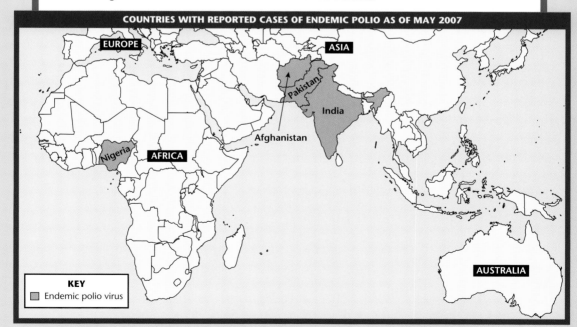

COUNTRIES WITH REPORTED CASES OF ENDEMIC POLIO AS OF MAY 2007

KEY
Endemic polio virus

Source: World Health Organization Global Polio Eradication Initiative.

through food or water contaminated by feces or saliva from an infected person. Transmission is possible for up to six weeks while the virus is alive in the digestive system of the host. The *incubation period* (the amount of time from infection to the first sign of symptoms) ranges from 3 to 35 days. However, infected people are most contagious for 7 to 10 days before and after their symptoms appear. Infected people can transmit the virus to others even if they never develop any symptoms themselves. An estimated 90 to 95 percent of all polio infections are transmitted by infected people who never develop any symptoms themselves.

Some people experience only mild symptoms that are similar to those of the flu. This lesser illness is called *abortive poliomyelitis*. In these cases, the virus never reaches the central nervous system. These patients display such symptoms as fever, headache, sore throat, and vomiting within a few days after exposure, but usually recover completely in less than a week. Some patients experience severe headache as well as pain

POLIO TIMELINE

Although polio was not identified as a disease until the 1700's, epidemics have occurred throughout history. The first image of a polio survivor may be an ancient Egyptian engraving from about 1200 B.C. that shows a king named Siptah with a deformed foot (right). ────

1789	British physician Michael Underwood provides the first clinical description of polio.
1840	German physician Jacob Heine describes the clinical features of polio and its involvement with the spinal cord.
1894	Vermont suffers the first U.S. polio epidemic, with 132 cases.
1908	Austrian physicians Karl Landsteiner and Erwin Popper determine that polio is caused by a virus.
1916	

The first major epidemic of polio occurs in the United States.

1921	Future U.S. president Franklin Delano Roosevelt (FDR) contracts polio at age 39.
1927	Roosevelt forms the Warm Springs Foundation in Georgia for polio rehabilitation.
1929	Engineer Philip Drinker and physician Louis Shaw develop the first practical iron lung.
1930	Two of the three strains of poliovirus are discovered.
1935	Maurice Brodie and John Kolmer unsuccessfully test polio vaccines.

and stiffness in the neck and back. These symptoms are due to a type of *meningitis* (inflammation of the outer layer of the brain and spinal cord). Nevertheless, the vast majority of people who get this nonparalytic form of polio recover within 10 days.

Fewer than 1 percent of people infected with the poliovirus develop paralytic polio, the most severe form. Some of them may feel ill at first, followed by a few days with no symptoms at all. Then symptoms begin again, including headache and pain in the back and neck. These symptoms are caused by an invasion of the nerves that control muscles.

Spinal poliomyelitis occurs when the poliovirus attacks the nerves that control the muscles of the legs, arms, trunk, abdomen, and pelvis. This is the most common form of paralytic polio. If the virus attacks the nerve cells of the brain stem, where the brain is connected to the spinal cord, the disease can be even more serious. In this form, called *bulbar poliomyelitis*, the disease affects the muscles for swallowing and

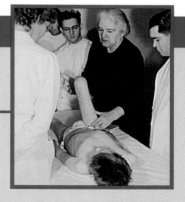

1938	Roosevelt founds the National Foundation for Infantile Paralysis, which became the March of Dimes in 1960.
1940's	Sister Kenny, an Australian nurse, arrives in the United States to promote her new heat treatment for polio.
1953	Medical researcher Jonas Salk and associates develop an effective polio vaccine using a killed virus.
1954	Nearly 2 million children in the United States participate in clinical trials for Salk's vaccine.
1955–1957	Inoculation reduces the incidence of polio in the United States by 85 to 90 percent.
late 1950's	Medical researcher Albert Sabin develops an oral vaccine using a weakened virus.
1979	The last case of polio caused by a wild virus is reported in the United States.
1980's	Post-polio syndrome is identified.
1981	The poliovirus genome sequence is published.
1988	International health agencies begin a campaign to eradicate polio throughout the world.
1999	Last reported case of wild Type 2 polio worldwide.
2006	Endemic polio is confined to four countries: Afghanistan, India, Nigeria, and Pakistan.

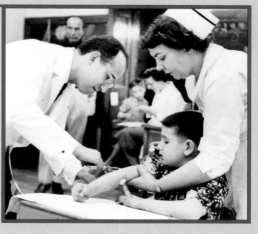

MARCH OF DIMES

In 1938, President Franklin D. Roosevelt, himself a victim of polio, grew concerned about the expanding polio epidemic in the United States. In response, he established the National Foundation for Infantile Paralysis. During a radio campaign to raise public awareness of polio and funds for fighting the disease, comedian Eddie Cantor came up with the phrase *March of Dimes*. The phrase was used to encourage listeners to send their dimes to the president.

The dimes rolled in—for years. The campaign was so successful that the National Foundation for Infantile Paralysis officially changed its name to the March of Dimes in 1979. With the donations from the public, the March of Dimes funded research for a vaccine against polio. In 1952, medical researcher Jonas Salk tested the vaccine on children who had recovered from the poliovirus since it was known they could produce antibodies to attack the virus. After these tests and other clinical tests had successfully been carried out, millions of children were inoculated with the vaccine. With the help of the March of Dimes and the vaccine, polio was effectively wiped out in the United States by the late 1970's.

Franklin Roosevelt, the 32nd president of the United States, was stricken with polio in 1921 at the age of 39. Because of the disease, Roosevelt had to rely on braces and crutches or a wheelchair for support and mobility for the remainder of his life. As president, Roosevelt established the National Foundation for Infantile Paralysis to provide support for polio victims and to find a cure for the disease.

for moving the eyes, tongue, face, and neck. It may also attack the nerves that control breathing and the circulation of vital body fluids.

When the virus attacks nerve cells, they can become inflamed and ultimately are destroyed. Dead nerve cells can no longer send out impulses to muscles; the muscles stop contracting and become limp and, eventually, paralyzed. The muscles then start to *atrophy* (shrink). The extent of the paralysis depends on which cells are hit and how many are destroyed. Most commonly, one or both legs are affected. The muscles become weak and movement is difficult. Pain may occur, especially when the limbs are stretched or straightened. When paralysis develops, the person may not be able to stand or walk (though patients still have feeling in those limbs).

The virus can also strike the muscles of the back or abdomen, affecting posture; those of the face and neck, causing the head to droop; or even the muscles that control breathing and heart rate, which can lead to death. As many as 5 percent of children who develop paralytic polio die.

In most polio cases, the nerves are not completely destroyed and the patient recovers. Healthy nerves branch out in an attempt to compensate for the dead ones. Within about a month, nerve impulses begin to return. Most muscle function is recovered within six months, though it may take up to two years. Only in rare cases, where the nerve cells are completely destroyed, is paralysis permanent, leaving the patients with serious disability.

Researchers have not found a drug that can kill the poliovirus or stop it from spreading in the body. The degree of recovery from polio often depends on immediate medical attention and good nursing care. Complete rest is perhaps the most important treatment; fatigue may worsen the disease. In the early 1900's, physicians used casts to immobilize stricken limbs and prevent muscle contraction. Thanks to the work of Sister Elizabeth Kenny, an Australian nurse, in the 1940's, health care providers now use hot, moist bandages to relieve pain. Movement is prescribed to maintain flexibility. After the fever goes down, physical therapists gently move the patient's limbs to help prevent deformities. Later, more intensive exercises strengthen and retrain the muscles. Even extensively paralyzed patients often develop enough motion to carry on many activities. Less severely paralyzed people usually resume most of their previous activities. Some may need splints, braces, or crutches. When breathing muscles are paralyzed, physicians may use a mechanical device, such as a respirator, to help the patient breathe. About two-thirds of such patients recover natural breathing.

Dianne Odell watches her favorite soap opera at home in Jackson, Tennessee, in 2007. Odell has lived in an iron lung for 57 years. She is among only 30 to 40 people in the United States who depend on the devices. Most of them were children when they contracted polio, which left them unable to inhale on their own.

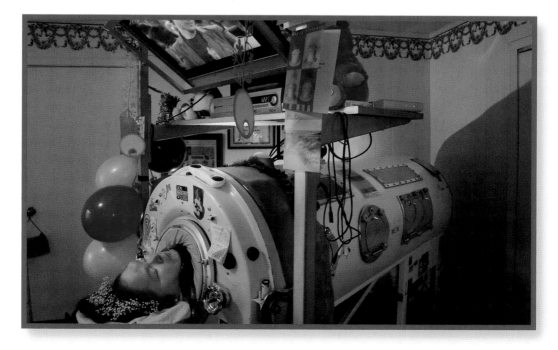

Polio vaccine

Prevention is a far more powerful tool than treatment for fighting epidemic diseases such as polio. Prevention is accomplished through vaccination. All vaccines contain material that stimulates the body to produce antibodies against a particular infectious disease. The antibodies protect the person if he or she is later exposed to the actual disease-causing organism. The modern concept of vaccination for infectious disease has been known since the 1790's, when British physician Edward Jenner noticed that milkmaids who had contracted the relatively harmless cowpox disease did not contract smallpox. Based on this observation, Jenner safely immunized a boy against deadly smallpox by *inoculating* him (giving a preparation to provide immunity) with material taken from a cowpox sore on the hand of a milkmaid.

The Austrian immunologist Karl Landsteiner identified a virus as the cause of the disease in 1908. (Immunologists study the cells, molecules, and tissues that help defend the body against diseases and other harmful invaders.) Soon after, U.S. pathologist Simon Flexner isolated the virus and discovered polio antibodies in patients.

In the 1920's and 1930's, many researchers sought to understand the disease and develop a vaccine, but early attempts were unsuccessful. By 1936, U.S. physician Albert Sabin had succeeded in growing poliovirus in laboratory cultures. Sabin was working on a vaccine using a live,

Women and children collect water from a muddy stream. In many areas of Africa, war or lack of development leaves people with no access to clean water supplies, forcing them to take their drinking water from polluted streams. The lack of sanitation contributes to the spread of such diseases as polio.

attenuated (weakened) virus when U.S. researcher Jonas Salk developed a vaccine using a *killed* virus (virus that was modified so it could not infect its host). Even though it contained no live virus, Salk's vaccine remained strong enough to provoke an immune response and prevent infection by the live virus. Live vaccines work faster and induce longer-lasting immunity. However, they also have the potential to cause infection in people with weak immune defenses, though this is extremely rare. Both types of vaccine are currently used against polio, and both protect against all three types of poliovirus.

The Salk vaccine, which is given by injection, was declared safe and effective in 1955 by the U.S. government. The Sabin vaccine, which was approved for use in the United States in 1961, is an oral vaccine. That vaccine is typically given in four doses—at 2 months, 4 months, 6 to 18 months, and 4 to 6 years of age. By 1965, U.S. health officials recorded only 61 cases of paralytic polio, compared with 2,525 cases in 1960. The use of the oral vaccine has been or is being phased out in areas where *wild* (naturally occurring) polio has been eliminated because of the slight risk of contracting vaccine-associated paralytic poliomyelitis (VAPP). In countries that still have outbreaks of wild polio, however, the oral vaccine is still being used.

Global Polio Eradication Initiative

In 2007, polio continued to hang on in the developing world long after it was eradicated elsewhere. In 1988, the World Health Organization (WHO), along with Rotary International, the United Nations Children's Fund (UNICEF), and the U.S. Centers for Disease Control (CDC), launched the Global Polio Eradication Initiative. It is the largest international health project ever undertaken, with more than $3 billion spent by 2007. Rotary International is a network of international volunteers who, along with UNICEF and WHO workers, go into underdeveloped regions to ensure polio vaccinations are administered and polio cases are reported. Thanks to these efforts, the annual number of polio cases worldwide has fallen by more than 99 percent, from an estimated 350,000 cases to fewer than 2,000.

In addition, by the end of 2006, the number of countries with wild poliovirus was down to 16 from 125 before the initiative was launched. The virus remains endemic only in Afghanistan, India, Nigeria, and Pakistan. Health workers have never succeeded in vaccinating enough people in those countries to permanently interrupt transmission of the disease. The four countries account for more than 90 percent of the world's polio cases. Unfortunately, polio has continued to spread to previously polio-free areas. Ten countries—Angola, Bangladesh, Cameroon, the Democratic Republic of Congo, Ethiopia, Kenya, Namibia, Nepal, Niger, and Somalia—reported cases in 2006. All were associated with outbreaks originating elsewhere.

Polio vaccination field officials carry vaccine supplies as they make house-to-house visits to immunize children in Lagos, Nigeria. Nigeria is the only African country in which polio is still endemic. By 2007, most of the nations of Africa were polio free because of the National Immunization Day campaign. During NID's, children receive free vaccinations against diseases such as polio.

WHO set 2000 as its original target year for wiping out polio worldwide. Despite extraordinary progress, the goal remains elusive, and some experts question whether worldwide eradication is possible. In addition to being extremely contagious, polio is often transmitted by people who are immune to the disease themselves or who are infected but have no symptoms. There are other obstacles as well.

Barriers to eradication

The polio vaccine is not always effective. Even though the quality or potency of the vaccine is not a problem, some people in certain populations seem to require 10 or even 12 doses of the vaccine to achieve immunity—far more than is normally recommended. Health officials believe the vaccine may be less effective in these cases because of malnourishment or the presence of gastrointestinal disorders, such as diarrhea, which may interfere with the body's ability to absorb and process the vaccine.

One reason the disease remains endemic in Nigeria, which has more than half the cases in the world, is that immunization campaigns were suspended in 2003 and 2004 after tribal leaders announced that the vaccine was tainted. Rumors spread that the immunization campaign was a plot to spread AIDS or to make young girls infertile. Similar propaganda has been spread in Pakistan. Some Islamic clerics there have falsely claimed that the vaccine contains *estrogen* (a hormone that promotes development in females) and that it will make men impotent.

Three official investigations in 2004 concluded that the Nigerian vaccine was safe. Similarly, investigations in 2006 confirmed that the vaccine

in Pakistan did not contain estrogen. Nonetheless, many Nigerians and Pakistanis remained suspicious of the vaccine. The rumors in Pakistan have left more than 160,000 children unprotected. Although immunizations resumed in Nigeria, the 11-month suspension is blamed for the reemergence and spread of polio in 10 previously polio-free countries.

In Afghanistan, Somalia, and parts of Pakistan and Ethiopia, armed conflict and political instability have created additional inoculation difficulties. To conduct immunization campaigns, public health workers must negotiate "days of tranquility" on which the warring parties agree to suspend the violence. Health officials may also find their own safety at risk in these regions. In February 2007, the chief of health services of the tribal agency of Pakistan's Bajaur region was killed by a roadside bomb.

Eradication efforts have also been challenged by incidents in which the vaccine itself triggered cases of polio, which then spread to other people. One such outbreak occurred toward the end of 2005 on the island of Madura, in Indonesia, where 46 cases were documented.

A health care worker in Al Gabeen, Yemen, has arrived by burro to vaccinate children against polio. Although Yemen had been certified polio free in 2003, the disease reemerged in 2005 when the infection spread from Nigeria.

New ways to fight the disease

New tools and research findings have revitalized the eradication effort. In 2005, health workers in India introduced a *monovalent* vaccine (containing antibodies to only one antigen) that showed promise in wiping out the virus in the impoverished states of Uttar Pradesh and Bihar, which were also among the last refuges of the wild smallpox virus. The traditional *trivalent* vaccines contain weakened forms of each of the three types of poliovirus. The three strains can interfere with one another in-

Therapist Lea Morgan works with Elaine Ricks in a pool during a reunion of polio patients who had been treated at the Warm Springs Institute in Warm Springs, Georgia. Ricks was at the Institute in the 1950's and is now suffering from post-polio syndrome.

side the body, producing immunity to one strain but not another. The monovalent vaccine, by contrast, is specific to the Type 1 virus—the dominant strain—and may, therefore, prove more effective. The Advisory Committee on Polio Eradication, which is part of the Global Polio Eradication Initiative, reported at the end of 2005 that the monovalent oral vaccine appeared to have stopped transmission of polio in Egypt and most areas of India. The committee recommended that the new vaccine be used to mop up the remaining polio outbreaks worldwide.

For decades, international health workers have monitored outbreaks of polio by keeping track of how many cases occurred in each part of the world. Now they have tools that make it possible to track the virus at the molecular level. Scientists have succeeded in *sequencing* (analyzing the arrangement of DNA) in the polio *genome* (all the genes in a cell), enabling them to create a genetic profile of every wild virus. Because the genetic material of the virus is constantly mutating, researchers can use patterns of genetic similarity to figure out where a particular strain came from, how it evolved, and how it was transmitted. For example, genetic sequencing confirmed that polioviruses reported in 2006 in Niger were imported from Nigeria. Those in Nepal came from India. Genetic sequencing also makes it possible to monitor the progress of eradication efforts—for example, to tell when a particular country no longer has endemic polio—and to determine whether the source of an outbreak is importation or previously undetected internal transmission.

Post-polio syndrome

Unfortunately, even if health workers achieve the goal of global eradication, it could take several generations before the last traces of polio disappear. Some polio survivors develop a newly identified condition, known as post-polio syndrome (PPS), from 15 years to, more typically, 30 to 40 years after the initial attack. The symptoms of PPS include fatigue, progressive muscle weakness or atrophy, pain in the joints, skeletal deformities, and difficulty breathing. Post-polio syndrome is not contagious and is rarely life threatening. More than 440,000 polio survivors in the United States may be at risk for PPS. Researchers estimate that between 25 and 60 percent of survivors may be affected by the condition.

The cause of PPS is unknown. Some experts have suggested that it may be related to the overuse of the new branches developed by nerves that were damaged by the poliovirus years before. They suggest that over time the new branches may themselves weaken.

Researchers have not yet identified a cure for PPS. Several medications have been tested and found ineffective. However, nonfatiguing exercises can improve muscle strength. Researchers are studying whether intravenous *immunoglobulin* (protein in blood plasma that acts as an antibody) may be helpful in relieving pain and improving strength.

A new goal

In February 2007, the Stakeholder Consultation (nongovernment agencies, including businesses that are accredited by WHO and will benefit from the eradication of polio) for the Global Polio Eradication Initiative reported, "The world now has a second and best chance to eradicate polio." Although the group missed its original deadlines, this statement is more than simple optimism. Polio has been eliminated in most of the world. No cases have been reported in the Americas, Europe, or the western Pacific since 1998, and only 2,000 cases worldwide were reported in 2006. The Global Polio Eradication Initiative is committed to achieving global elimination by 2008. If it meets this goal, polio will be a vanished epidemic, a disease that future generations will only read about in history books.

■ FOR ADDITIONAL INFORMATION

Books and periodicals

Brooks, Tim, and Khan, Omar A. *The End of Polio? Behind the Scenes of the Campaign to Vaccinate Every Child on the Planet.* Apha Press, 2006.
Kluger, Jeffrey. "Polio's Back: Why Now?" *Time,* May 9, 2005, pp. 46-47.
Wilson, Daniel J. *Living with Polio: The Epidemic and Its Survivors.* University of Chicago Press, 2005.

Web sites

World Health Organization: Poliomyelitis Web site—http://www.who.int/topics/poliomyelitis/en/
Post-Polio Health International Web site—http://www.post-polio.org/

Renewable Energy: *Power* for the Future

By Tom Clynes

Without energy, modern societies would cease to function. Energy runs our lights, our cars, and our computers. It supports our transportation and communication systems, water and waste treatment, agriculture, and health care.

All of the different types of energy fall into one of two categories. Nonrenewable energy comes from sources that are being used up and cannot be replenished quickly. Such sources include the fossil fuels coal, natural gas, and petroleum. Fossil fuels were formed beneath Earth's surface over millions of years from the remains of prehistoric plants and animals. Renewable energy (also known as alternative energy) is energy from resources that are easily replaceable or, for all practical purposes, cannot be depleted. Renewable energy sources include sunlight, wind, certain crop plants, water, the heat found deep inside Earth, and the element hydrogen.

For thousands of years, people used renewable energy sources. They burned wood to keep warm and to cook their food. They harnessed the power of wind and water to grind grain. In the 1900's, as societies became more industrialized, energy consumption increased, and people turned to fossil fuels for their main source of energy. The price of oil began to rise in the 1970's. In the 1990's, prices soared even higher, as rapidly developing nations such as China and India increased their demand.

By the summer of 2006, oil prices had hit a record high. (They rose again in 2007.) At the same time, evidence increased that rising levels of carbon dioxide in the atmosphere could result in unprecedented climate change and environmental devastation. Also in 2006, according to energy analysts, energy alternatives finally hit the mainstream. The research firm New Energy Finance Limited of London reported that total investment in alternative energy reached $63 billion in 2006, compared with $30 billion in 2004. The use of geothermal, solar, water, wind, and *biomass* energy increased for such uses as generating electric energy and heat and producing transportation fuel. (Biomass is any organic material that can be converted into energy or into a source of energy.)

Renewable energy sources can limit the emissions of *greenhouse gases* (gases such as carbon dioxide that trap heat in the atmosphere) and bring economic benefits to regions where such resources as wind and farmland are abundant. Renewable resources can also be easily incorporated into distributed-energy systems. Such systems consist of small power-generating sources located near or at the site of the energy consumer.

Nevertheless, to make renewable energy sources economically viable, one significant challenge remains. Systems that can store renewable energy and make it available at the flick of a switch still need to be developed.

The author:
Tom Clynes is a journalist and photographer who covers conservation and environmental conflicts, science, culture, and adventure travel for a wide range of publications, including *National Geographic Adventure* and *Popular Science*.

The sun is about 150 million kilometers (93 million miles) from Earth, and only a tiny fraction of the sun's energy strikes Earth—about one-hundredth of one-millionth of 1 percent. Yet the sunlight that hits Earth every hour carries enough energy to meet the world's entire energy demand for a whole year.

Why solar power?

Solar power has many environmental and economic benefits. Because it comes from the sun, solar energy is free. Unlike power generated from fossil fuels, solar power produces no greenhouse gases or radioactive wastes. Solar power systems can be mass-produced and require little maintenance after they are installed. There is a strong market for solar power in rural parts of developing countries, where it is less expensive to use solar panels for small electric devices than to transmit electric power from central plants. Nevertheless, though solar technology is advancing rapidly, solar power systems in the early 2000's were still more expensive to build than fossil fuel systems. They also had limited efficiency. However, once a solar power plant is built, solar energy can be harvested inexpensively.

Solar power also has limitations. Solar collection can occur only during daylight, and some solar collection systems do not work well on cloudy days. To fill around-the-clock energy needs, energy storage systems (such as batteries) must be used at night. Finally, depending on how much solar energy is needed, solar panels can take up a lot of surface area—even the entire rooftop of a house. Despite these limitations, more and more people in the early 2000's began to embrace solar energy.

How solar power is used

Homeowners can use solar energy to power lights, heat and cool the house, and heat water. Businesses can use solar power for these purposes and for industrial processes as well. Some solar power users are able to produce enough electric power to end their reliance on power companies or even sell their surplus current to electric utilities.

Utilities and power plants also take advantage of the sun's energy. *Concentrating solar power systems* (systems that use specially shaped panels that concentrate the solar energy to specific points on the panel) give consumers the benefit of solar power without investing in personal solar systems. Worldwide, more than 3,696,800 *kilowatts* (1,000 *watts*, or units of electric power) of *photovoltaic power* was produced in 2006. (Photovoltaic power is electric current generated when the energy in sunlight causes electric charges to flow through layers of a conductive material.) The United States produced more than 479,000 kilowatts. Even with these amounts, solar energy provided less than 1 percent of the energy the world consumes.

Photovoltaic solar cells

Photovoltaic cells—solar panels mounted on roofs to collect energy from the sun—are the most familiar form of solar power. Photovoltaic solar devices use *semiconductors* to convert sunlight to electric power. (Semiconductors are mineral substances that conduct electric current more efficiently than insulators but less efficiently than metals.)

By the early 2000's, solar cells had gained broad acceptance in remote areas where extending electric power lines would be too difficult or too costly. The cells are often used to operate such devices as remote weather stations, irrigation pumps, and ocean navigation aids.

By 2006, manufacturers had also developed photovoltaic technology that allowed people to charge cell phones and MP3 players through solar-collecting backpacks. In the future, hybrid cars might be refueled through solar-collecting surfaces, and solar-powered airplanes might fly the skies.

The photovoltaic effect was discovered by French physicist Edmond Becquerel in 1839. Becquerel found that when sunlight hits the semiconductor silicon, the solar energy knocks electrons loose from their atoms, allowing the electrons to flow through the silicon to produce an electric current. In 1954, U.S. scientists at Bell Laboratories (now part of Lucent Technologies) introduced a photovoltaic cell capable of producing a useful amount of energy. The National Aeronautics and Space Administration (NASA) began using photovoltaic cells in 1958 to power electrical components on satellites.

The first photovoltaic cells had a conversion efficiency of less than 4 percent. In other words, the cells only converted about 4 percent of the solar energy hitting them into usable electrical energy. In fact, the amount of energy produced was so small that a lifetime of use would never recover the energy that went into the cell's production. In 2007, commercially available solar photovoltaic cells had a conversion efficiency of 12 to 18 percent, and typically recovered the energy that went into their manufacture after one to three years.

Conventional photovoltaic cells are made with two thin slices of the extremely purified mineral silicon. Impurities are added to the layers so that an electrical field develops at the boundary between the layers. When sunlight strikes the cell, the light dislodges electrons from the silicon atoms. An electrical field in the photovoltaic cell separates free electrons from one layer and forces them into the other layer. The flow of electrons creates a current that is collected by metal contacts at the top and bottom of the cell. That current can be used to power a variety of devices.

Solar cells are usually constructed in panels that hold about 40 cells. About 10 panels are arranged in groups called arrays, which can measure several meters (yards) on a side. Photovoltaic arrays can be mounted at a fixed angle facing south (in the Northern Hemisphere) or on a device that moves to follow the sun and capture the most sunlight throughout the day. From 10 to 20 photovoltaic arrays can harness enough power for a household. For electric utilities or industrial applications, hundreds of arrays can be interconnected to form a single power system. The main drawback of photovoltaic cells is their high cost of manufacture, largely because of the scarcity of silicon. Silicon is used to make about 93 percent of the world's photovoltaic cells.

Another form of photovoltaics, thin-film solar cells, uses layers of semiconductor materials only a few micrometers thick. These clear films can be added to rooftop shingles, building facades, or even windows, transforming them into devices that harvest energy. But thin film is less efficient than conventional photovoltaic cells, so more area must be covered to harvest the same amount of energy. The best thin-film solar cells achieve efficiencies of 10 to 13 percent.

Solar concentrators

Photovoltaic cells convert sunlight directly to electric power. Other types of devices convert sunlight to heat and then to electric power. Such devices are called solar concentrators. Most conventional power plants burn fossil fuels to boil water. The steam produced by the boiling water rotates a turbine that produces electric power. Solar concentrator systems use the sun as their heat source. They are made of reflective materials that focus the sun's heat energy, which then drives a generator to produce electric current. Parabolic-trough systems concentrate the sun's energy through rectangular, curved mirrors. (A parabola is a geometric shape similar to a shallow bowl.) The mirrors tilt toward the sun, focusing sunlight onto a pipe that runs down the center of a trough. Oil or another heat-absorbing fluid flowing through the pipe becomes heated to as high as 400 °C (750 °F). The hot fluid is then pumped to a conventional steam generator, which produces electric power.

Solar concentrators called parabolic troughs line the Mojave Desert near Barstow, California. The curved mirrors of parabolic troughs, which are tilted toward the sun, concentrate sunlight onto a pipe in the center of the trough that contains heat-absorbing fluid. The hot fluid is piped to a steam generator that produces electric power.

In 2007, the largest parabolic-trough facilities were located at Kramer Junction and Harper Lake in the Mojave Desert northeast of Los Angeles, California, where they produced more than 300 *megawatts* (one million watts) of energy. The electric power generated could power more than 90,000 homes. The parabolic trough is considered the most well-established and most versatile concentrator technology.

A *dish/engine system* uses a mirrored dish that looks like a very large satellite dish. The reflective surface concentrates the sun's heat onto a fluid-filled receiver in front of the dish. The receiver transfers the heat to fluid within an engine, causing the fluid to expand and push against a piston or turbine to produce mechanical power. This power is used to run a generator to produce electricity. Dishes raise fluid temperatures to 750 °C (1,380 °F). Thus, they hold great promise for generating large amounts of electric power.

In early 2007, construction was to begin on the world's largest solar energy farm, which uses dish/engine technology. When the Stirling Energy Systems solar power plant is completed, some 20,000 dishes, stretching over approximately 1,800 hectares (4,500 acres) of the Mojave Desert, will produce up to 600 megawatts of electric power—enough to power 278,000 California homes. The plant will be the first commercial application of the Stirling solar dish, which can convert about 30 percent of the sun's energy into electric power, making it the most efficient solar-electric technology available in 2007.

A *power tower system* (also called a *central receiver system*) uses a large array of mirrors to focus sunlight onto a fluid-filled receiver at the top of the tower. The mirrors heat molten salt, which flows into a conventional steam generator.

Because molten salt retains heat efficiently, it can be stored for several days before being converted into electric power, allowing solar-powered electricity to be produced on cloudy days or even several hours after sunset. In Spain, the first commercial power tower plant, called Solar Tres, was being built in 2007 using technology developed at the pilot Solar One and Solar Two projects in Barstow, California. A large thermal storage system will enable this solar power plant to produce power 24 hours a day in the summer.

Passive solar

Building designers also take advantage of the power of the sun by using techniques called passive solar heating and daylighting.

To use passive solar heating in the Northern Hemisphere, designers position the south side of a building so it is exposed to the most sunlight possible. Modern passively heated buildings usually have large windows facing south. The floors and walls that are exposed to the sun are built of materials that absorb the sun's heat and release it at night when it is needed. This passive solar design characteristic is called *direct gain*.

Many passive solar structures also use daylighting and solar lighting. Daylighting is simply the use of natural sunlight to illuminate a building's interior through windows and skylights. Solar lighting relies on roof-mounted solar concentrators to collect sunlight. The sunlight is brought through optical fibers to lighting fixtures that illuminate the building's interior spaces.

Solar hot water

Most solar water-heating systems are mounted on rooftops. The solar collector usually consists of a rectangular box with small tubes running through it. These tubes carry fluid—usually water or an antifreeze solution—and are attached to an absorber plate. The plate is painted a dark color to absorb the sun's heat, which radiates into the fluid passing through the tubes. The tubes then transfer the heated fluid to an insulated storage tank. Systems that use fluids other than water usually make use of a *heat exchanger*, a device that keeps the fluid separate from the water to be heated.

Solar collecting boxes on the roof of a home absorb heat from sunlight and transfer it to small tubes inside the boxes. The tubes contain a fluid such as water or antifreeze. The heated fluid flows to an insulated tank, where it is stored until needed.

Trainers from Solar Cooker International, a nonprofit organization based in Sacramento, California, demonstrate an inexpensive solar cooker at the Kakuma Refugee Camp in Kenya. The cooker, made of such materials as cardboard and foil, generates temperatures hot enough to pasteurize water and cook meals for an entire family.

Solar water-heating systems can be used in any climate but almost always require a backup system for cloudy days. In China, solar energy is a primary source for heating household hot water. In the United States, more than 1.5 million homes and businesses use solar water-heating systems. The state of Hawaii, which offers both utility rebates and tax breaks, accounts for 41 percent of the U.S. solar water-heating equipment market.

Solar cooking

Solar cookers, also called *solar ovens*, allow people to use the sun's power to cook. A simple solar cooker consists of nothing more than a foil-lined cardboard reflector and a dark pot inside a plastic bag. Such a device can convert sunlight into enough heat to *pasteurize* (remove disease-causing microbes, such as bacteria) water or cook one or two pots of food at a time. Used primarily in developing countries close to the equator, solar cookers are inexpensive to buy and maintain.

Future prospects for solar energy

In 2007, more than 1.5 million homes and businesses in the United States—including the

White House—derived at least some of their energy needs from solar cells. Photovoltaics make up the biggest growth area of solar technology, with yearly, worldwide growth rates exceeding 35 percent. World photovoltaic energy outputs reached a record high of 1,460 megawatts in 2005.

In 2006, Portugal started work on what will be one of the world's biggest photovoltaic power plants. The plant, comprising 52,300 photovoltaic modules, is being built in Serpa, one of Europe's sunniest areas. With no fuel cost or emissions, the facility will produce electric power sufficient to power 8,000 homes and save more than 27,000 metric tons (30,000 tons) in greenhouse gas emissions annually, compared with equivalent fossil fuel generation.

Research in the photovoltaic sector in the 2000's has focused on capturing more energy per area and lowering the cost of solar-conducting materials. In 2006, an experimental solar cell achieved a world-record conversion efficiency of 40.7 percent. Researchers are also making use of *nanotechnology* (the techniques, machines, tools, and processes needed to manipulate matter the size of atoms and molecules) to improve solar energy collection. The Global Climate and Energy Project (GCEP), a collaboration of academic and private research facilities based at Stanford University in California, is looking into ways to harness *photosynthesis* (the process by which plants convert energy from the sun into food) to produce "bioelectricity." The idea, said GCEP managing director Richard Sassoon, is to capture energy directly from living algae cells by inserting extremely small electrodes into their *chloroplasts*, the parts of the plant where solar energy splits water into oxygen and the subatomic particles protons and electrons. "If we can extract a few electrons as they flow across a single cell, then we can create arrays of cells," said Sassoon. "In a sense, it's like plugging into a tree."

Some engineers at NASA have even proposed locating photovoltaic panels in space. They say that rows of photovoltaic arrays could be placed either in a *geostationary* Earth orbit (orbiting over a fixed position above the equator and therefore at the same rate as Earth moves) or on the moon. The system would collect solar energy in space, convert it to *microwaves* (high-frequency electromagnetic waves), and transmit the microwave radiation to Earth, where it would be captured by a ground antenna and transformed to electric power.

Wind Power

People have harnessed wind energy for thousands of years. A 5,000-year-old drawing, found in Egypt, of a sailboat on the Nile River depicts a wind-driven craft. As early as 200 B.C., windmills were used to grind grain in the region that is now Iran. Beginning in the mid-1800's, farmers and other landowners in the United States built small windmills to pump water. The windmill's modern counterpart—the wind turbine—uses the wind's energy to generate electric power in extraordinary abundance, making it the centerpiece of the alternative energy economy.

Beginning in the mid-1990's, global wind-energy capacity increased nearly tenfold, from 6,259 megawatts in 1996 to more than 59,000 megawatts by 2006. In the United States, wind-energy capacity grew from 1,698 megawatts in 1996 to more than 10,400 megawatts by the end of 2006—enough to serve 2.5 million households. In 2007, wind energy is expected to grow by about 3,000 megawatts, or about 30 percent.

Wind power basics

A wind turbine works like a fan, only in reverse. Instead of using electric energy to generate wind, wind turbines use wind to generate electric energy. The force of the wind turns the blades of a rotor that converts the *kinetic energy* (energy of motion) of the wind into the rotation of a horizontal or vertical shaft. The shaft is connected to an electrical generator through a set of gears.

Small turbines, below 100 kilowatts, are used to power houses, telecommunication dishes, and water pumps. They can be used in combination with diesel generators, batteries, and photovoltaic systems. Such systems, called hybrid wind systems, are often used in remote locations far from electric utility grids.

Utility-scale turbines range from a little less than a megawatt to 2 megawatts or more in generating capacity. Larger turbines are grouped into wind farms, which distribute bulk electric power through transmission lines for use in homes and businesses.

Modern wind turbines fall into two basic groups: horizontal-axis designs, the most common, which typically have two or three blades, and vertical-axis designs, such as the eggbeater-style turbine named after its French inventor, Georges Darrieus.

Advantages of wind power

One of the advantages of wind power is its extraordinary abundance. A 1991 government inventory of wind resources concluded that just three states—Kansas, North Dakota, and Texas—have enough usable wind energy to meet the entire country's electrical energy needs.

Another advantage is that the technology to produce wind power efficiently is available now, in contrast to other renewable technologies—such as solar technology—which are less advanced. Wind typically provides electric energy at a lower cost per kilowatt-hour than geothermal or solar energy. The cost of wind power today is competitive with that of conventional power plants being built.

Wind power also has many environmental benefits. Wind turbines do not produce airborne toxins, acid rain, global warming emissions, or hazardous waste. Local water supplies are not affected and nonrenewable resources are not consumed. Wherever the wind blows, wind turbines can produce power without burning any fuel; regions that rely on wind power to replace some of their fossil fuel power plants can reduce levels of air pollution. Because wind power is produced domestically, there is no need to rely on politically unstable regions of the world such as the Middle East, which produces much of the petroleum used in the United States.

Disadvantages of wind power

One of the most serious disadvantages of wind power is that wind is not constant. In much of the United States, wind tends to blow strongest on winter nights when electrical demand is low. The least windy days are often the hottest, with the highest demand for electric power to run air conditioners.

Because wind sometimes fails to blow when electric energy is needed most, power companies must have standby systems to ensure that they can deliver power during periods of peak demand. These standby generators are generally conventional coal or natural gas generators that can be started and stopped quickly.

Wind power researchers are confident that the issue of unpredictable supply can be addressed as technology evolves and the electric power industry gains experience with the use of wind power. One solution would be to divide the electric power grid into bigger geographic areas. Such a move would allow energy supplies to be distributed from a larger pool of wind farms. Thus, a drop-off in wind in one place could be balanced by an increase somewhere else, reducing the need for conventional backup. Another answer lies in more sophisticated wind-forecasting techniques that can accurately predict hourly wind power generation a season, a day, or an hour in advance. The forecasting would allow electrical system operators to react to rapid wind changes and extreme weather events. But unless methods for storing wind energy for use during calm periods are developed, engineers say, wind turbines will not be suitable as a utility's primary source of power.

A nontechnical disadvantage to wind power is its high visibility. As turbines get bigger, they become more vulnerable to not-in-my-backyard (NIMBY) sentiment. Since the mid-1990's, many communities have rejected industrial-scale wind farms that were planned for their regions. These controversies cast doubt on whether wind power is well suited to environmentally delicate or tourism-dependent locations.

Balancing out the so-called NIMBY syndrome is a growing put-it-in-my-backyard (PIMBY) chorus.

In the Midwest, many farmers are eager to gain extra income by leasing quarter-acre lots to electric companies that pay yearly royalties for each turbine. Depending on the size of the turbine and other factors, farmers can earn $2,000 to $4,000 or more per year for each turbine installed on their property. The farmers can continue to grow crops up to the base of the turbines.

A major disadvantage of wind power is that the windiest parts of the United States are located far from the areas that consume large amounts of electrical energy, such as big cities and industrial regions. This geographic reality affects efficiency because 5 to 10 percent of electrical energy can be lost in long-distance transmission. Many transmission lines are reserved for older power plants, making it more expensive for newer technologies, such as renewables, to gain access. Development continues on land-based turbines that can efficiently exploit slower winds close to major urban areas and on systems that can harness the strong, steady winds that surge over the oceans within just a few miles of cities on both coasts. The development of wind power in recent years has centered in California, Texas, and the Midwest.

Some studies have shown that wind turbines can have negative effects on wildlife, particularly birds. In California, the first industrial-scale turbines

A wind farm operated by the Los Angeles Department of Water and Power stretches along Interstate 10 near Palm Springs, California. A turbine atop each windmill converts the energy of the wind as it turns the blades into electric power. Transmission lines carry the power to residences and businesses.

(which had small, quickly moving blades) were constructed without an understanding of how bird species used the area. Collisions with these turbines killed a number of birds, including *raptors* (birds of prey) that are protected by law.

The newest generation of turbines has blades with very large surface areas and gearboxes that turn *dynamos* (generators) quickly while the blades move slowly. Birds dodge these slow-moving blades with relative ease. In addition, environmentalists point out that the risk to birds from wind turbines must be weighed against the technology's environmental contribution as a clean energy source. For example, the *Exxon Valdez* oil spill in 1989 is estimated to have killed between 375,000 and 500,000 birds, and car and truck collisions kill 60 million to 80 million birds each year. Climate change, which may be slowed by wind power, also poses a massive threat to birds. In contrast, the U.S. National Academy of Sciences estimated in 2007 that less than 40,000 birds would be killed by wind turbines annually. Thus, the danger to birds because of wind farms is relatively small when compared to the stakes involved with continued levels of petroleum use.

Wind power advances

High equipment costs and mechanical unreliability slowed the growth of wind power in the 1980's. Engineers of early wind turbines underestimated the force that wind would produce. The rotors of early large wind turbines often broke in high winds, destroying generators, gearboxes, and other critical parts.

Engineers overcame many of these obstacles during the 1980's and early 1990's. They developed stronger materials, devised more efficient manufacturing methods, arranged turbines more effectively to capture more wind, and designed rotors to extract more energy from the wind. With an increasing understanding of wind force, engineers strengthened rotors, gears, and other components to withstand the stress of wind turbulence.

These engineering advances cut the price of wind-driven electric power by about 80 percent in the early 2000's. Whereas wind turbines installed in 1990 were able to convert about 44 percent of total kinetic energy into electric power at peak efficiency, 15 years later wind turbines reached efficiencies of 50 percent or greater.

The newest turbines exploit technology from the aeronautics and aerospace industries. In general, researchers have found that longer blades are more efficient, since they can reach higher-altitude winds that are stronger, more reliable, and less turbulent. The largest of these new turbines are taller than the Statue of Liberty (which is powered by wind-generated electric energy) and can generate up to 5 megawatts of electrical energy.

Starting in the 1990's, researchers have focused on creating lighter, stronger, and more reliable turbines. Streamlined manufacturing processes and flexible components reduce costs and increase the amount of energy captured. Computer-controlled gearboxes help turbines stabilize voltage on the electrical grid.

Researchers have developed new turbine blades incorporating lightweight materials such as carbon-fiber and carbon-glass hybrid composites. Although carbon fibers are more expensive than traditional fiberglass materials, they are stronger and lighter. Researchers are also experimenting with different blade shapes to take maximum advantage of all wind speeds, including slower speeds. Instead of the traditional linear shape, some of the new blades have curves at the trailing edges, designed to relieve pressure on blades and turbine drive trains.

Advances have also been made in matching a turbine's design to specific wind conditions. Turbines for the Plains states, for instance, are built differently than those designed for the hurricane-prone Gulf Coast. Turbine manufacturers are also working to develop advanced *small-wind systems* (which generate 100 kilowatts or less of electrical power) for the U.S. rural population. The industry estimates that 60 percent of the United States has enough wind resources to make small-wind systems a good option.

TOP TEN WIND ENERGY PRODUCING COUNTRIES IN 2006

Ranking	Country	Total capacity
1	Germany	20,622
2	Spain	11,615
3	United States	11,603
4	India	6,270
5	Denmark	3,136
6	China	2,405
7	Italy	2,123
8	United Kingdom	1,963
9	Portugal	1,650
10	France	1,567

Source: World Wind Energy Association.   megawatts

Energy production

The wind-energy industry grew by about 29 percent in the early 2000's compared to the 1990's. In March 2006, the cost of wind-generated electric energy in some markets dropped below that of natural gas for the first time. In 2005 and 2006, the United States installed more new wind-energy capacity than any other country in the world. By the end of July 2006, the nation's wind-energy capacity had topped 10,000 megawatts—enough to power 2.5 million average American households.

In early 2007, some 12,000 to 15,000 megawatts of wind-generation capacity was under construction or in planning for that year worldwide—3,000 megawatts in the United States alone. Experts say that this growth will continue through the year 2010 if prices of natural gas remain high and if the U.S. Congress continues favorable tax policies.

According to the U.S. Energy Information Administration's 2007 Energy Outlook, an estimated 46.21 billion kilowatt-hours are expected to be generated from wind power in 2007—nearly a 60 percent increase over the 2006 total. The agency's long-term analysis predicts generation of nearly 52 billion kilowatt-hours by 2030. The agency also says that a little more than 4,000 megawatts of wind power capacity will be added in 2007, which would follow a record-setting 2,750 megawatts in 2006.

The U.S. Department of Energy recently committed to developing an action plan that would provide up to 20 percent of the nation's electric power from wind energy. The wind community has set a target of 100 gigawatts of wind-generated electric capacity installed in the United States by 2020. At that level of use, wind will displace about 3 quadrillion BTU's (British thermal units) of primary energy and 65 million metric tons (71.6 million tons) of carbon emissions a year.

The first industrial-scale wind farms were built in 1981 in California, which soon had more than 80 percent of the world's wind power capacity. Within 20 years, however, Texas, the state that leads the nation in oil and gas production, became the top producer of wind energy. By 2007, Texas had a cumulative 2,634 megawatts of wind power capacity—enough to power more than 600,000 average American homes. More than 1,140 megawatts were under construction in Texas— nearly half of all construction planned for the United States in 2007.

In Europe, the largest project under development in the early 2000's was the Whitelee wind farm, south of Glasgow, Scotland. With 140 turbines, it has the capacity to generate an estimated 322 megawatts of electric energy—enough to supply electrical energy to nearly every home in Glasgow.

New frontiers

Development continues on turbines that can efficiently exploit slow winds close to heavily populated areas and on systems that can harness the strong, steady winds that surge over the oceans. Energy researchers estimate that turbines off the shores of the United States could produce 20 percent more energy than onshore turbines. This is because winds blow harder at sea and larger turbines can be used to generate electric energy. In fact, a Department of Energy study published in September 2005 found that out to a distance of 80 kilometers (50 miles) from the shoreline, enough energy could be harnessed to satisfy national needs. America's first offshore wind farm has been proposed for Nantucket Sound off the coast of Massachusetts. However, the 130-turbine project has met with substantial public and political opposition.

In the United States in 2006, Department of Energy officials were looking at locations for the site of the first laboratory for testing blades for offshore wind turbines. The facility will test blades 50 to 100 meters long (164 to 328 feet) that could be installed along U.S. coastlines or the Great Lakes in the future. The $11.5 million lab (scheduled to begin operation in 2009) will research the strength, flexibility, durability, and ice resistance of blades.

Meanwhile, other developers of wind technology are reaching for the sky. So-called *flying electric generators* would run at altitudes above 3,050 meters (10,000 feet), tethered to the ground with a cable that conducts electric power. If the designs can overcome challenges posed by anchoring, maintaining, and safely retrieving the devices, these generators will access winds that are the strongest, smoothest, and most energy rich on the planet.

For wind energy to reach its full potential, the industry will need to develop better methods for storing wind energy for use during calm periods. Greater storage potential would allow researchers to find ways to use wind energy not only as a renewable energy source but also to produce other renewables. Wind power could be used to create hydrogen fuel, to clean and move water, and to work together with hydropower to provide a stable supply of electric power.

People have been burning biomass for hundreds of thousands of years, ever since early human beings used wood fires to warm dwellings and cook food. Even now, hundreds of millions of people around the world rely on wood as their primary source of *bioenergy* (energy obtained from *biofuel*, fuel created from biomass).

Since 2000, unstable energy markets and increased acceptance by the general public and the environmental community have created unprecedented enthusiasm for biomass. A new generation of technologies is making it possible not only to fuel vehicles but also to produce electric energy from grassy plants, agricultural residues, and even sewage.

Primary biofuel sources

Agricultural products grown to make biofuels include corn and soybeans in the United States, flaxseed and rapeseed in Europe, sugarcane in Brazil, and palm oil in Southeast Asia. *Biodegradable* (able to be broken down by biological processes) waste from industry, agriculture, and households can also be used to produce bioenergy. Such waste products include paper-mill residue, lumber-mill scrap, city and agricultural waste, animal waste, and food leftovers. Over the

long term, energy scientists are working on plans to grow dedicated energy crops, such as fast-growing and sustainable trees and grasses, on lands that cannot support large-scale food crops.

Advantages of biofuels

Biomass energy has the potential to ease the demand for fossil fuels, which discharge carbon dioxide into the air and increase potential for climate change. Biomass energy also releases carbon dioxide, but it is usually balanced by the carbon dioxide captured during the growth of the materials from which the fuel is harvested. Because biomass energy does not introduce new carbon dioxide into the atmosphere, it can greatly reduce greenhouse gas emissions. Greenhouse gases, such as carbon dioxide, methane, and nitrogen oxide, trap heat in the atmosphere. In order to maintain life on Earth, a certain level of greenhouse gases is needed; however, too much can cause climate change and danger to life. The levels of pollutants produced by biofuel are lower than those produced by fossil fuel. The use of biodiesel in vehicles reduces the emission of carbon monoxide and other hydrocarbons by 20 to 40 percent.

In addition to being environmentally friendly, biomass fuels ease U.S. dependence on foreign sources of fuel. Biomass fuels are relatively abundant, and some biomass fuel sources, such as poplar and willow trees, can be grown on depleted forestland to help restore forest growth. Biomass energy supports domestic agricultural and forest-product industries, and biomass facilities and harvesting operations provide jobs.

Many biomass power technologies that produce electric energy can be particularly useful in the developing world, where remote villages often

A homeowner refills his corn-burning stove with grain. Although *biofuels* (fuels created from biomass) are generally more environmentally friendly than fossil fuels, policy makers in the early 2000's were concerned that their use may result in higher food prices for U.S. consumers and a decrease in grain exports to developing nations.

do not have access to electric power. In these areas, small biomass electric generators can be provided to produce electric power.

Drawbacks to biofuels

In order to make biofuels, a lot of material—and, thus, a large amount of land—are needed to produce biomass. Nevertheless, the use of biofuels can reduce the amount of land that is needed to extract nonrenewable energy sources, such as coal and oil.

As the explosive growth of the ethanol market draws increasing amounts of grain into fuel production, less grain is available for livestock feed and exports. According to the Earth Policy Institute, an environmental organization located in Washington, D.C., ethanol distilleries in the United States will pull an estimated 132 million metric tons (146 million tons)—or more than half—of corn from the 2008 corn harvest to produce automobile fuel. Reducing the harvest devoted to food will probably result in higher food prices for U.S. consumers and decrease the export flow to hungry people in other nations. In February 2007, participants in the "Tortilla Protest" in Mexico City expressed their anger that they could not afford to make tortillas because the price of corn had increased by 400 percent.

The scientific and environmental communities are divided over the environmental benefits of some biofuels, especially ethanol. Most ethanol is made from corn, and industrial corn production uses significant amounts of products made from fossil fuel, such as fertilizer and the gasoline that powers farm equipment. Some scientists argue that the fossil fuel energy required to grow corn actually exceeds the amount of energy yielded by the resulting ethanol. Such a discrepancy is called a *negative energy balance.*

Several recent studies, including a 2006 article in the journal *Science*, conclude that biofuels such as ethanol are energy positive but do little to cut greenhouse gases. Researchers from the University of California at Berkeley determined that ethanol use results in a *net energy gain* (the surplus of energy after factoring in the amount of energy used) of about 20 percent, but the pollution generated in processing the corn offsets most of ethanol's gains in emissions of greenhouse gases. An analysis by the Massachusetts Institute of Technology (MIT) in Cambridge released in 2007 shows that the energy balance is actually so close that several factors (such as the amount of fertilizer used) can easily change ethanol's status as a net energy winner or loser.

In early 2007, liquid biofuels were not yet widely available as primary transportation fuels. As of 2006, only about 1,000 of the approximately 168,000 fueling stations in the United States sold the E85 (85 percent ethanol and 15 percent gasoline) blend.

Ethanol

Ethanol is essentially grain alcohol fermented and distilled from plants such as corn in a process that is similar to that used in making alcoholic liquors. Ethanol was used in one version of the first cars—the Model T produced from 1908 to 1927 in Detroit by Ford Motor Company, now headquartered in Dearborn, Michigan. Pure ethanol is used in about 40 percent of the cars in Brazil, and the use of blended ethanol is climbing in the United States.

The year 2006 was a record year for the U.S. ethanol industry. Some 19 million liters (5 billion gallons) were produced from corn to blend with gasoline, accounting for 3 percent of vehicle fuel. Ethanol can be added in small amounts to conventional gasoline without modifying a vehicle's engine; in 2006, it was blended into more than 45 percent of the nation's gasoline.

According to the National Association of Automakers of Brazil, more than 80 percent of the new cars sold in Brazil in 2006 were flexible-fuel vehicles (FFV's) capable of burning up to 100 percent ethanol. In the United States, some 6 million FFV's were on the road at the end of 2006—but the vast majority rarely ran on E85 because of its limited availability.

Most energy experts agree that the future of ethanol is not in corn, but in such higher-*cellulose* (the woody parts of plants and trees) plants as switchgrass and willow trees. The amount of energy used to grow, harvest, and produce cellulosic ethanol is six times less than the energy it produces as a fuel. Such a high-energy balance is possible because switchgrass and other cellulosic crops can grow without the fossil fuel consumption (such as fertilizers and harvesting equipment that runs on gasoline) that corn needs.

In 2007, construction was to begin on the first U.S. ethanol plant to make fuel from wood chips, switchgrass, and waste from the paper industry. The plant, to be built in Rochester, New York, was to use *engineered* (altered or made by people) enzymes to break down the woody bits of plants in order to cut production costs.

Biodiesel

Biodiesel is a *nontoxic* (not poisonous to living things), biodegradable liquid fuel produced from vegetable oils. Biodiesel can be used in its pure form or as an additive to petroleum diesel (typically 20 percent) to reduce vehicle emissions. It can be used in diesel engines with little or no modification. The primary benefits of biodiesel are that it reduces petroleum diesel usage and, as a result, lowers the emissions of carbon dioxide, toxins such as sulfur, and *particulate matter* (tiny bits of waste material that can cause pollution). According to an analysis by the Department of Energy's National Renewable Energy Laboratory in Golden, Colorado, roughly 80 percent of the energy in biodiesel is renewable and can be used to replace petroleum fuel in cars. However, biodiesel can also increase nitrous oxide emissions (a greenhouse gas). Researchers are working to develop fuel formulation, fuel additives, and engine-operation strategies to eliminate such emissions.

Biodiesel is made by mixing alcohol (usually a type called methanol) with vegetable oil, animal fat, or recycled cooking grease in a process known as *transesterification*. The market for biodiesel is smaller than for ethanol but by 2007 was showing rapid growth.

Among the plants most frequently used for biodiesel production are canola, rapeseed, and soy. Researchers also hope to utilize *algae* (organisms that create their own food through photosynthesis but are not plants) as an energy source for biodiesel since some species have a very high oil content. Engineers hope that algae can be used by big producers of carbon dioxide, such as factories and power plants. This would help to reduce carbon emissions by as much as 40 percent.

The potential of liquid biofuel

In 2006, the Renewable Fuel Standard (RFS) went into effect in the United States, requiring increasing levels of renewable fuel use through 2012. Included in the Energy Policy Act of 2005, the RFS required the use of 15 billion liters (4 billion gallons) of renewable fuel in 2006, increasing to 28 billion liters (7.5 billion gallons) of renewable fuel use annually beginning in 2012.

In 2006, the United States used more than 19 billion liters (5 billion gallons) of ethanol, outpacing RFS requirements by more than 25 percent. Demand from American consumers for cleaner-burning, renewable fuels contributed to unprecedented growth in this industry. In Europe and Asia, where facilities producing ethanol and biodiesel have also sprung up, governments have focused on biofuels as a critical way to meet environmental and energy needs. By 2010, the European Union planned to have bioethanol replace more than 5 percent of the gasoline market.

Biopower

Biopower, also called biomass power, is the use of biomass to produce electric energy. Biopower technologies include direct-firing, cofiring, gasification, pyrolysis, and anaerobic digestion.

Most biopower plants use *direct-fired* systems, in which a solid *feedstock* (fuel) such as wood is burned in a boiler to produce steam. The steam drives a turbine, which turns a generator to produce electric energy. In some biopower facilities, the spent steam from the power plant is used to heat buildings or for manufacturing processes. Such combined heat and power systems greatly increase overall energy efficiency. Paper mills are currently the biggest producers of biomass power.

Power companies also fuel some old coal-powered plants with a mixture of biomass and coal, a practice called *cofiring*. Cofiring reduces the power plant's emissions of sulfur dioxide, a major contributor to acid rain, because most biomass fuels contain little sulfur and coal dust.

Processed waste can also be used for combustion. Most sorts of biomatter, including dried manure, can be burned to heat water and to drive turbines. Corncobs, sugarcane residue, wheat straw, and other plant matter can be burned successfully.

Automobile pioneer Henry Ford stands beside his highly successful Model T, a vehicle designed to run on ethanol, gasoline, or a combination of the two. In 2006, only about 1,000 of the 170,000 gas stations in the United States sold E85, a blend of 85 percent ethanol and 15 percent gasoline.

TOP FIVE ETHANOL PRODUCING COUNTRIES IN 2006

(in millions of gallons)

Country	2004	2005	2006
Brazil	3,989	4,227	4,491
United States	3,535	4,264	4,855
China	964	1,004	1,017
India	462	449	502
France	219	240	251

Source: Renewable Fuels Association

Solid biomass can also be gasified. Gasification systems use high temperatures and an oxygen-controlled environment to break down biomass, producing a mixture of hydrogen and carbon monoxide known as *synthesis gas*, or *syngas*. Syngas can be burned in a conventional boiler or used in place of natural gas in a gas turbine. Gasification increases the fuel's power-generating efficiency by about 10 percent when compared to direct burning. In addition, exit gases (hydrogen and carbon monoxide) can be harnessed to run a steam turbine for a second round of power generation. Waste heat from the entire process can be used to warm buildings or entire towns.

Another *thermochemical* process (a process dependent on chemical reactions involving heat), pyrolysis, totally excludes oxygen from the gasification process, transforming biomass into a liquid. Pyrolysis oil can be burned to generate electricity or used to make such products as plastics and adhesives.

A new process called *thermal depolymerization* (a process that uses high heat and pressure to create oil) has made it possible to transform agricultural waste, plastics, sewage, used tires, animal carcasses, or nearly any biomass into oil. Thermal depolymerization uses the same principles that cause fossil fuels to form, but on a smaller scale over a much shorter period of time.

Naturally decaying biomass produces methane. To capture this gas and use it for power production, wells are drilled into landfills to release the methane from decaying organic matter. Pipes carry the methane to a central point, where it is filtered and cleaned before burning. This process produces electricity and prevents methane from being released into the atmosphere.

Methane can also be produced from biomass through a process called a*naerobic digestion*. Natural bacteria are used to decompose organic matter

in the absence of oxygen in closed reactors. Gas suitable for power production is produced, and wastes (such as those at sewage treatment plants or feedlots) are turned to usable compost.

In Vermont in 2006, one electric company began offering its customers "cow power." The power is generated via anaerobic digestion of cow manure at dairy farms. The high temperatures reduce unpleasant odors and destroy potentially dangerous bacteria such as *E. coli*. The excess generator heat is used to heat the farm's water. The nation's first direct farm-to-consumer renewable energy program has created a market for manure from farms.

In the San Francisco Bay area in 2007, waste management officials were beginning a pilot program in which dog excrement would be collected from dog-walking parks around the city. The waste is combined with food scraps from restaurants, then digested by bacteria and turned into methane that can be used to power electric generators.

Biopower potential

Developing countries are the largest consumers of biofuels, using them for cooking and heating rather than for producing electric energy. This is because many rural, isolated areas in these countries have limited municipal utilities that are found in developed nations.

Although interest in biomass power increased during the early 2000's, issues of climate protection and rural development proved to be greater driving forces behind bioenergy legislation and action. Since 2002, according to the U.S. Department of Energy, the use of biomass has risen steadily. In 2006, 4 percent of the energy produced in the United States came from biomass. Based on these trends, experts are hopeful that by 2027, the nation's dependence on gasoline will be reduced by 15 percent by switching to biofuels.

Water Power

Water constantly moves through a vast global cycle. The sun's heat evaporates water from lakes and oceans, forming clouds, from which water falls as rain or snow and then flows back down to large bodies of water. The energy of this cycle, known as hydropower, is driven by the sun and can be tapped to provide power for machinery or to create electric energy.

Traditionally, hydropower has referred to power derived from falling water in rivers or streams. In the early 2000's, new technologies were developed to also exploit the energy of the ocean's waves and tidal systems and of the temperature differences between layers of ocean water.

Traditional hydropower

Hydropower usually refers to electric energy generated by *hydroelectric plants* in dams. As long as the sun's heat pulls water into the air through evaporation, rain and snow cause riverbeds to fill with water, and gravity pulls river water downstream, water's kinetic energy can be used to do work.

A water wheel is a simple example of traditional hydropower technology. For centuries, people constructed water wheels along rivers. The flowing water turns the wheel, providing the force needed to operate machinery such as grain mills. Textile mills relied heavily on water wheels for power during the Industrial Revolution of the 1700's and early

An artist's rendering (left above) depicts a series of turbines to be installed 9 meters (30 feet) beneath the surface of New York City's East River (left), on the eastern side of Roosevelt Island. As the tide flows in and out of the river, the heads of the turbines will pivot to face the current. The spinning blades will generate power, which will be delivered to a control room on the island through attached cables. By early 2007, the first turbine in the experimental system was installed and was supplying energy to a grocery store and a garage on Roosevelt Island.

1800's in Europe and the United States. The world's first hydroelectric power plant began operation on the Fox River in Appleton, Wisconsin, in September 1882.

Most dam designs require that dams be built between two high points. To construct a dam, engineers use strong materials such as concrete and steel to block a river, creating a reservoir of water. Water from the reservoir flows down pipes or tunnels through the dam. Near the bottom, the rushing water drives a turbine. The turbine is connected to a generator, which produces electric energy. The energy of 3.8 liters (1 gallon) of water per second falling 30 meters (100 feet) can generate about 1 kilowatt of electric energy.

Hydroelectric power offers several important advantages over fossil fuels. Although it can be expensive to construct a hydroelectric plant, producing electric energy at an existing facility costs little. The "fuel" for the plant—water—is free, and it is not reduced or used up in the process of producing power. Electric power production from hydropower plants can thus be less than half as expensive as production at traditional plants using fossil fuel, according to the U.S. Department of Energy.

In addition, hydropower can be produced on demand. Operators can control the flow of water through turbines to produce electric energy as needed. Also, unlike fossil fuel power plants, hydroelectric plants emit no air pollution. By 2003, hydroelectric plants accounted for 17 percent of the world's electric power, producing the same amount of electric energy as burning 3.6 billion barrels of petroleum oil.

Since the 1980's, the environmental drawbacks of hydroelectric dams have become more apparent. In fact, some dams in the United States are scheduled for demolition for such reasons. In Washington and Oregon alone, seven dams, including two large dams on the Elwha River in Olympic National Park, are slated for demolition, beginning in 2007.

Hydropower plants can harm the environment by reducing the amount of dissolved oxygen in water, damaging riverbank habitats. In tropical climates, vast quantities of methane are produced by decaying vegetation in reservoirs created by the dams. Dams can also disrupt ecosystems by blocking the flow of water, silt, and nutrient-rich sediment down a river. The blockage can lower the fertility of farmland downstream and reduce the productivity of fisheries, both in the river itself and in ocean fisheries near the *mouth* of the river

(where a river flows into a larger body of water such as the ocean). Such a blockage has built up, for example, below the Aswan high dam, constructed in the 1960's along the Nile River in Egypt.

The flooding caused by a dam can destroy *spawning* (mating) areas for some fish species, and the dam itself may block other fish species, such as salmon, that swim upstream to spawn. Because large hydroelectric dam reservoirs flood hundreds of square miles, people living in the area may be forced to leave their homes. In China, officials estimate that the nation's Three Gorges Dam (scheduled to be completed around 2009) will submerge dozens of towns and cities and force the relocation of from 1.3 million to 1.9 million people.

In addition, the structural failure of a hydroelectric dam could be catastrophic. Hydroelectric dams are designed to withstand the tremendous pressure of water behind them, as well as shocks from earthquakes. However, severe earthquakes could damage some dams. Because of their high visibility, hydroelectric dams may also be appealing targets for terrorists.

Limitations of traditional hydropower

Hydroelectric plants are built in different sizes, depending on how much water is available to operate the turbines and the distance the water falls. Some hydroelectric dams supply power to a few thousand people. Others, such as the massive 6,000-megawatt Grand Coulee Dam on the Columbia River in the state of Washington, supply millions of people with power.

In North America, most usable rivers have been dammed for electric production. Starting during the Great Depression of the 1930's, the U.S. government built thousands of dams, bringing inexpensive power to many states. By 2007, these dams supplied 7 percent of U.S. demand— some three times the combined share of wind power, solar power, and other forms of renewable energy. Yet even as some of these existing dams were being upgraded, environmental concerns have thwarted new construction.

Several factors limit the expansion of hydroelectric power worldwide. Among them are the high cost of building large dams and opposition from environmentalists and people living in the area—many of whom may be forced from their homes. Although construction costs for hydroelectric plants are, on average, only about 30 percent more than for advanced coal plants, many of the nations that could most benefit from hydroelectric plants are heavily in debt, so they are reluctant to spend the extra amount.

In addition, development institutions such as the World Bank, headquartered in Washington, D.C., and dedicated to alleviating global poverty, have curtailed funding of dams because of pressure from activist groups. According to critics, the World Bank, the largest single source of funding for dam construction around the world, has promoted and financed dams that have displaced more than 10 million people, caused severe environmental damage, and pushed developing nations further into debt. Critics also point out that in countries that limit political protest, dams have been built without weighing the effects on human populations and the environment.

Ocean-wave energy devices

Compared to traditional sources of hydropower, the ocean offers new reserves of untapped power. The energy of ocean waves is driven by the moon's gravity and by tides, currents, and winds. The sun warms the ocean's surface water more than the ocean's deep water, creating temperature differences that can be used as an additional energy source. All these forms of energy can be used to produce electric power.

Wave-power systems extract energy directly from the movement of the ocean's surface or from pressure changes below the surface. According to a report from the Electric Power Research Institute published in September 2005, only 24 percent of available wave energy is needed to produce the equivalent to the output of all existing hydropower in the United States.

Countries with long shorelines can use the vast energy-producing potential contained in ocean waves and tides. Wave-rich areas of the world include the northeastern and northwestern coasts of the United States, as well as the western coasts of Scotland, northern Canada, southern Africa, and Australia. Energy experts estimate that in the Pacific Northwest alone, wave energy could produce 40 to 70 kilowatts per meter (3.3 feet) of coastline.

By the early 2000's, more than two dozen companies worldwide were developing systems to unlock the power of waves and currents. Ocean Power Delivery Ltd. of Edinburgh, Scotland, installed the first commercial "wave farm" in operation off the coast of Portugal in 2006 and 2007. Its Pelamis Wave Energy Converter resembles a large, semisubmerged snake 120 meters (394 feet) long floating in the ocean water. The

snakelike tube consists of four segments that are hinged so they move in concert with the ocean waves. At each hinge, or joint, is a *hydraulic* motor (one that is powered by changes in liquid pressure). The movement of the segments causes high-pressure oil to be pumped into the motors, producing electric energy. The electric current is then transmitted onshore through a cable that is attached to the seabed. Projected to be fully operational by 2008, the system is expected to power about 15,000 homes.

Onshore wave-power systems, built along shorelines, extract the energy from breaking waves. These technologies include oscillating water columns, tapered channel systems, and Pendulor devices.

An *oscillating water column* is a partially submerged structure with an opening below the waterline. It traps a column of air above a column of water. As a breaking wave enters the structure, it forces the water and air column up. Such a motion creates airflow. When the wave retreats from the structure, the column of air and water goes down, again creating airflow. The airflow turns a turbine, which produces electric energy.

A *tapered-channel system* (also called a *tapchan system*) makes use of a tapered channel that feeds into a tank constructed on cliffs above sea level. As the channel narrows, the waves are forced higher as they move toward the cliff face. At the top, the waves spill into a reservoir. The stored water then flows downward into a turbine where electric energy is produced.

The *Pendulor* wave-power device uses a rectangular box with a hinged flap over an opening at one end. The waves' action causes the flap to swing back and forth, powering a hydraulic pump and a generator.

Tidal systems

The technology for tidal turbines—which are essentially wind turbines operating in water—was rapidly developed in the early 2000's. Coastal areas experience two cycles of high and low tides over a period of slightly more than 24 hours. Conditions are good for tidal-power generation in both the Pacific Northwest and Atlantic Northeast regions of the United States.

In 2006, the first power-producing tidal-turbine farm in the world began operating in New York City's East River. The six slow-turning propellers, which are anchored to the riverbed, were expected to generate 525,000 kilowatt-hours of electric power within their first year—enough to power 60 homes. Depending on the results of an 18-month trial, enough turbines could be added to produce 26 million kilowatt-hours and power 8,000 homes. Energy experts believe that the prototype could lead to a new, steady, nonpolluting energy source.

Other tidal-power systems include *tidal barrages* and *tidal fences*. A tidal barrage, also called a tidal dam, works in a way that is similar to a hydroelectric dam. A huge dam called a barrage is built across a body of water with substantial tidal flow. As the tide flows in and out, water moves through tunnels in the dam, turning generators to produce electric energy. A tidal fence looks like a giant turnstile. Arranged across fast-flowing tidal channels, the turnstiles spin as tidal currents move through, driving electric generators.

The benefits of ocean power

Ocean power has several advantages over wind power. Ocean power systems are less visible than wind farms, and water is 10 to 40 times as energy-dense as wind. Tidal and wave power are renewable, abundant, and much more predictable and dependable than many other renewable sources of power. According to Virginia Technical University oceanographer George Hagerman, tides are more predictable forces than the rain and snow that feed dam-based hydroelectric generators. "The wind may or may not blow an hour from now, but you can predict the moon and tide a thousand years from now," says Hagerman. "I call it lunar power."

Tidal-turbine systems are expensive to build but cheap to operate in terms of fuel usage. The fuel they use—seawater—is free. A major drawback of tidal-power stations is that they can generate electric energy only when the tide is flowing in or out—in other words, only for 10 hours each day. Also, the ocean is a demanding environment for any kind of machinery. Maintenance to keep away barnacles and similar "biofouling" generally runs higher than for wind turbines.

Some types of tidal-power plants (especially tidal barrages and fences) can harm sea life. Since barrages and fences can cross an entire channel, the paths for migratory sea life are blocked. In addition, the water in the immediate environment becomes cloudy with sediment, which eventually builds up in other areas, changing the balance within the ecosystem.

Careful site selection can reduce the environmental impacts of wave- and tidal-power systems. Still, as of 2007, wave- and tidal-power systems were not able to compete economically with tradi-tional power sources or even with some of the other renewable alternatives.

Ocean thermal energy conversion

Another type of ocean power—ocean thermal energy conversion (OTEC)—taps the vast amount of heat energy trapped in the oceans in order to generate electric energy. The sun continually heats the oceans, which cover nearly 70 percent of Earth's surface.

The OTEC method involves pumping cold water from the ocean depths—as deep as 1 kilometer (0.6 mile)—to the surface, then utilizing the temperature difference that exists between deep and shallow waters to run a *heat engine* (an engine that converts heat energy into mechanical energy, such as energy that runs an electric power generator). OTEC is viable when the temperature difference between the warm top layer of water and the cold deep water is about 20 °C (36 °F). The amount of energy available through OTEC is higher than other ocean energy options such as wave power, but the small size of the temperature difference at most sites makes energy extraction difficult and expensive. As of 2007, OTEC systems had an overall efficiency of only 1 percent to 3 percent.

Some energy experts say that if OTEC could be made cost-competitive with conventional power technologies, it could produce billions of watts of electrical power. But OTEC power plants require substantial capital investment. Also, there are only a few hundred land-based sites in the tropics where deep ocean water is close enough to shore to make OTEC plants feasible.

The potential of ocean energy

In the early 1990's, the Department of Energy eliminated ocean-energy funding from its budget. Also at that time, deregulation and declining prices for fossil fuel reduced the cost of electric energy, so emerging wave and tidal energy technologies were no longer considered economically viable.

In many countries, government-funded research and development on ocean-energy projects continued. However, in the United States, private companies drove new developments in technology, proposing projects in Washington, New York, and Hawaii. In 2005, the United States reexamined its role in the advancement of hydropower. Congress passed legislation that included funding for the study of ocean and *hydrokinetic* (moving fluid) technologies. In 2007, new hydropower technologies were ready for initial commercial deployment.

Geothermal Power

The word *geothermal* refers to the heat deep inside Earth. As Earth was forming, intense pressures and high temperatures turned the rock inside the planet *molten* (reduced to liquid form by heating). Earth's inner layers, which remain in a hot, molten state, heat underground reservoirs of water. The hot water and steam in the reservoirs provide the heat for geothermal energy.

Modern technology has developed various ways to use Earth's heat as an energy source. For example, a utility company can use hot water and steam to drive a turbine, which turns a generator to produce electric energy. Homeowners and businesses can use geothermal heat directly from the ground to control the temperature in homes and other buildings.

In 2007, electric energy from geothermal sources provided less than 1 percent of the world's total electric energy when compared to other sources of electric power. However, exploitation of this abundant resource was growing—particularly in developing nations with underground heat reservoirs that are easily accessible.

In the United States, electric energy from geothermal sources was expected to nearly double by 2010. A new generation of power plants was being developed that can produce geothermal electricity with cooler water. The National Renewable Energy Laboratory (NREL) reported that, based on 2006 consumption, the United States has enough geothermal resources to meet the energy needs of the nation for another 30,000 years.

Getting energy from Earth

The use of geothermal energy is not new technology. *Paleo-Indians* (people who lived 10,000 to 40,000 years ago) of the United States used geothermal hot springs for warmth and bathing. As early as 1200 B.C., Romans built bathhouses that made use of warm waters from hot springs. The world's first large-scale geothermal electric plant opened in Larderello, Italy, in 1904, and continues to operate today. The first commercial U.S. geothermal power plant opened at The Geysers in California in 1960, producing 11 megawatts of net power. In 2007, it was the largest single source of nonhydropower renewable energy in the world. Today, many people in Iceland, New Zealand, the western United States, and elsewhere use water from hot springs to heat houses and other buildings.

Hot springs and geysers are found in only certain places on Earth's surface, however, so engineers drill deep into the earth to access geothermal energy. Temperatures rise about 30 °C (80 °F) for every kilometer below the surface. Deep drilling is technically difficult and expensive, though, so most drill holes extend no lower than the top 4 kilometers (2.5 miles) of Earth's crust.

The most promising places to drill are areas where molten rock rises close to Earth's surface. Such sites are typically located near the intersection of *tectonic plates* (gigantic plates that make up Earth's crust). These regions include the western portions of much of North and South America, many areas of the western Pacific Ocean, and the eastern Mediterranean Sea.

Pipes rising in a tropical rain forest in Salak, Indonesia, are part of a geothermal power plant that captures steam and heat from deep inside the earth and converts them into electric power. Indonesia's location on the Ring of Fire—a horseshoe-shaped zone along the edge of the Pacific Ocean that has many volcanoes—has given it what is believed to be the world's greatest source of geothermal power. The country has the potential to produce 21,000 megawatts, enough to supply all its electric power needs.

A visitor enjoys an open-air swimming pool heated by a geothermal power plant in Erding, Germany. Tighter emissions' controls and rising fuel costs have increased demand for renewable energy and prompted utility companies throughout the world to tap geothermal sources previously considered too costly to develop.

Geothermal power is generally used in three different forms: as direct heat, for producing electric power, and in heat pumps.

Direct use of geothermal energy

For the direct use of geothermal energy, hot water is brought up through a natural spring or a drilled well, and a mechanical system delivers the steady stream of hot water directly for its intended use. As of 2007, direct uses included heating buildings (either individually or whole towns), warming greenhouses for plants, drying crops, heating water at fish farms, and powering industrial processes, such as pasteurizing milk. A disposal system then either injects the cooled water underground or releases it on the surface.

Electric power from geothermal energy

Geothermal energy can also be used to produce electricity. After a hole is drilled to access geothermal heat, the superheated water is brought to the surface and piped to a power plant. There are three kinds of geothermal electric power plants: dry steam, flash steam, and binary cycle.

Dry steam power plants draw from underground resources of steam. The steam is brought from underground wells through pipes to a power plant, where it is directed into a turbine or generator. In the United States, there are only two known underground resources of steam: Yellowstone National Park in Wyoming and The Geysers in northern California. Because Yellowstone is protected from development, the only dry-steam plants in the country are at The Geysers.

Flash steam power plants use geothermal reservoirs with water temperatures higher than 182 °C (360 °F). As this very hot water flows up through wells, the pressure decreases and some of the hot water boils into steam. The steam is then used to power a turbine or generator. Leftover water and condensed steam are injected back into the reservoir, making it a sustainable resource.

Binary cycle power plants use water at lower temperatures, from 107 °C to 182 °C (225 °F to 360 °F). These plants use the hot water to boil a working fluid, usually an organic compound (such as pentane or isobutane) with a low boiling point. The working fluid is vaporized in a heat exchanger from which it is directed into a turbine. The water is then injected back into the reservoir. Because the water and the working fluid are separated during the whole process, this creates few or no air emissions.

A new generation of binary power plants will allow power production at low-temperature hot springs in Arkansas, Georgia, and New York. Abandoned oil wells represent another opportunity since they often produce large quantities of very hot water that is otherwise wasted as it comes to the surface. Engineers are developing technology to produce power from these well fields; one study showed 5,000 megawatts of geothermal potential in western Texas oilfields alone.

Geothermal heat pumps

Even in places where there is no reservoir of superheated water close enough to the surface to be harvested in a cost-effective manner, people can take advantage of geothermal energy to heat and cool buildings. Throughout the year, the upper 3.05 meters (10 feet) of Earth's crust maintains a nearly constant temperature of from 10 °C to 16 °C (50 °F to 60 °F). This ground temperature is warmer than the air above it in the winter and cooler than the air in the summer. Geothermal heat pumps (also called *geoexchange systems*) take advantage of this difference in temperature to heat and cool buildings. Geothermal heat pumps use much less energy than conventional heating and cooling systems, saving money and reducing air pollution.

There are three parts to a geothermal heat pump system: the ground heat exchanger, the heat pump unit, and the air delivery system (ductwork). The heat exchanger consists of a system of pipes called a *loop*, which is buried in the ground near the building. A fluid (usually water or a mixture of water and antifreeze) circulates through the pipes, carrying the heat of the ground into the building. There, a vapor compression cycle—the same principle employed in a refrigerator—concentrates the heat and releases it inside the building through ducts. In summer, the process is reversed; the heat pump removes heat from the indoor air into the heat exchanger. This heat can then be used to heat water before it is expelled to the loop, where the heat is absorbed by the earth.

Environmentally friendly?

Electric energy produced from Earth's super-heated center is an ideal source for *baseload* (continuous) power. It is virtually emission free, and the technology for harnessing accessible geothermal resources is proven and readily available. Because geothermal plants produce very little particulate and carbon dioxide emissions, they contribute little to global warming and air pollution. According to the geothermal division of the U.S. Department of Energy, the average operating geothermal plant emits about 90 percent less carbon dioxide than a coal plant of the same size. Advanced geothermal plants currently under development are expected to produce almost no carbon dioxide emissions.

Geothermal plants also require very little land. A typical geothermal plant requires nine times less land than a coal plant to produce the same amount of electric energy, if the amount of land necessary for coal mining is taken into account. Another advantage is that geothermal plants usually require less maintenance than plants that use fossil fuel.

Geothermal energy is considered renewable because Earth contains vast stores of heat that are maintained by natural processes. The supply of geothermal energy is essentially limitless since Earth's heat is essentially limitless. Scientists have determined that the center of Earth has been extremely hot for some 3.9 billion years and will continue to be hot for at least that far into the future.

Nevertheless, geothermal resources are difficult to find and use, and geothermal plants are expensive to build. Plants can emit hydrogen sulfide, a compound that smells like rotten eggs and is poisonous at high concentrations. Hydrogen sulfide can break down in the atmosphere to form sulfur dioxide, a major contributor to acid rain. Although producers can avoid this problem by treating emissions with special chemical filters, the chemicals that filter sulfur can themselves be hazardous and must be taken to approved hazardous-waste disposal sites. However, experts say this is not a major obstacle to geothermal energy production.

Another disadvantage is that water extracted from deep underground may contain hazardous chemicals, such as arsenic, lead, and mercury. Operators can reinject this water deep into the ground, but they must take care that the chemicals do not accidentally contaminate water supplies.

Developing technologies

To overcome the limitations of accessing traditional locations of geothermal energy, researchers and engineers are looking at other ways of getting to Earth's heat resources. One of the alternatives they have considered is *geopressured resources*, deeply buried reservoirs of hot *brine* (water combined with salt) containing dissolved methane under extremely high pressure. Such reservoirs are

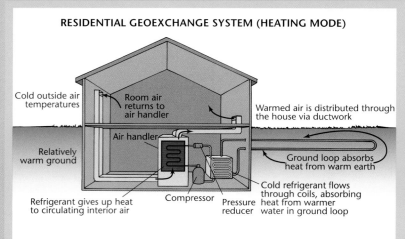

RESIDENTIAL GEOEXCHANGE SYSTEM (HEATING MODE)

Cold outside air temperatures

Room air returns to air handler

Warmed air is distributed through the house via ductwork

Relatively warm ground

Air handler

Ground loop absorbs heat from warm earth

Refrigerant gives up heat to circulating interior air

Compressor

Pressure reducer

Cold refrigerant flows through coils, absorbing heat from warmer water in ground loop

In a residential geoexchange system, water circulates through a buried ground loop, absorbing heat from the earth. The ground loop water transfers its heat to coils filled with refrigerant inside the building. The coils give up their heat to circulating air in an air handler. The heated air is forced through ductwork, warming the house. Room air is recirculated to the air handler through return ductwork.

known to occur both onshore and offshore beneath the coast of the Gulf of Mexico, along the Pacific coast, in Appalachia, and in deep sedimentary basins elsewhere in the United States. Deep wells required to extract these brines are very expensive, and scientists believe that only a limited portion of U.S. geopressured resources would be commercially exploitable in the foreseeable future.

Another resource may be *magma* (molten rock). Magma occurs close to Earth's surface where the crust is thinned or fractured by plate tectonics. When magma's near-surface heat is transferred to water, a usable form of geothermal energy is created. Geologists believe that the heat within magma bodies will yield sufficient quantities of energy to justify the potentially high cost of extraction. But formidable technical problems make the economical development of magma resources in the near future unlikely. The very high temperatures surrounding magma bodies (such as volcanoes) can cause drilling equipment to fail, and the risk of exploding gases is very high.

Hot dry rock (HDR) heat mining, despite its name, is not a completely dry process. Holes are drilled into rocks, typically to depths of less than 5 kilometers (3 miles), to create a well, or artificial reservoir. Water is then injected into the well. *Fractures* (tiny cracks) in the rocks, caused by the drilling, allow deep-earth heat to superheat the water, which is then pumped to the surface. The heat is converted into electric energy in steam turbines or binary power plant systems. Wastewater from electric energy production is reinjected into the rock, beginning the cycle again.

Pilot programs have demonstrated that HDR heat mining is feasible, but continued progress awaits the development of improved drilling, rock-fracturing, and circulation techniques. Although HDR resources could potentially yield enormous quantities of energy, exploitation still requires significant technological development. In 2007, HDR systems were being developed and tested in Australia, France, Japan, Switzerland, and the United States.

Geothermal energy use today

According to renewable energy company Enel North America Inc. of Andover, Massachusetts, geothermal energy supplied 8,900 megawatts of electricity to 24 countries worldwide in 2005, meeting the total electric power needs of some 60 million people. From 2000 to 2005, geothermal generation tripled in France, Kenya, and Russia. By 2007, three other countries—Austria, Germany, and Papua New Guinea—were producing geothermal power for the first time. El Salvador, Iceland, and the Philippines generated an average of 25 percent of their electric energy from geothermal sources, and Tibet met 30 percent of its energy needs through geothermal power.

In the mid-2000's, the United States was the world leader in online capacity of geothermal energy and geothermal generation of electric power. According to the U.S. Department of Energy's Energy Information Agency, geothermal energy in 2005 produced approximately 16,010 gigawatt-hours of electric generation, or about 0.36 percent of the annual U.S. total. California produced the greatest amount of electric energy using geothermal resources, accounting for 5 percent of its total in 2003 on a per-kilowatt-hour basis.

Geothermal potential

In the early 2000's, worldwide geothermal power production represented a small fraction of the resource's potential. As the technology advances, the cost of using geothermal resources is expected to continue to decline, while geothermal contribution to energy needs will continue to expand.

Geothermal heat pump installations were increasing at an annual rate of 15 percent, with more than 600,000 units in operation in the United States in 2005. All U.S. regions have nearly constant shallow-ground temperatures, which are suitable for geothermal heat pumps.

In 2006, more than 40 new geothermal electric projects were under development in 10 states. A U.S. Geological Survey assessment found sites capable of producing 20,000 to 26,000 megawatts of geothermal energy in the country. Of this amount, a 2005 report for the Western Governors' Association estimated that 5,600 megawatts would be viable for commercial development by about 2015.

In addition, the Energy and Geosciences Institute of the University of Utah estimated that thermal *aquifers* (a layer of underground rock that contains water) alone could provide 15.3 billion kilowatt-hours of electric power in the United States—five times the total U.S. electrical production in 1990. Other geothermal resources—such as magmatic systems, geopressured basins, and those available only with enhanced geothermal techniques— are estimated to contain significantly more energy. As technology and research advance, new methods will enable scientists to tap the enormous potential of heat energy beneath Earth's crust.

Hydrogen Power

Someday people may fill their vehicle fuel tanks with hydrogen instead of gasoline. They may pipe hydrogen into their homes for heating and cooking and use it to generate electricity. Many energy analysts see hydrogen technologies as necessary in the long-term transition from a *hydrocarbon economy* (an economy based on the consumption of fossil fuels) to an economy based on renewable energy.

Hydrogen, the most abundant element on Earth and in the universe, can be found in water and many *organic compounds* (living or once living substances that contain carbon). Hydrogen does not occur naturally as a gas. It is always combined with other elements. For example, hydrogen combined with oxygen is water. However, if hydrogen is separated from other elements, it can be burned as a fuel or converted into electric energy.

Hydrogen can be produced from a wide variety of domestic resources using many different technologies. It has very high energy for its weight, and when it is burned in air, the main byproduct is water. When pure hydrogen is burned, it does not produce carbon dioxide, so its use could slow global warming.

Hydrogen production

In spite of its great potential, hydrogen technology has fallen far short of expectations set in the 1990's, when some energy experts predicted a fast transition to a hydrogen economy. The problem is that the process of extracting hydrogen requires energy. If hydrogen is taken from natural gas, the process releases carbon dioxide (a waste product), adding to the greenhouse effect. Another method of producing hydrogen, called electrolysis, requires large amounts of electric energy, which largely comes from the burning of fossil fuels.

Most hydrogen production is based on *steam reformation* of natural gas. In this process, a natural gas such as methane or propane is combined with

HOW A FUEL CELL WORKS

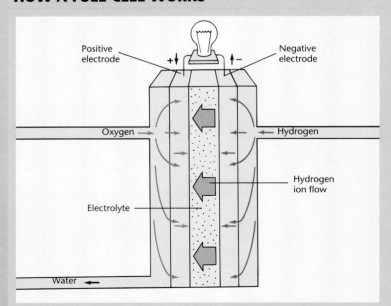

Positive electrode

Negative electrode

Oxygen

Hydrogen

Hydrogen ion flow

Electrolyte

Water

A fuel cell has two electrical terminals called electrodes. In the fuel cell shown at left, hydrogen gas (H_2) is fed to the negative electrode. There, the hydrogen undergoes a process called oxidation, which releases hydrogen ions and electrons. The hydrogen ions can pass through the electrolyte that separates the electrodes, but the electrons cannot. The electrons instead flow to the positive electrode through a circuit outside the cell, thus powering the light bulb. At the positive electrode, oxygen gas (O_2) reacts with these electrons and the hydrogen ions that have passed through the electrolyte, producing water and some heat as by-products.

high-temperature steam, from 700 °C to 1,000 °C (1,290 °F to 1,830 °F). The gas reacts in the presence of a *catalyst* (a compound that triggers a chemical reaction without being changed itself) that breaks the bonds of the natural gas and creates hydrogen, carbon monoxide, and carbon dioxide. The carbon monoxide is treated with more steam, producing more hydrogen and carbon dioxide. The carbon dioxide is removed from the mixture and released into the atmosphere. Unfortunately, this conversion uses more energy than it creates, resulting in an energy loss.

Hydrogen can also be produced from water through *electrolysis*, which electrochemically splits water into hydrogen and oxygen. This process produces no emissions, as long as the electric energy used to separate water into its elements is produced from a nonpolluting source. As of 2007, Iceland, which produces electric energy through hydrothermal and geothermal power, was the only nation that could economically use electrolysis to convert water into hydrogen. In North America, it is likely that hydrogen electrolysis will someday be powered by surplus wind power.

Another process, called *thermochemical* hydrogen production, involves the heating of biomass or fossil fuel with limited or no oxygen present. This treatment turns the material into a mixture of hydrogen and carbon monoxide known as synthesis gas. The fuel can also be liquefied into pyrolysis oil and then processed further to extract the hydrogen.

Researchers are also exploring ways to use solar energy directly for hydrogen production, mimicking methods used by nature. *Biological photolytic hydrogen* is one promising avenue. Certain types of algae and photosynthetic bacteria use photosynthesis to make hydrogen instead of sugar and oxygen. Although this conversion has been successfully replicated in laboratories, researchers say they are years away from making it work on a commercial scale.

Hydrogen storage

Although hydrogen is an ideal fuel, some of its properties make storage difficult. Hydrogen has a very low *density* (the mass in a given volume of a substance); one gram of unpressurized hydrogen requires a container that can hold 11 liters (nearly 3 gallons). Hydrogen's *boiling point* (the temperature at which a substance turns into a gas) is very low: –253 °C (–423 °F). To maintain hydrogen in a liquid state requires keeping it at temperatures even lower. Maintaining these extremely cold conditions requires expensive, insulated tanks.

Storing hydrogen as a pressurized gas instead of a liquid takes up less space and does not require such cold temperatures. Hydrogen is, therefore, often compressed in pressurized tanks, allowing it to be stored in smaller containers. However, these containers are still bulky and impractical for use in vehicles.

Hydrogen is also extremely explosive; a small spark can cause it to ignite. Scientists are concerned about the effects of excess hydrogen leaking into the atmosphere. As reported in *Popular Science* in January 2005, leakage might actually promote global warming because "hydrogen added to the atmosphere will combine with oxygen to form water vapor, creating noctilucent clouds—those high, wispy tendrils you see at dawn and dusk. The increased cloud cover could accelerate global warming."

To overcome storage pitfalls, researchers are looking to high technology for a solution. In recent years, researchers explored the use of nanostructures, which have large surface-to-volume ratios and readily absorb hydrogen on their surfaces. Although the research was still in its early phases in 2007, it held great promise.

Fuel cells

Fuel cells are devices that convert chemical energy to electrical energy. In this way, they are similar to batteries. However, a battery contains all of the components required to produce electric power; a fuel cell must constantly be fed a fuel and an *oxidizer* (substance that removes electrons in a chemical reaction) to produce power.

Hydrogen is a common fuel used in fuel cells. In one type of fuel cell, hydrogen fed to one catalyst-containing electrode splits into a positively charged hydrogen ion—a proton—and a negatively charged electron. Positive ions travel through an *electrolyte* (nonmetallic conductor of electrical ions) to a second catalyst electrode. There, they combine with electrons and oxygen to produce water and heat. The electrons are drawn through an external electric circuit that generates electric power.

Hydrogen fuel cells have a long history of successful use in spacecraft and in stationary applications such as emergency power generators. However, fuel cell technology for other uses, such as to power automobiles, is still in early development. Much more work will be required before fuel cells become competitive and hydrogen gains widespread commercial use. Researchers hope that advanced hydrogen and fuel cell technologies will eventually reduce U.S. dependence on foreign oil, improve air quality, and curtail global warming.

Although the use of fuel cells in automobiles is far away, several stationary fuel cell generators are already on the market. Collectively, fuel cell power systems had a peak generating capacity of about 69 megawatts in 2006; that is less than 0.01 percent of the total 944,000 megawatts of U.S. generating capacity.

Hydrogen-powered vehicles

Hydrogen can be used as a fuel for internal combustion engines that are very similar to engines fueled by gasoline. However, an average gasoline-powered automobile can travel about 480 kilometers (300 miles) before having to refuel, while a hydrogen vehicle can travel only 240 kilometers (150 miles) This is because hydrogen has a lower density than gasoline; thus, when compared gallon to gallon, it takes more hydrogen than gasoline to run a vehicle. In order for a hydrogen car to travel as long between fill-ups, its fuel tank would therefore need to be more than four times larger than conventional gasoline tanks. This size is not practical for an automobile.

Fuel cells could someday replace internal combustion engines in vehicles since they are energy-efficient, clean, and fuel-flexible. Fuel cell vehicles (FCV's) use hydrogen that is usually stored as a pressurized gas in onboard fuel tanks. The electric energy generated by the fuel cell feeds a storage battery (as in electric/gasoline hybrid vehicles) that energizes the vehicle's electric motor. However, by 2007, fuel cells still had not come close to the automotive industry's standard for internal combustion engines—a lifespan of 15 years, or about 270,000 driving kilometers (170,000 miles).

The hydrogen economy

In 2003, the world's first hydrogen fueling station opened in Reykjavík, Iceland. At this station, hydrogen powers a fleet of fuel cell buses and is produced onsite from electrolyzed water. Meanwhile, an association of energy companies, automakers, and the Icelandic power company is planning to convert the rest of the island nation to a hydrogen system.

A hydrogen economy is viable in Iceland because 72 percent of the country's electric energy comes from geothermal and hydroelectric power. With so much clean, readily available energy and plenty of water, Iceland can cost-effectively use electric power to *electrolyze* (decompose a chemical compound into its ions) water. In the United States, such a system would not be feasible because only about 15 percent of the nation's electric power comes from geothermal and hydroelectric sources, while the burning of fossil fuels generates 71 percent.

Most analysts think it will take several decades for hydrogen to make a large impact on worldwide energy consumption, even if hydrogen technologies were affordable and readily available to the general public. In 2006, a U.S. government-sponsored report published by the National Research Council identified "major hurdles on the path to achieving the vision of the hydrogen economy." The report urged lawmakers to legislate tougher tailpipe-emission standards, thus making fossil fuels more expensive to use, and to earmark additional funding for research on renewable energy and alternative fuels, which include hydrogen.

A zero-emission, hydrogen-powered fuel cell bus waits at Aldgate bus station on its first day of service in central London, England, in 2004. The bus emits only water vapor and is part of a European trial aimed at reducing air and noise pollution in nine cities.

Moving energy from a power source to consumers or storing it at the site where it is produced or used are essential to using renewable energy effectively. Although wind and solar energy alone could generate all the electric energy needed in North America, they are limited by availability and the lack of systems to distribute and store the energy they produce. To make these and other renewable energy sources economically viable, systems must be developed to store renewable energy and make it readily available.

Storing energy from renewable sources allows supply to more closely match demand. For example, a storage system attached to a wind turbine could capture energy contained in the strong winds that blow at night. Then it could distribute that energy during high-demand periods in the middle of the day. A storage system for solar energy would allow solar-generated energy to be used both day and night.

Distributed energy refers to many small sites providing electric power to an area instead of one large power-generating facility, thus improving the delivery of electric energy. Distributed-energy technology is becoming increasingly important as the U.S. electric grid reaches capacity and as renewable, intermittent power sources become available for regular use. Distributed-energy systems can be used to help provide base load, peak power, backup power, and some cooling and heating needs.

Batteries

Among the many devices used to store electrical energy, batteries are the most widely used. Lead-acid batteries, the most common type, are used in automobiles, consumer devices, and utilities. Traditional lead-acid batteries consist of plates of lead and lead oxide submerged in a solution of sulfuric acid and water called an *electrolyte*. The electrolyte triggers a chemical reaction that produces electrons. New variations on the traditional lead-acid battery include valve-regulated lead-acid (VRLA) batteries, which are sealed and require less maintenance, and gel-type lead-acid batteries, which are filled with a gel and thus less likely to spill.

Another type of battery, called a flow battery, works like lead-acid batteries, except the liquid electrolyte is stored externally and circulated through the battery cells as needed. The electrical storage capacity of a flow battery is limited only by the capacity of its electrolyte reservoirs. Often used for *load-leveling* (compensating for fluctuations in electrical demand) on the electricity grid, flow batteries provide high power and high capacity. In the United States, a two-megawatt-hour battery installed in Castle Valley in southeast Utah has allowed the local power company, PacifiCorp, to meet increasing peak power demands without increasing the capacity of its aging distribution line that feeds the area.

Several other types of advanced battery technology—lithium-ion, lithium polymer, nickel sodium sulfur, and metal hydride—have smaller "footprints" (use less space) than traditional lead-acid batteries. As of 2007, such batteries were too costly for large-scale utility applications, but they were used in such smaller goods as cell phones, computers, and hybrid-electric automobiles.

Lithium and lithium-ion batteries could potentially bring a new level of performance to everything from MP3 players to hybrid vehicles. Advances in nanotechnology are particularly promising. The additional surface area of nanoscale particles on electrode materials allows ions to move more freely, which gives them a rapid charge rate and allows them to maintain their charge for a longer period of time than other types of rechargeable batteries.

Hybrid cars of the early 2000's ran primarily on nickel metal hydride batteries, which can power an electric motor and recharge rapidly. Lithium batteries do not have the rapid charging capability or safety level needed for use in cars. But energy experts say that advances in lithium-ion battery technology may soon advance the performance of electric vehicles.

Compressed air energy storage

Compressed air energy storage (CAES) uses off-peak electric energy to power a combined motor/generator unit. At off-peak times, the unit drives compressors that force air into an underground storage reservoir (such as an abandoned mine or salt cavern). The process is reversed when there is high demand for electric power. The compressed air is withdrawn from the reservoir, heated by natural gas in combustors, blended with natural gas, and then used to drive a gas turbine to generate electric energy. As of early 2007, two CAES facilities were operating: an 11-year-old plant in McIntosh, Alabama, and a 23-year-old plant in Germany, both in caverns created by salt deposits.

Flywheels

Flywheels are rotors that spin at high speeds, storing kinetic energy. A flywheel is connected to a motor/generator that interacts with the utility grid. At off-peak times, the motor spins the flywheel faster. The faster the flywheel turns, the more energy it retains. In high-demand times, energy is drawn off by the generator, which slows the flywheel. The most advanced flywheels operate in a vacuum environment to reduce *drag* (resistance to forward motion). They also use superconducting electromagnetic bearings that minimize energy loss due to friction.

In mid-2006 in San Ramon, the California Energy Commission began final-stage field trial testing of an advanced flywheel system designed to regulate power on the electrical grid.

Pumped hydropower

Pumped hydropower systems use off-peak electric energy to pump water from a lower reservoir to a higher-elevation reservoir. Electric energy is then generated during peak periods by allowing the pumped water to flow downhill through turbines

connected to generators. Although the amount of electric power needed to pump water uphill is greater than the amount gained when the water is released, the pumped-storage facilities are cost effective because they consume low-cost, off-peak electric power but generate high-peak energy.

An additional advantage is the ability of pumped hydropower systems to store large quantities of energy for long periods of time. When a plant shuts down unexpectedly, the pumped hydropower system provides emergency power for an electric grid.

Supercapacitors

Supercapacitors (also known as ultracapacitors or electrochemical double-layer capacitors) are electrochemical devices that store energy. They consist of a positively charged surface and negatively charged surface separated by a gap.

Supercapacitors can be recharged hundreds of thousands of times. However, their power is available only for very short durations. They are often used to start diesel trucks and railroad locomotives. They can also be used as emergency power sources in uninterruptible power supplies, much like flywheels.

In 2007 at the Laboratory for Electromagnetic and Electronic Systems (LEES) at the Massachusetts Institute of Technology, engineers were using nanotechnology to increase the storage capacity of supercapacitors. Researchers say a new generation of supercapacitors could replace conventional batteries in everything from digital cameras to electric automobiles and even trains.

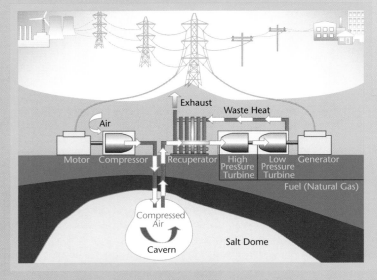

In a compressed air energy storage (CAES) facility located in salt caverns or mines, compressors use off-peak electricity to fill the cavern with compressed air. When demand for electricity increases, the compressed air is withdrawn from the cavern and blended with natural gas that is piped in from a nearby gas plant. The air and fuel mixture is used to drive a gas turbine to generate electricity.

DISTRIBUTED ENERGY GENERATION

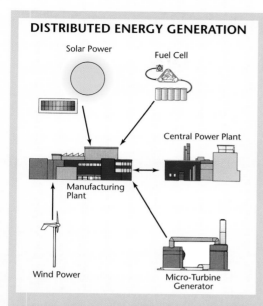

A facility such as a manufacturing plant may be supplied with electrical power from several different renewable energy sources in a distributed energy system. Such a facility may also be connected to a central power plant. Distributed energy systems can supply power more efficiently and at lower costs than central power plants.

The MIT researchers hope to make the LEES "batteries" available to consumers by 2010.

Superconducting magnetic energy storage

Magnetic storage is traditionally associated with data and media storage. *Superconducting magnetic energy storage* (SMES) systems break this tradition by providing energy storage within a magnetic field. The magnetic field is created by the flow of *direct current* (electric current that flows in one direction) through a coil of superconducting material that has been *supercooled* (cooled below the freezing point without solidifying).

SMES systems offer several advantages. The most important is that they can deliver very high power output almost instantaneously for a short period of time. Little power is lost with SMES power systems because electric currents encounter almost no resistance. In addition, SMES systems have no major moving parts—a design feature that makes them highly reliable.

SMES systems are used to address power-quality problems, short-term power losses, and voltage instability. The systems ensure that companies, such as manufacturers of computer chips, receive a steady, uninterrupted flow of electric energy.

Low-temperature SMES systems cooled by liquid helium were commercially available in 2007, and high-temperature (less cold) SMES systems cooled by liquid nitrogen were in development. Energy researchers are studying ways to maintain the special qualities of SMES systems at higher temperatures.

Distributed energy systems

Existing U.S. power grids are one of the biggest barriers to the widespread use of renewable energy technology. These grids were designed for centralized distribution. Electric energy is generated at large-scale power plants and then transmitted along power lines to consumers.

Renewable energy sources work more efficiently through distributed energy systems in which power sources are located near the site of consumer use. Distributed energy systems can address the nation's most serious electric power problems—blackouts and brownouts, security concerns, power-quality issues, transmission bottlenecks, and pollution emissions.

Some experts say that the growth of distributed energy is similar to the evolution of computer technology. At one time, people relied on mainframe computers with remote workstations that had no processing power of their own. Now, most people work on personal computers connected to a network of servers (the Internet). Just as the availability of smaller and cheaper computers has enabled individuals to purchase and manage their own computing power, distributed-energy technologies enable consumers to purchase and run their own electrical power systems. While central generating plants continue to provide most of the power to the grid, distributed resources can meet peak demands on a local basis.

Distributed-energy technologies can lead to improved efficiency and lower energy costs, particularly when renewable technologies are used in combined cooling, heating, and power (CHP) applications. CHP systems provide electricity along with hot water, heat for industrial processes, space heating and cooling, and refrigeration.

Unfortunately, aging centralized power grids cannot yet efficiently manage large flows from intermittent sources such as wind turbines and solar panels. Connecting thousands and then perhaps millions of energy sources will require sophisticated digital control mechanisms to route energy traffic during peak and off-peak periods. Innovations such as "smart" electric meters that can talk to storage and generation devices—and even to appliances and industrial motors—are all under development.

The Road Ahead

Renewable energy resources are abundant around the world, and people already have the technology they need to begin shifting toward clean, renewable power. Why, then, as of early 2007, did renewables account for only 13.2 percent of world energy consumption?

The many obstacles to greater use of renewable energy involve the higher cost of renewables compared to fossil fuels. The reasons for this price difference have to do with economies of scale, technological maturity, and governmental policies.

Economies of scale

Implementation of most renewable energy sources requires new financial investments in the technology and infrastructure necessary to produce and distribute the energy. By comparison, the infrastructure for producing and delivering fossil fuels has been built over many decades. This infrastructure has already been paid for with large investments on the part of industry and governments, which are naturally reluctant to replace existing, expensive systems with new ones.

The technology for producing, storing, and transporting fossil fuels is well established. Investment in newer technology and infrastructure carries much greater risk, requiring extensive experimentation to develop efficient systems to manage and maintain.

Finally, many governments heavily subsidize fossil fuel production and research. Shifting subsidies away from these industries into renewable energy development will require time and political persuasion.

Technological challenges

Each renewable energy source—biomass, geothermal, hydrogen, solar, battery, water, and wind power—has a unique set of technological challenges that present barriers to its development and limits to full implementation. To make such renewable energy sources economically viable, it will be necessary to develop advanced systems to store renewable energy and make it available when it is needed. The existing electrical grid must become far more efficient and sophisticated in order to deal with renewable power sources such as wind and solar farms located far from urban users.

The number of refineries producing biofuels has steadily increased and is predicted to continue to grow in the immediate future. New vehicles capable of using fuels such as ethanol and biodiesel are becoming more commonplace.

Geothermal electricity is virtually emission-free and inexhaustible. But geothermal energy has not reached its full potential as an energy alternative because of limitations in extraction technology, accessibility of resources, and insufficient research funding. Low-temperature (binary) electric generation technology may greatly expand the geothermal resources that can be developed economically. In addition, geothermal heat pumps represent a readily available technology for heating and cooling homes and businesses.

To boost renewables' share of the energy market, a breakthrough in the efficiency of solar power systems would be most significant. Photovoltaic technology is quickly gaining acceptance, thanks to its ability to produce power at points of consumption. Recent research has focused on capturing more energy per area and lowering the cost of solar-conducting materials. There have been encouraging signs that both challenges may be met in the future.

Although a complete solution to storing renewable energy is many years away from full implementation, new developments in battery technology show promise of a short-term solution for storage limitations. Advanced batteries may be able to support industrial power-distribution networks. They may also reduce fossil fuel consumption with the large-scale adoption of electric vehicles that rely on batteries for storing electric energy.

As hydroelectric dam technology has matured, the environmental drawbacks have become more apparent. Technologies to harness wave and tidal-stream power were at early stages of development in 2007, but they offer substantial potential as renewable energy resources. The costs associated with their development and implementation were expected to decrease.

Among the various technologies for harvesting renewable energy resources, wind power is the fastest growing. Tax incentives and high fossil fuel costs have combined with advances in wind turbines to establish the technology's widespread acceptance. By 2007, the U.S. wind industry had the capacity to generate nearly 10,500 megawatts—enough energy to power 2.5 million homes. Now that wind-turbine efficiency is close to its theoretical limit, the challenge is to boost reliability and equipment life spans and to lower costs. Industry experts forecast that wind could eventually supply up to 20 percent of the nation's electric power.

Policy challenges and actions

According to a 2007 report by the European Renewable Energy Council (EREC), headquartered in Brussels, renewables could satisfy half the world's energy demand by 2050. The report warns that this will be possible only if governments encourage efficiency and enact policies that discourage the use of fossil fuel. The International Energy Agency (IEA), a Paris-based group of 26 countries that develops energy policy, claims that there is "potential to achieve a greater share for renewables, if more vigorous policies are implemented." The IEA states that the share of renewables could more than quadruple by 2020 if market barriers, such as lack of economic funding for research, were removed.

According to global investment bank Goldman Sachs, headquartered in New York City, at least 49 governments have established targets to increase the use of renewable energy sources. The European Union has set a target of 18 percent for power from renewable sources by 2010. In the United States, there is no official federal target for overall use of renewable energy, although the Energy Policy Act of 2005 provides tax credits to individuals and businesses for purchase of products that use certain types of renewables, such as hybrid vehicles that run on electric batteries and gasoline. Nevertheless, annual U.S. federal spending for alternative energy research and development in 2006 was less than half what it was in the mid-1970's.

In the United States, state and municipal governments have taken the lead in developing policies that encourage production and use of alternative energy. Many states have passed or are considering emissions standards and renewable energy requirements. As of early 2007, 21 of the 50 states had established renewable energy standards for local utilities. New Jersey, for instance, requires that 22.5 percent of its electricity should come from renewables by 2021.

Renewables are at a tremendous disadvantage in terms of governmental policies and research budgets. According to a 2004 report from the New Economics Foundation in London, the World Bank alone funds about $235 billion a year in fossil fuel projects, money that could be better allocated to projects that promote the use of renewables.

Another hurdle for alternate energy resources is that fossil fuels are touted as cheaper than renewables. However, economists say that the true costs of fossil-based energy are not included in consumer utility or fuel bills, nor do the companies that produce or sell the energy pay them. These costs include human health problems caused by air pollution; damage to land from coal mining; environmental degradation caused by global warming, acid rain, and water pollution; and national security costs, such as protecting foreign sources of oil. Fossil fuels seem cheaper than renewable energy only because their true high costs are not apparent to individual consumers but paid by society as a whole.

Many energy experts and economists believe that the best way to encourage energy production that is less costly to society would be to tax carbon dioxide emissions. "Setting a price on carbon emissions is the single most important policy step to take," said Robert N. Stavins, director of the environmental economics program at Harvard University in Cambridge, Massachusetts. Such a step would add a significant cost to oil, gas, and coal—and encourage production and consumption of renewable fuels.

Just as important as the development of renewable energy technologies is conservation and efficiency. In a 2006 report, the McKinsey Global Institute, headquartered in New York City, estimated that the yearly growth in worldwide energy demand could be cut by more than half through 2020, from a projected annual rate of 2.2 percent to 0.6 percent, using current technologies. These technologies include improved insulation, fluorescent lighting, and more energy efficient appliances.

In the long term, the world will need a large-scale technological revolution to transform the global economy—in which the vast majority of our energy is derived from fossil fuels—to an economy that is largely free of fossil fuel emissions through the use of clean, renewable energy sources.

CONSUMER SCIENCE

Topics selected for their current interest provide information that the reader as a consumer can use in understanding everyday technology or in making decisions—from buying products to caring for personal health.

Low-Calorie Alternatives for a Sweet Tooth

In any supermarket, shelves are lined with candy, ice cream, and soft drinks peddled as "sugar-free," "zero-calorie," and "guilt-free." These goods are made with artificial sweeteners and are helping many Americans, according to the United States Department of Agriculture, kick a 20-teaspoons-of-sugar-a-day habit. Craving sweets is nothing new; since ancient times, sweeteners have been used to improve the flavor of food. In ancient civilizations, sweeteners were reserved for the elite and special occasions because they were difficult to obtain. Today, the only challenge most people face in seeking a sweet fix is from which store to buy it. We consume a vast quantity of candy, sodas, cakes, and other processed sweets that are high in calories. Unfortunately, due to inactivity and over consumption, many people do not burn all of the calories they consume, and there is now a rise in harmful health conditions, such as obesity and diabetes.

For nearly 100 years, artificial sweeteners have provided a solution to satiate sugar cravings without the side effects of excess sugar consumption. Artificial sweeteners supply the sweetness of sugar with few or no calories. This is either because they are made of compounds that are *indigestible* (unusable) by our bodies or because they have sweetening powers that are so great that only a small amount is needed to achieve the sweetness we desire. On average, artificial sweeteners are 200 to up to 13,000 times as sweet as sugar. Their molecular structures are thought to connect more tightly or longer to receptors found in our taste buds, thus signaling our brain that they are "supersweet."

Artificial sweeteners are helpful for individuals who are monitoring their caloric intake or who suffer from diabetes. Diabetics do not produce enough insulin to keep their blood *glucose* (sugar) levels in check. Artificial sweeteners contain very little or no carbohydrates, unlike natural sources of sugar, which can contain 5 to 25 grams of carbohydrates in a single serving. As a result, diabetics are able to consume products containing sugar substitutes without having excessive increases in their blood glucose levels.

The U.S. Food and Drug Administration (FDA) categorizes artificial sweeteners as food additives, and they must be approved as safe before products containing these additives can be sold. Five artificial sweeteners are approved by the FDA: acesulfame potassium, aspartame, neotame, saccharin, and sucralose. Like many artificial products that we consume, these sweeteners have been scrutinized by scientists, nutritionists, and the U.S. government. These studies and tests have concluded, according to the July–August 2006 *FDA Consumer Magazine,* that FDA-approved these

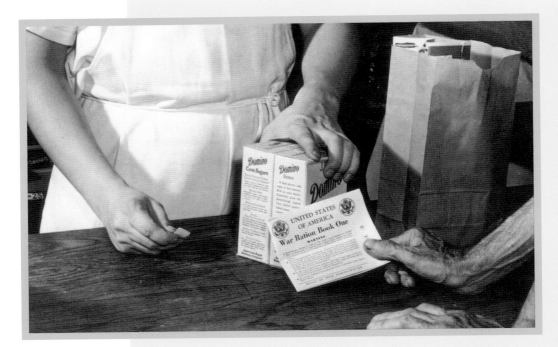

The rationing of sugar during World War II (1939-1945) resulted in the popularization of saccharin, a sugar substitute that previously had been used primarily by people with diabetes.

sweeteners pose little or no risk to health when used in moderation.

Artificial sweeteners have a serendipitous history that began in 1879. Chemists Ira Remsen and Constantin Fahlberg were conducting experiments on substances made from coal tar in Remsen's laboratory at Johns Hopkins University in Baltimore. Following their experiments, Fahlberg tasted an extraordinary sweetness while eating bread. Defying all safe laboratory practices, he began tasting residue found on clothing and hands and traced the sweetness back to the materials that he and Remsen were working with in the laboratory. The *American Chemical Journal* published the first article about the discovery in 1880. After leaving Baltimore, Fahlberg streamlined his techniques to produce large quantities of the compound inexpensively. He called the compound *saccharin*, which comes from the Medieval Latin word *succarum* and the Greek word *zacharono*, meaning *sugar*.

By 1907, saccharin was being used in foods for patients with diabetes. During World War II (1939-1945), saccharin was popular because sugar was

in short supply due to rationing, which ensured that armed forces overseas had enough supplies. Today, saccharin is marketed in the United States as Sweet'N Low®, Necta Sweet®, and SugarTwin®. Saccharin dissolves readily in water and remains *stable* (does not break down) at high temperatures—practical qualities for food preparation. It is used as a tabletop sweetener and in such products as soft drinks, baked goods, candies, salad dressings, and medicines. Saccharin is approximately 300 times sweeter than sugar, but it has a somewhat bitter aftertaste—thought to be detected by taste bud receptors that are "tuned" for bitterness.

Like its predecessor, aspartame was discovered by accident in 1965. Chemist James Schlatter had been assigned by G. D. Searle & Company in Illinois to create a new medicine to treat stomach ulcers. After crystallizing the compound L-aspartyl-L-phenylalanine methyl ester into powder, Schlatter unknowingly got some of the powder on his hand. Later on, while licking his finger to grab a piece of paper, he noticed a sweet taste. Although he never should have put an unwashed finger in his mouth, this accident led to the discovery of aspartame. Twenty years later, it was introduced to the public as a sugar substitute. Aspartame is recognized by the public under the names of NutraSweet® and Equal®. It is composed of two *amino acids* (organic molecules that form proteins) and the bond that holds them together breaks apart at high temperatures. This makes aspartame the only artificial sweetener that is not stable enough to use in cooking. The FDA approved aspartame for use as a table sugar substitute and a food additive in 1981. In 1983, it was approved for use as a sweetener for carbonated beverages, and in 1996, it was approved for general use. Aspartame can be found in breakfast cereals, chewing gum, instant coffee and tea, gelatin, candy, and yogurt.

In the late 1960's and early 1970's, another sugar substitute was developed—acesulfame potassium (acesulfame K). This sweetener is about 200 times sweeter than sugar, and because of its chemical structure, it enhances the sweetness of other substances. Due to its enhancing properties and because it, like saccharin, has a bitter aftertaste, acesulfame K is often combined with aspartame. Acesulfame K is sold under the brand names Sunett® and Sweet One®. Its chemical structure remains intact during heating and is stable during long-term storage. The FDA approved acesulfame K for use as a table sugar substitute in 1988 and for beverages in 1998. In 2003, acesulfame K was approved as a general-purpose sweetener for baked goods, dairy products, candy, breath mints, and other items.

In 1975, another artificial sweetener was created by accident. At Queen Elizabeth College in London, Professor Leslie Hough and his student, Shashikant Phadnis, were conducting experiments to see if they could create a new insecticide. The two created a solution of sugar water and slowly began adding drops of sulfuryl chloride. The mixture reacted strongly, exploding into powder. Hough asked his student to test this new chlorinated sugar. Misunderstanding "test," Phadnis tasted the powder, putting a tiny bit on the tip of his tongue. It was sweet—extremely sweet. Fortunately, the powder was not an insecticide, so Phadnis did not become ill. The new substance became known as sucralose. Over time, more stable methods were established to create sucralose. Today, it is marketed as Splenda®.

Sucralose is heat-stable, so it can be used in baking, canning, and other manufacturing processes that require high temperatures. On average, it is 600 times sweeter than sugar. Sucralose was granted approval by the FDA in 1998 for use in 15 food and beverage categories. In 1999, approval was extended for use as a general-purpose sweetener. Sucralose is available as a tabletop sweetener and is used as a replacement for sugar in baking. Products sweetened with sucralose include soft drinks, applesauce, frozen desserts, and gelatin.

In the 1990's, Claude Nofre and Jean-Marie Tinti, two chemists in Lyons, France, greatly enhanced aspartame's sweetness by modifying it—adding 3, 3-dimethylbutyl molecules (molecules that break down into methyl alcohol and are eliminated from the body). This new compound was called neotame. Gram for gram,

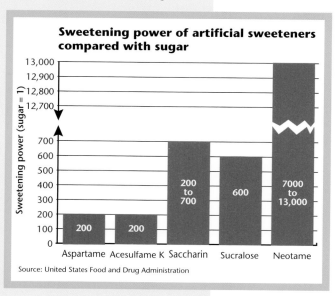

Sweetening power of artificial sweeteners compared with sugar

Source: United States Food and Drug Administration

neotame is approximately 7,000–13,000 times sweeter than sugar. Unlike aspartame, neotame remains intact when heated. In 2002, the FDA approved the use of neotame as a general-purpose sweetener. The NutraSweet Company is marketing neotame directly to food manufacturers for use in chewing gum, soft drinks, yogurt, and other fresh and frozen dairy products.

Artificial sweeteners have been surrounded by controversy ever since they were introduced to the public as a food additive. In the early 1900's, attempts were made to ban saccharin, and decades before that, it was even labeled an *adulterant* (a product that does not belong in food). However, this label was removed because of the need for alternative sweeteners during sugar shortages in wartime. In 1958, Congress added the Food Additives Amendment to the Food, Drug and Cosmetic Act. Because saccharin had been used for many years and was not known to be harmful, the FDA gave it GRAS (Generally Recognized as Safe) status under this act.

During the 1970's, scientists reported that saccharin might be responsible for bladder tumors in rats. In 1971, the FDA removed saccharin from the GRAS list until it could be tested further. A few years later, the FDA proposed to ban it. Concerned that individuals with diabetes would not have access to saccharin, Congress in 1977 passed the Saccharin Study and Labeling Act, which prevented a saccharin ban. Instead, the act required foods containing saccharin to have warning labels on them. After further studies, the National Cancer Institute and the National Toxicology Program determined that the ill effects from saccharin observed in rats did not occur in humans. As a result, the warning label was no longer required on foods containing saccharin after 2001.

Beginning in the 1980's, scrutiny shifted to aspartame. When aspartame was first introduced, the NutraSweet Company had a toll-free number for consumers to call for information related to aspartame and to report health complaints. Each month, the company shared the collected information with the FDA. The company collected complaints from 1982 through 1993. Such an extensive program to monitor product safety had never before been conducted for a food additive. In 1984, at the request of the FDA, the Centers for Disease Control and Prevention (CDC)

U.S. Food and Drug Administration acceptable daily intake (ADI) for artificial sweeteners

Artificial sweetener	Products that contain this sweetener	ADI per kilogram (2.2 pounds) of body weight	ADI for a 150-pound adult	Equivalent product consumption
Aspartame	NutraSweet®, Equal®	0.050 grams	3.4 grams (0.12 ounces)	15 cans of diet soda
Acesulfame K	Sunett®, Sweet One®	0.015 grams	1.02 grams (0.04 ounces)	25 cans of diet soda
Saccharin	Sweet'N Low®	0.005 grams	0.34 grams (0.01 ounces)	8.5 sweetener packets
Sucralose	Splenda®	0.005 grams	0.34 grams (0.01 ounces)	5 cans of diet soda
Neotame	No U.S. products available	0.018 grams	0.018 grams (0.00063 ounces)	No U.S. products available

Source: MayoClinic.com

evaluated the health complaints associated with aspartame. The CDC concluded that no specific symptoms were identified that could be associated with aspartame. In addition to NutraSweet's collection of health complaints, several experimental scientific studies were conducted to investigate aspartame. By 1995, the FDA concluded that data were sufficient to confirm that aspartame was safe. The FDA continues to review complaints alleging adverse reactions to aspartame.

In 2006, the European Ramazzini Foundation (ERF) reported finding cancer and other illnesses in rats fed aspartame from eight weeks of age until death. However, the European Food Safety Authority reviewed this data and released a statement in May 2006 that the ERF's conclusions were not supported by the data. The FDA requested the ERF to review its data but has yet to announce any changes to current regulations.

The only limitation set by the FDA for aspartame is a warning label for people who have phenylketonuria (PKU). This is a very rare genetic disorder in which a person is unable to process the amino acid phenylalanine. As a result, an excess of phenylalanine can build up in the bloodstream, leading to neurological disorders. People with PKU eat a diet that is very low in phenylalanine. One of the by-products of aspartame when it is broken down in the human body is phenylalanine. Since this can contribute to phenylalanine levels in individuals with PKU, the FDA requires the following warning on all products containing aspartame: "This product contains phenylalanine." It is also recommended that pregnant women should not consume products containing aspartame since it is only possible to determine if an infant has PKU after it is born.

Like saccharin and aspartame, the newest artificial sweeteners also underwent rigorous review and testing before being approved. In determining the safety of neotame, the FDA reviewed data from more than 100 studies of its use by animals and humans. Although neotame is derived from the amino acid phenylalanine, the FDA considers that its chemical form and the minimal amount introduced into the body do not pose any safety risk for individuals with PKU. The FDA concluded in 2002 that neotame is safe, so products containing this sugar substitute do not require warning labels.

Sucralose is an inert compound, meaning it passes rapidly through the body and is excreted unchanged. After reviewing more than 110 animal and human safety studies, the FDA approved the use of sucralose in food. Sucralose has been gaining popularity that may soon equal that of aspartame (currently the most commonly used artificial sweetener).

The FDA considers acesulfame K to be safe because it passes through the body unchanged. One concern was raised that methylene chloride, a cancer-causing chemical, might be created in the initial manufacturing step of acesulfame K. However, the FDA was convinced that the final packaged product does not contain this chemical because the production of acesulfame K involves many purification steps; since methylene chloride is volatile, it would not stay in the product but would evaporate into air. By 2003, acesulfame K was approved as a general-purpose sweetener.

Artificial sweeteners offer the sweetness of sugar with few or no calories. These attributes make them ideal for people who are on weight-control diets or who must avoid sugar because of diabetes. The sweeteners also do not promote tooth decay. Is it safe to consume these sugar substitutes? The FDA says yes. According to the 2006 *FDA Consumer Magazine,* testing of FDA-approved artificial sweeteners has shown that "the typical amount used by U.S. consumers is well within designated 'acceptable daily intake levels (ADI),' or levels that can be consumed safely every day over a lifetime." In other words, just as you should consume candy, baked goods, and sodas that contain sugar in moderation, you should practice the same moderation when eating foods made with artificial sweeteners.

■ Catherine Klein

Antibacterial Cleansers: Do They Clean Up?

A special lotion designed to resemble bacteria appears blue under ultraviolet light on volunteers' hands during a demonstration on the importance of washing hands properly. After applying the lotion, volunteers view their hands under the light. They then wash their hands and check for the amount of "bacteria" that remains.

The average home teems with germs. A dishwashing sponge may hold more than 1 billion colonies of bacteria, viruses, and other disease-producing microorganisms. Refrigerator door handles can harbor another 1 million. The interior of a shower may contain more than 1 million colonies per square centimeter, and a washbasin, more than 10 million. Consumer interest in antibacterial products, including items for washing hands and bathing and for cleaning kitchens and bathrooms, has grown dramatically in the past decade. In fact, the sales of antibacterial products generate billions of dollars for businesses in the United States. More people are traveling throughout the world, expanding the reach of many microbes. And new studies, made public every year, illustrate the pervasiveness of germs in our environment and how they affect our health. Consumers can purchase hand sanitizer gels and wipes containing an alcohol called ethanol; liquid soaps, deodorants, and toothpastes that contain the antibacterial agent triclosan (TCS); and bar soaps that use triclocarban (TCC), also an antibacterial agent. Some scientists question whether these products carry the risks of creating resistant strains of bacteria and causing danger to the environment.

About 1,500 bacteria live on each square centimeter of your hands. For many of these microorganisms—known as resident bacteria—your skin is permanently home. Resident bacteria actually help keep humans healthy by producing beneficial substances that support and nourish cells. These bacteria also fight off transient bacteria—bacteria that you pick up from doorknobs, faucet handles, elevator buttons, shopping carts, and—especially—other people's hands. Transient bacteria are responsible for many *infectious diseases* (illnesses caused by microorganisms that invade and reproduce inside the body). Infectious diseases caused by bacteria range from sinus infections and cholera to leprosy (Hansen's disease), pneumonia, and whooping cough.

According to a 2003 report from the Centers for Disease Control and Prevention (CDC)," the infectious diseases influenza and pneumonia are the seventh-leading cause of death in the United States, despite the widespread availability of vaccines, antiseptics, and powerful antibiotics. As many as 80 percent of infectious diseases are spread through person-to-person contact. As a result, most health experts agree that the single most effective way to protect yourself against them is to wash your hands. Washing generally does not remove the resident bacteria on your hands—nor should it. Washing does not even remove all the transient bacteria. However, it reduces transient bacteria populations, so they are less likely to get into your body and make you sick.

Soap consists of an acid and a base. The acid is in the form of a fatty acid; the base is an alkali metal. Within the mixture, the base acts upon the acid to form salts. These salts decrease the surface tension (the ability of molecules below the surface film of a liquid to attract molecules to the film) of water. They can also attach to soil and bacteria. Thus, "plain soap" not only gets you clean, but it also removes bacteria. The difference between plain and antibacterial soap is that additional ingredients are added to the latter. These include TCS and TCC. Both these chemicals prevent the growth of bacteria. But do these chemicals make antibacterial soap more effective than plain soap in the fight against bacteria?

Elaine Larson, a professor at Columbia University's School of Nursing, conducted two studies to assess how well antibacterial cleansers worked. Her research found little difference between the amounts of microbes found on hand washers using plain liquid soap or soaps that contain TCS.

Another study headed by Larson tested the effects of antibacterial products on the incidence of infectious disease symptoms, such as a runny nose, cough, and sore throat, or vomiting, diarrhea, and fever. The tested antibacterial items, including products for general cleaning, laundry soap, and hand soap, were placed in households that consisted of essentially healthy persons. The study concluded that using antibacterial products did not reduce the occurrence of infectious disease symptoms. However, in homes where family members' health or immune systems were compromised, the products could contribute to reducing bacterial symptoms that might aggravate existing conditions.

Hand-washing discovery saves lives

During the 1800's, as many as one in three mothers died after delivering their babies in hospitals. Hungarian physician Ignaz Phillipp Semmelweis campaigned to get doctors to wash their hands before treating a patient. This simple advice introduced the concept of *antisepsis* (the process of preventing infection) and paved the way for the measures used today for controlling infection in hospitals. In the early 1840's, Semmelweis began to investigate the causes of *puerperal fever* (commonly called childbed fever). He observed that women who gave birth at home and those who were assisted by midwives in the hospital clinic in which he worked had high rates of survival. In a second clinic within the hospital, women giving birth were attended by physicians. This clinic had a higher death rate. Semmelweis concluded that the doctors were transmitting various diseases from other patients to the birthing mothers, who then got sick and often died.

To prevent the spread of disease, Semmelweis established a policy requiring doctors to wash their hands in a chlorine solution to rid them of potential disease-causing particles. Hand washing proved successful. The maternal mortality within Semmelweis's hospital was reduced by more than 50 percent.

A 2005 study in Karachi, Pakistan, conducted by Stephen Luby of the CDC, assigned one group either antibacterial soap or plain soap and offered instructions on how to wash hands properly. Another group was given a *placebo* (containing no active ingredients) to use without any hand-washing instructions. The results found that both "soap groups" had a decreased rate of respiratory infection, impetigo, and diarrhea, the latter two of which can be caused by bacteria. There was no added benefit from use of the antibacterial product; rather proper hand washing seemed to be the key to reducing symptoms of infection.

So are antibacterial soaps any more effective than plain soap? The answer is no, according to conclusions presented in 2005 by an advisory panel of the U.S. Food and Drug Administration (FDA). These studies show that what prevents the spread of bacteria and infection is proper hand washing with warm water and soap—and any soap will do. Furthermore, antibacterial cleansers will not kill the microbes, such as viruses, that cause most infectious diseases. Fungi and parasites are also resistant to antibacterial products.

Hand washing guidelines

Keeping your hands clean is one of the most important steps you can take to avoid getting sick and spreading germs to others. It is best to wash your hands with soap and clean running water for 20 seconds. However, if soap and clean water are not available, use an alcohol-based product to clean your hands. Alcohol-based hand rubs significantly reduce the number of germs on skin and are fast acting.

When washing hands with soap and water:
- Wet your hands with clean running water and apply soap. Use warm water if it is available.
- Rub hands together to make lather and scrub all surfaces for 20 seconds.
- Rinse hands well under running water.
- Dry your hands using a paper towel or air dryer. If possible, use your paper towel to turn off the faucet.

When using an alcohol-based hand sanitizer:
- Apply product to the palm of one hand.
- Rub the product over all surfaces of hands and fingers until hands are dry.

When should you wash your hands?
- Before preparing or eating food
- After going to the bathroom
- After changing diapers or cleaning up a child who has gone to the bathroom
- Before and after tending to someone who is sick
- After blowing your nose, coughing, or sneezing
- After handling an animal or animal waste
- After handling garbage
- Before and after treating a cut or wound

Source: "Clean Hands Campaign," U.S. Centers for Disease Control and Prevention.

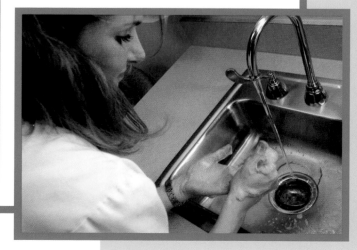

Are antibacterial gels more effective than antibacterial soaps? Antibacterial gels are actually solutions containing alcohol and are used as a supplement to hand washing or as an alternative when water is not available. Alcohol rubs must contain 70 to 95 percent alcohol to kill germs effectively. Health care facilities use products containing these levels of alcohol, in addition to gels containing a second ingredient used to kill germs. Many consumer products, however, contain less than 70 percent alcohol, so they are less effective. A 2003 study conducted by Children's Hospital of Boston found that families who used antibacterial gel for hand washing, as opposed to antibacterial soap or regular soap and water, had almost half the amount of infectious disease symptoms in their homes. The study pointed out that people's homes, especially those with children, are a common source of bacterial infections.

Antibacterial wipes contain the same ingredients as gels but are used where liquids are not appropriate or difficult to apply. They are also used by consumers as an alternative to gel.

Some have questioned whether consumer antibacterial products are harmful. In response to the growing concern over the effectiveness and safety of these products, the FDA convened a meeting in 2005 to review the data. Scientists warned the FDA that antibacterial cleansers, like other chemicals found in food and medicines, may pose some risk to the user.

Some researchers wondered whether the use of TCS and TCC contributes to antibacterial resistance among some pathogens. Researchers worry that the way TCS kills bacteria may play a role in creating antibiotic-resistant strains of bacteria. In the late 1990's, Tufts University researcher Stuart Levy reported in the scientific journal *Nature* that constant usage of antibacterial products caused genetic changes in bacteria in laboratory studies. He warned of the possible development of "supergerms"—bacteria that would be resistant to all antibiotics. Recent laboratory studies, however, conducted by Allison Aiello of the University of Michigan School of Public Health and her colleagues, found that participants using antibacterial soaps for an entire year showed no significant increase in *cross-resistance* (tolerance as a result of exposure) to antibiotics. However, Aiello noted, "But just because we did not measure an increased resistance at the population level, in an environment less controlled than a laboratory, does not mean there is no risk. We may not be able to detect small changes in antibiotic resistance in an epidemiological study. ... One year of exposure to antibacterial soap may be too short a time for resistance to develop, especially with such widespread use of these products in the community setting. It could take several years to measure changes." Her research group urged further surveillance on the effect of long-term use of antibacterial cleaning and hygiene products.

As medical scientists continue to study the safety of antibacterial cleansers, environmental scientists have expressed concern about the effects of TCS and TCC on the environment. TCS shares chemical similarities with dioxin, a *toxic* (poisonous) chemical, and TCC transforms in the environment to create chemical compounds that are toxic to blood cells and may promote the development of cancers. Studies show that TCS and TCC can accumulate in soil and sediment and persist in the environment, thus exposing marine life and mammals, including humans, to these toxins. Keeping the environment free of these agents is not easy since consumers introduce the agents into the environment simply by washing their hands and allowing the rinse water to drain into the sewer system.

Jochen Heidler and Rolf U. Halden of the Johns Hopkins University Bloomberg School of Public Health looked at how well a high-functioning sewage cleaning plant cleared TCS and TCC from the water. They found that half of TCS and three-quarters of TCC—all of which came from antibacterial products—remained detectable in the *sludge* (a by-product of the wastewater treatment). This sludge is used by some farmers as a crop fertilizer. "We estimate that 150,000 pounds [68,000 kilograms] of triclosan (TCS) and 175,000 pounds [79,000 kilograms] of triclocarban (TCC) are applied every year in sludge on agricultural fields used for either grazing or crop production. Neither of these pesticides [TCC and TCS] is approved or tested for agricultural use," Halden told the FDA's advisory committee. In 1999 and 2000, a U.S Geological Survey assessed whether 139 streams across 30 states were polluted with organic wastewater contaminants. TCS, found in 58 percent of the river water samples, ranked among the top 10 pollutants. TCC was not included in the survey, so Halden studied waterways near Baltimore and found TCC in 60 percent of the samples.

According to Halden, the FDA committee felt that there was not, to date, enough convincing scientific evidence that personal-care products containing TCS or TCC offer any measurable benefit over use of regular soap and water for the general population. "Given this assessment and the confirmed pollution of U.S. streams," he claimed, "use of these products should be discontinued." In other words, products that certainly play a useful role in health care settings are not needed in the normal household.

Although drugstore and supermarket shelves may be packed with antibacterial products, the best advice is wash your hands. Plain soap and water will do. If water is not accessible, use gels and wipes containing alcohol. "Alcohol-based hand antiseptics appear to have very good to excellent activity against many bacteria and some enveloped [surrounded and destroyed] viruses," according to the CDC. In general, the agency says, "The efficacy of most alcohol-based hand antiseptics approximates simple hand washing."

■ Deborah Kowal

Voice over Internet Protocol: A Revolution for the Telephone

Advancements in technology, including Voice over Internet Protocol, allow users to make local and long-distance phone calls without the use of a traditional telephone.

The ability to make telephone calls over the Internet through a technology called Voice over Internet Protocol (VoIP) is revolutionizing the telephone industry. VoIP's cost-saving advantages, flexibility, and efficiency will almost certainly radically affect the use of traditional telephone systems worldwide. High-speed communication has already altered the way people do business, send mail, and conduct research. Making telephone calls is next.

The roots of VoIP can be traced to 1973, when the first voice signals were carried over the Internet. The technology did not become commercially available, until 1995 and was not available to consumers until 2004. VoIP uses a *broadband* (high-speed) connection to send data, specifically the human voice, from one site to another. The transmission may occur over a physical channel—such as a cable television system or digital subscriber line (DSL), which uses traditional copper telephone lines or fiber-optic lines—or through energy waves within the air—as in a satellite television system.

Voice over Internet Protocol can be installed in a home in three ways. All three require a broadband connection. This connection can be a DSL (lines provided by telephone companies to subscribers to carry data at high speeds) or a cable modem (an electronic device that sends data to or from a computer, telephone, or other communication lines). The DSL system uses a regular telephone and special equipment called an *analog* (continuous data) telephone adapter (ATA). The telephone wire that would typically go into a wall jack plugs instead into the ATA, which then plugs into the computer. The ATA converts the analog signals used by traditional telephones into digital signals that can be sent over the broadband connection.

A second VoIP setup requires a special telephone that may look like a traditional telephone but has wiring that connects it directly to the *router* on a computer, rather than to a phone jack. A router is a device that forwards data *packets* between computer networks. Packets are the bits of communication—voice conversations, music files, e-mails, pictures—sent over a connection.

The third and simplest way to use VoIP connects one computer to another with software and a few extra pieces of hardware. With the addition of a microphone, speakers, a sound card, and the appropriate software, the computer itself becomes a modified telephone.

Some systems allow subscribers to use VoIP to call any local or long-distance phone number, just as they would with a traditional telephone. However, other systems restrict calls to other subscribers on the same system. Such restricted systems are often used by businesses to reduce telephone charges and long-distance costs, especially if the company has employees or branches in other parts of the world.

Traditional telephones rely on *circuits*. A circuit is simply the connection of two points with data moving in both directions. During a telephone call, a circuit is opened between the caller and the recipient. The voice data are sent in a continuous stream over the circuit and arrive in the same order in which they were sent. While a circuit is active, no other call can use it. That means that when data are not being sent, such as during pauses in the conversation, empty circuit space is being wasted.

VoIP, however, does not use circuits. Instead, in the same way that information is sent over the Internet, the data are broken into packets, each one containing a piece of information. There is no dedicated path of transmission; the packets are sent through a fiber-optic cable over the network, following random paths. Packets travel from router to router, filtering into less crowded lines amid the other network traffic, until they reach the recipient's computer. Lines may be more or less crowded depending on the number of users on a system. Because the packets may take different routes to reach the recipient and may arrive out of order at their destination, they need to be compiled into the correct order to reproduce the original message.

Think of the message as a puzzle and the packets as puzzle pieces. Initially, the pieces form a complete unit, but the pieces are broken apart to transmit because it is easier and faster to send small puzzle pieces of information over multiple channels than to send the entire puzzle through one channel. The re-

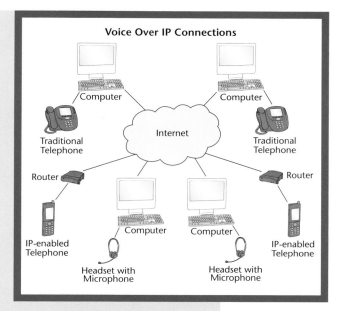

Voice Over IP Connections

cipient will not recognize the puzzle by simply looking at the individual pieces, so, once the pieces reach their destination, the puzzle has to be put back together. This type of transmission allows multiple messages to use the same lines, increasing efficiency, eliminating unused space, and reducing costs.

From a technical standpoint, the other difference between VoIP and the traditional telephone is a matter of signals. Telephone lines use analog signals to transmit voice data. Analog data are received in a continuous stream of electrical impulses. The Internet relies on digital signals. Digital data consist of information broken down into numbers. To allow analog and digital systems to interact so that voice data can be sent over an Internet connection, VoIP must convert the signals into the appropriate format at each stage of the process.

From a user's standpoint, phone calls made with VoIP are very similar to calls made with a standard telephone. Subscribers dial phone numbers using either the appropriate telephone or their computer. The person being called is often unable to distinguish a VoIP call from a traditional telephone call. (However, VoIP calls may be detected by garbled sound quality if the caller's computer is running other

Voice over Internet Protocol connections can be created with traditional telephones connected to a computer, with Internet Protocol-enabled telephones and a router, or with a headset with a microphone and computer. Regardless of setup, there must be a broadband connection to the Internet.

Because VoIP can be cost-effective, especially for long-distance calls, many small businesses are replacing their traditional telephone service with VoIP systems.

Advantages and disadvantages of VoIP

Advantages	Disadvantages
VoIP computer-to-computer calls are free.	VoIP users must be connected to the Internet in order to make phone calls.
Long-distance calls to traditional telephones may be billed as local calls.	VoIP systems do not work during an electric-power outage.
Services such as call waiting, caller ID, and conference calling are often included at no additional charge.	Emergency (911) calls are not as efficient and cannot be made during a power failure.
Subscribers can choose their area code.	Voice quality may not be as good as that on traditional phones.
VoIP systems are portable and can be used in any location with an Internet connection.	Some systems require the host computer to be on in order to transmit and receive messages.
Subscribers can send data including pictures and documents while talking on the phone.	VoIP systems may be susceptible to computer viruses.

programs during the call and lacks the processing power to handle them all.) Subscribers also receive calls the same way they would using a telephone line; the telephone or computer attached to the broadband connection will ring to alert them when there is an incoming call. For VoIP systems that rely on the computer to transmit messages, the computer and the VoIP software must be turned on in order to receive calls. However, because the other configurations (ATA's and specialized phones that connect to routers) use a phone connected directly to a broadband connection, they will work even if the computer is off, as long as the connection remains active.

As of 2007, VoIP was in use in more than 5 million homes in the United States. VoIP's popularity can be attributed to the advantages it has over traditional telephones: cost and flexibility. Although there are charges for the broadband connection and necessary hardware and software, VoIP still is less expensive than traditional phone service. The ability to transmit multiple conversations over the same lines keeps maintenance and operating costs lower than with traditional phone lines. These savings are passed on to the subscribers. Some VoIP services are free; others charge a flat monthly rate for unlimited phone calls to anyone in the world. Some VoIP systems, however, require a traditional phone line for the broadband connection, so subscribers pay both the phone carrier and the VoIP provider. People calling a VoIP phone are charged the same local or long-distance fees that they would pay to call any other telephone number in that area.

Many VoIP packages include such typical telephone services as call waiting, caller ID, and conference calling. Because a subscriber can use the computer while on a VoIP phone call, additional Internet-related services may also be included.

VoIP is more flexible than the standard telephone system. Subscribers can choose service in any area code because Internet addresses are not tied to a local area. This turns otherwise long-distance calls into local calls, eliminating the charges associated with traditional long-distance service. However, once an area code is selected, it cannot be changed without selecting a new phone number as well. Some business owners choose to have an area code in a region they service even if they are based elsewhere.

Many VoIP systems are also portable. Subscribers can use their VoIP system adapter anywhere they have an Internet connection. This is ideal for travelers because they retain the same phone number, and so calls to and from their "home" area code are still considered local calls. And, as more wireless (wi-fi) locations crop up, VoIP users may be able to connect to the Internet while sitting in a café or airport, making and receiving calls at a lower rate than would be charged for using a cellular telephone.

Despite VoIP's advantages, there are also disadvantages. Traditional telephone lines do not rely on electric power, but VoIP needs it to maintain the broadband connection. A power failure will leave the VoIP system unavailable, which is especially dangerous in an emergency. Battery backup or some type of generator that maintains a continuous power supply to the home or business will prevent interruption of service. Network problems will also affect VoIP services. If the Internet fails, the broadband connection will be dropped, along with the VoIP system.

Another safety concern involves 911 emergency calls, which do not work the same way with VoIP as with traditional phones. Traditional phone numbers are tied to a geographic location. A 911 operator receiving a phone call also receives information about where that caller is located and where to send emergency services. With VoIP, the reliance on a broadband connection, the ability to use a number in a different area code, and the option of connecting to a VoIP system from anywhere make it more difficult to pinpoint a caller's location.

In addition, most 911 operators merely route calls to emergency personnel. On a traditional phone line, this process just takes a minute or two. Because operators require more information from those using VoIP, however, precious time is wasted. Recognizing these concerns, the Federal Communications Commission has begun to issue regulations for enhanced 911 systems for VoIP users that make use of traditional telephone networks. These regulations require VoIP providers to notify subscribers about the issues and record a physical address that is linked to the subscriber. Subscribers are responsible for keeping the information current.

The use of a network connection makes VoIP susceptible to such security threats as viruses, worms, and computer crashes. Viruses and worms are computer programs designed to modify—and, in some cases, destroy—information saved on a computer's hard drive. Many VoIP-service providers have not developed effective *encryption methods* to prevent other people from eavesdropping on a conversation. Encryption programs convert transmissions into code so they cannot be read by unauthorized persons. *Hackers*—individuals who illegally gain access to computer systems, usually for theft or corruption—may also be able to modify the caller ID information so that it displays a different number. This misrepresentation can enable hackers to collect personal and financial data from people who believe they are calling or receiving a call from a legitimate organization. New technology and new laws may lessen these risks in the future.

As VoIP continues to evolve, many of these problems will likely be addressed and resolved. And just as the Internet has inspired new technologies and applications, VoIP may expand and be implemented in new ways, notably in the development of wireless devices. For now, VoIP is a supplement, rather than a replacement, for the traditional telephone system. However, most communications experts believe this economical, efficient technology will undoubtedly become the standard in voice communication in the next decade.

■ Mindi McDowell

Chocolate: Rich in Health, History, and Taste

Bittersweet, dark, milk, or white—chocolate inspires such passion that enthusiasts often describe themselves as chocoholics. Rich in history as well as taste, chocolate has been brewed as an offering to gods, used as a form of money, and flaunted as a sign of status and wealth. In modern times, chocolate became a sweet indulgence. More recently, however, this delectable food has been attracting public and scientific interest for its possible health benefits, one of the reasons that the ancient Maya and Aztec prized it 1,500 years ago. Several recent studies, for example, suggest that eating some types of chocolate—as part of a healthy diet—may lower blood pressure and reduce the risk of heart disease, stroke, and diabetes.

More than 3 billion kilograms (3 million tons) of cocoa is processed around the world each year. Americans rank 11th among chocolate consumers, enjoying about 5 kilograms (12 pounds) per person annually. Europeans are the world's top consumers; people in the top chocolate-loving countries—(in order of consumption) Switzerland, Austria, Ireland, Germany, and Norway—consume an average of 8 to 11 kilograms (18 to 22 pounds) annually.

The history of chocolate began more than 2,000 years ago in the jungles of Mesoamerica—today, Mexico and Central America. Archaeologists have uncovered murals and pottery depicting chocolate being prepared and presented to royalty. Spouted chocolate pots found in the Central American country of Belize contain residues that date from 600 B.C. to A.D. 250. The Maya and their ancestors cultivated the cacao tree, which was native to their area. When the beans were ripe, the Maya would gather them from the trees and grind them into a paste. They mixed the paste with such spices as chilies and vanilla and sweetened it slightly with honey. The mixture was combined with water to create a frothy beverage. This spicy, bitter chocolate drink was very different from the hot chocolate that we enjoy on cold winter days.

The Aztec, who ruled much of Mesoamerica after the Maya, also revered chocolate. Unfortunately, the cacao tree was not suited for the climate of the Aztec capital, which was located in what is now Mexico City. As the Aztec conquered the lands where cacao grew, their defeated enemies were required to pay tribute to their overlords in the form of cacao beans. In the 1500's, Europeans were introduced to chocolate when Spanish explorers arrived in Mesoamerica. In fact, Hernán Cortés, who would later conquer the Aztec, was served "xocolatl" by the Aztec emperor, Montezuma II.

Spanish explorers took chocolate back to Spain. The Spanish court, disliking the bitterness of the Aztec version of chocolate, added such flavors as sugar and cinnamon to their drink. By the 1600's, the drink had spread to the rest of Europe. Soon, the French, Dutch, and British established plantations devoted to growing cacao in their tropical colonies, and large shipments of cocoa beans were imported to Europe. (Because of a mistake in spelling, probably made by English importers many years ago, cacao beans became known as cocoa beans in many English-speaking countries.)

Cocoa beans and sugar, two key ingredients of the European chocolate drink, were expensive commodities, so only the elite could enjoy the pastime of sipping chocolate. Drinking chocolate was a measure of status and rank within European high society. The Industrial Revolution in the 1800's paved the way for the mass production of chocolate, making it affordable and available for almost all social classes to enjoy.

As a medicine used by the ancient Mesoamericans, chocolate was administered to encourage weight gain, stimulate the nervous systems of weak patients, and provide a source of nourishment for pregnant women. The bitter chocolate beverage was also used to treat stomach and intestinal ailments. Sometimes, cocoa was combined with a liquid from the bark of the silk cotton tree to create a medicine for curing infections. Early remedies used in South America for childhood diarrhea and coughing combined cocoa with different additives and herbs. By the early 1600's, these same medicinal qualities were acknowledged in Europe, where chocolate was also used to treat anemia, tuberculosis, fever, gout, and kidney stones. The stimulant properties of chocolate led to its early use to improve one's mood.

Today, cacao is cultivated on more than 70,000 square kilometers (17 million acres) all over the world. The largest producer of cacao is the western African nation Côte d'Ivoire (Ivory Coast), which produces 40 percent of the world's harvest. Other top producers are Ghana and Indonesia, accounting for about 15 percent each; and Brazil, Nigeria, Cameroon, Guatemala, Ecuador, and Venezuela, which share in producing the remaining 30 percent.

The ancient Maya and Aztec ground up fermented, dried cocoa beans with maize, chilies, and spices to create a spicy chocolate drink. The drink was reserved for the elite, including rulers and priests.

The cacao tree begins to bear fruit when it is about five years old. A mature cacao tree may have 6,000 flowers, but as few as 20 pods—the fruit from which cocoa beans come. When harvested, cacao pods may be red, yellow, green, or a combination of these colors. Workers open the pods with sharp machetes and remove the cocoa beans along with the pod's pulp. The pulp and wet beans are then allowed to ferment. During the process of fermentation, microorganisms break down the fleshy pulp, which liquefies and drains away. Fermentation also causes the flavor we associate with chocolate to develop within the cocoa beans.

To prevent the growth of molds and to maintain the flavor of the cocoa beans, the beans must be dried.

A woman in Ghana harvests cacao pods, from which workers obtain the main ingredient in chocolate. The cacao tree, an evergreen, produces pods throughout the year. The pods grow directly from the trunk or branches of the tree, without a stem.

The beans are dried either naturally, by sunlight, or by mechanical means. However, these latter methods cannot involve smoke oils, which can weaken the chocolate flavor. Once dried, the beans are bagged and shipped to cocoa processors.

When the cocoa beans arrive at a processing plant, they are washed and roasted. Roasting further enhances the chocolate flavor. The beans are then *hulled* (the outside shell of the bean is removed) by a machine. All that is left is the chocolate *nib*. The nibs are then ground by a mill until a thick, grainy paste, called cocoa liquor, is produced. For *alkalized* cocoa, or Dutch chocolate, alkali ingredients, such as potassium carbonate, are added during the milling process. Alkalization, first developed in the Netherlands during the 1800's, is what gives Dutch chocolate its distinct, mild flavor.

Once cocoa liquor is produced, it may be pressed to separate the cocoa butter from the cocoa mass or used to create chocolate. To make cocoa powder, the cocoa liquor is put into a press. During this process, various amounts of fat, called cocoa butter, are separated from the solid portions of the cocoa liquor—the cocoa mass. If all of the cocoa butter is removed from the liquor, equal amounts of cocoa mass and butter are created. The solid mass is then pulverized to form fine cocoa powder. Cocoa powder is often used in baking and drink mixes.

The product that we know and love as chocolate is created by blending the cocoa liquor with additional cocoa butter in varying quantities. The chocolate then undergoes *conching*. During this process, the chocolate is kneaded smooth. High-quality, very smooth chocolate may be conched for 72 hours, whereas lesser grades are conched from 4 to 6 hours. The final processing step, known as tempering, manipulates the temperatures at which the chocolate is heated and then cooled. The proper tempering of chocolate results in a hard product that snaps when it is broken.

A melanger, a type of mill, grinds chocolate nibs into cocoa liquor in a chocolate factory in San Francisco. Cocoa liquor is processed to make other forms of chocolate.

Different varieties of chocolate result from the mix of ingredients used in the blending. Unsweetened chocolate is 100 percent cocoa liquor. Dark (also called semisweet or bittersweet) chocolate is a combination of sugar, cocoa butter, at least 35 percent cocoa liquor, and sometimes vanilla. Milk chocolate also includes milk or milk powder and contains less cocoa liquor (at least 10 percent). White chocolate does not contain cocoa liquor or powder. It does contain cocoa butter (at least 20 percent). Because white chocolate does not contain cocoa solids, it was once not considered "chocolate" by the U.S. Food and Drug Administration (FDA). However, beginning in 2004, the agency officially acknowledged the identity of products made from cocoa butter, sweeteners, and other flavorings as "white chocolate."

The Maya and the Aztec knew that chocolate was not only tasty, but also good for people's health. Recently, scientists have identified the chemistry behind these health benefits. Research has shown that naturally occurring compounds, called *flavonoids*, within the dried cocoa nib can modestly lower an individual's risk of heart disease, blood clots, and stroke. Flavonoids, which are present in fruits and vegetables, tea, and red wine, can also lower higher-than-normal blood pressure. Chocolate's flavonoids have also shown to reduce insulin resistance. Insulin helps control blood-sugar levels. Some people who have high insulin resistance develop diabetes, a dangerous disease that, when not controlled, can lead to disabilities or death. The concentration of flavonoids in a particular chocolate product depends on the amount of cocoa mass. For example, a product that contains 35 percent cocoa mass has more flavonoids than another that contains only 10 percent cocoa mass. This is why chocolate's benefits are associated mainly with dark or unsweetened chocolate. Benefits are not associated with Dutch chocolate because the alkali processing decreases the levels of antioxidants.

Flavonoids are most commonly known for their *antioxidant activity*—that is, their ability to fight off damage to cells. Recent clinical studies with cocoa flavonoids have shown that they also help blood flow by relaxing blood vessels. This results in better blood circulation and lower blood pressure.

Chocolate contains a number of other potentially healthful substances. One is tryptophan, an essential *amino acid* (used by the body to

Types of chocolate

Chocolate	Description
Unsweetened	The purest form of chocolate sold commercially, it often consists of equal amounts of cocoa mass and cocoa butter (fat) and is used mainly for cooking. Unsweetened chocolate is also known as cocoa (chocolate) liquor.
Bittersweet (dark baking chocolate)	Contains at least 35 percent cocoa liquor to which sugar and sometimes vanilla are added. It is primarily a baking chocolate.
Semisweet (dark eating chocolate)	Contains the same percentage of cocoa liquor as bittersweet, but is mixed with additional sugar to make a sweeter taste.
White	Contains at least 20 percent cocoa butter and no cocoa liquor. Although some people do not consider it a true chocolate, its texture is similar to chocolate, allowing it to be used in baking and cooking.
Milk	A form of sweet chocolate that contains at least 10 percent cocoa liquor mixed with cocoa butter, vanilla, milk (or milk powder), and sugar. Most candies are made with this form of chocolate.

build proteins) that can be converted to *serotonin*, an important *neurotransmitter*. Neurotransmitters transmit messages between nerves. Serotonin transmits messages that play a role in shaping people's moods. Another chemical that affects mood is phenylethylamine. Although both of these mood-enhancing substances are present in chocolate, their levels in one serving of chocolate are far less than the levels used in medicines prescribed to relieve depression.

Chocolate is also a source of other important nutrients, including protein, calcium, magnesium, and potassium. A 41-gram (1.45-ounce) chocolate bar contains about 2 grams of protein, 12 milligrams of calcium, 13 milligrams of magnesium, and 206 milligrams of potassium.

Despite its health benefits, chocolate still remains a calorie-rich food. Fortunately, two-thirds of the fat in chocolate comes from stearic acid and oleic acid (which can lower cholesterol levels). Although stearic acid is a saturated fatty acid (which can raise cholesterol levels), it is unique in that it does not raise levels of low-density lipoprotein (LDL)-cholesterol—so-called "bad cholesterol"—in the bloodstream. LDL-cholesterol can lead to a build-up of *plaque* (fatty substances that form deposits and thicken over a period of years) in arteries, which eventually become narrowed and clogged, resulting in cardiovascular disease.

The other good news about chocolate is that many health concerns associated with eating chocolate are myths. Since the 1970's, clinical studies have shown that eating chocolate does not increase the chances of developing acne. The antioxidants present in chocolate may actually be beneficial for skin health. A second common myth is that eating chocolate leads to the development of *migraines* (severe headaches) or common headaches. By itself, chocolate does not cause migraines. Studies reported in 1991 and 2001 suggest that the very chemicals that elevate mood may work with other factors to trigger a migraine.

For centuries, chocolate has played a prominent role in the culture and customs of many different civilizations—from Mayan royalty to modern Americans. Today, many people view chocolate as a delectable treat to be consumed as a reward or during a holiday. Since chocolate provides antioxidants and other nutrients, it also can be part of a healthy plan when eaten in moderation.

■ Melissa White-Fournier

SCIENCE NEWS UPDATE

Contributors report on the year's most significant developments in their respective fields. The articles in this section are arranged alphabetically.

AGRICULTURE

Record-high oil prices, turmoil in the Middle East, global warming concerns, and a new United States Renewable Fuel Standard (RFS) created under the Energy Policy Act of 2005 pushed alternative renewable fuels like ethanol and biodiesel into the mainstream. The RFS requires 15 billion liters (4 billion gallons) of renewable fuels to be included in the nation's fuel supply by 2006, increasing by 2.6 billion liters (700 million gallons) a year until 2011, when the fuel requirement tops out at 28 billion liters (7.4 billion gallons). By 2012, the RFS will require 28.3 billion liters (7.5 billion gallons) of renewable fuel to be used by American motorists.

Ethanol, which is typically made from starch-based crops like corn and *sorghum*, a grassy plant, more than doubled in production capacity throughout 2006 and was set to grow an additional 50 percent by the end of 2007, according to the Renewable Fuels Association, the national trade association of the ethanol industry located in Washington, D.C. There were 120 ethanol plants in production as of May 2007, producing 23.5 billion liters (6.2 billion gallons) per year—an increase of 50 percent over May 2005 ethanol production numbers.

As a result, ethanol is eating up about 20 percent of the nation's corn crop, up from 5 percent several years ago, according to Keith Collins, the chief economist of the U.S. Department of Agriculture (USDA). In 2007, farmers were projected to plant 15 percent more corn acres (the highest acreage since 1944) as a result of ethanol demand, according to the USDA's Prospective Planting report released on March 30, 2007.

SEE ALSO

THE SPECIAL REPORT, **THE LATEST BUZZ ABOUT HONEY BEES,** PAGE 42.

SCIENCE STUDIES, **RENEWABLE ENERGY: POWER FOR THE FUTURE,** PAGE 100.

Biodiesel, which is made from vegetable oil or animal fats, is rapidly gaining ground among mainstream fuels. As of June 2007, there were 148 biodiesel plants in production in the United States, with a total annual production capacity of 5.3 billion liters (139 billion gallons), according to the National Biodiesel Board, the national trade association of the biodiesel industry located in Jefferson City, Missouri. Another 107 biodiesel plants are under construction. Biodiesel use, about 757 million liters (200 million gallons) annually, is much less than that of ethanol, at about 15.1 billion liters (4 billion gallons). Diesel engines can run on pure biodiesel, but most biodiesel is blended with petroleum-based diesel fuel.

So far, environmentalists support the use of ethanol and biodiesel, which burn clean and stem from virtually unlimited feedstocks, unlike crude oil. According to Argonne National Laboratory, a U.S. Department of Energy laboratory located in Argonne, Illinois, ethanol use in 2004, for example, reduced greenhouse gas emissions caused by burning fossil fuels by 7 million tons, or the equivalent of taking more than 1 million cars off the road.

INCREASED APPETITE FOR CORN

Corn grows outside an ethanol processing plant near Malta Bend, Missouri. The production of ethanol, which is typically made from such starch-based crops as corn and sorghum, more than doubled through 2006 and, according to the Renewable Fuels Association, was expected to grow by an additional 50 percent by the end of 2007.

Wheat rust causes global threat. The newest strain of wheat stem rust, an infection that afflicts wheat crops, is called Ug99. This most virulent strain of wheat stem rust in 50 years was first identified in Uganda in 1999 (hence the name Ug99) and has since spread to east Africa and toward the Indian subcontinent. The wheat rust strain is "a major, strategic threat to global wheat production," reported the International Maize and Wheat Improvement Centre, located in Mexico, the world's leading global wheat research organization.

"It is a major threat because this new strain of wheat rust can overcome the genetic resistance of many wheat varieties," says Kay Simmons, national program leader for USDA–Agricultural Research Service (ARS) grain crops research in Beltsville, Maryland. Preliminary testing under contained conditions determined that several U.S. wheat varieties are vulnerable to Ug99.

The wheat stem rust creates brick-red lesions (blisterlike rot) on the stem. Despite its name, stem rust, unlike a similar infection known as leaf rust, appears on all parts of the plant, including the stem and head.

One challenge in fighting stem rust is that it travels long distances as airborne spores. There are two possible ways for the disease to reach the United States and Canada. First, it could travel through the air via global wind patterns. For example, if Ug99 spreads north and then west across Africa to a country like Morocco, it could get swept up by tropical winds and brought to North America. The second possible way of transport is by human movement—for example, if people who were in an infected field got spores on their clothing and then traveled to the Western Hemisphere. Once the spores invade and infect, they can cause a 50- to 70-percent loss in a wheat crop.

BEE TROUBLE

A beekeeper removes a comb of honey bees from a hive. According to the American Beekeeping Federation, from October 2006 to February 2007, beekeepers throughout the United States lost 50 percent or more of their honey bees in a mysterious disappearance called colony collapse disorder. The loss threatened not only honey production, but also the estimated $14 billion worth of seeds and crops that honey bees pollinate annually in the United States.

Disappearing bees a mystery. Beekeepers throughout the United States have lost more than 50 percent of their honey bees since October 2006, according to the American Beekeeping Federation in Jesup, Georgia. Honey bees fly off in search of nectar and pollen, but do not return to their colonies. Beekeepers are calling the disappearance colony collapse disorder, or CCD. In December 2006, beekeepers' associations, scientists, and officials formed the CCD working group in hopes of identifying the cause and preventing the disappearance of more bees.

Aside from producing honey, bees pollinate an estimated $14 billion worth of seeds and crops annually in the United States, mostly fruits, vegetables, and nuts. According to beekeepers, a loss under 20 percent is considered normal in the off-season.

"Preliminary work has identified several likely factors that could be causing or contributing to CCD," said Dennis vanEngelsdorp, acting state apiarist with the Pennsylvania Department of Agriculture. "Among them are mites and associated diseases, some unknown pathogenic disease and pesticide contamination or poisoning." Initial studies of dying colonies revealed a large number of disease organisms present, but no one disease was identified as the culprit, vanEngelsdorp explained.

The bee disappearance is not a new problem. Since the 1970's, concern has risen around the world about the decline of pollinators. During this period in the United States, the honey bee, the world's premier pollinator, experienced a dramatic 40-percent decline, from nearly 6 million to less than 2.5 million. In 2005, for the first time in 85 years, the United States was forced to import honey bees in order to meet its pollination demands, according to the U.S. Department of Agriculture's National Agricultural Statistics Service. ■ Jeanne Bernick

ANTHROPOLOGY

Almost 3.5 million years ago, by a river in eastern Africa, a child was swept away in a flood and drowned. Her body was buried in river mud in a swampy delta. In 2006, a team led by Ethiopian paleoanthropologist Zeresenay Alemseged of the Max Planck Institute for Evolutionary Anthropology in Leipzig, Germany, announced the discovery of the child's fossilized remains. The child was an *australopithecine* (a human ancestor who walked upright but was still apelike in many ways), and her skeleton is the most complete one ever discovered of a child who lived so long ago. Alemseged and his colleagues placed her in the species *Australopithecus afarensis,* the same species as the famous Lucy, a partial australopithecine skeleton found in 1974 in Hadar, Ethiopia. The place where the child lived is now an area called Dikika in the Afar region of modern Ethiopia.

The team found the child's skull, most of her spinal column, parts of both arms and legs, and portions of her hands and feet. Her teeth indicate that she was about three years old when she drowned. Because children's bones are small and fragile, they do not often fossilize. This child's remains give scientists a rare opportunity to learn about how australopithecines developed in childhood. Modern human children grow up more slowly than apes, so knowing how fast australopithecines grew up is evidence for how apelike or humanlike our ancient ancestors were.

The child's remains show that typical australopithecine features— protruding jaws, a low, flat forehead, and a small brain—were present in childhood. Her knees and feet prove that she walked upright. Her shoulder blade,

LUCY'S DAUGHTER

A scientist displays the 3.5-million-year-old skull of a three-year-old girl discovered in October 2006 near a river in what is now Dikika in the Afar region of Ethiopia. Anthropologists believe that the child, nicknamed Selam or "Lucy's daughter," is an australopithecine, a member of the same early humanlike group to which Lucy, a female whose fossilized remains were discovered in Ethiopia in 1974, belongs. Australopithecines were about 110 to 150 centimeters (3.5 to 5 feet) tall and had large, projecting faces. Their brains were about one-third the size of a modern human brain. Although they stood upright and walked on two legs as modern human beings do, Selam's upward-pointing shoulder blades and slightly curved fingers seem to indicate that australopithecines may have still climbed and foraged in trees, as apes do.

however, is not at all like that of modern human beings. Instead of pointing straight out to the side, her glenoid fossa (shoulder joint) points slightly upward, very much like the shoulders of chimps and gorillas. Along with the fact that the bones of her fingers are long and slightly curved, the shoulder blade may mean that she and other australopithecines often climbed and foraged in the trees in addition to walking on the ground.

Most of the child's bones are still embedded in the block of sandstone in which they were found. Among them is her hyoid bone, the bone in the throat that anchors the base of the tongue. Even though the bone is still cemented to the bottom of the skull, it is clear that it is apelike rather than humanlike. Still to be studied and described are the child's collarbones, vertebrae, and ribs, and those bones are sure to add more to the knowledge of humankind's ancient ancestors.

Modern human beings in Europe. In January 2007, anthropologist M. V. Anikovich, of the Russian Academy of Sciences in Moscow, along with colleagues from Russia, Italy, and the United States, reported that modern human beings (*Homo sapiens*) may have reached eastern Europe as early as 45,000 years ago. That would make their arrival there 3,000 to 5,000 years earlier than previously thought and several thousand years before modern human beings expanded across central and western Europe.

Modern human beings first appeared in Africa sometime before 200,000 years ago. They began to expand into the rest of the world a little before 60,000 years ago. However, anthropologists still have doubts about the routes that modern human beings took and the timing of their expansion out of Africa. It is very difficult to get reliable radiocarbon dates for objects so old, and sometimes the dates seem contradictory.

The scientists analyzed samples of charcoal and mineral deposits from a group of archaeological sites near the villages of Kostenki and Borshchevo, on the west bank of the Don River about 400 kilometers (250 miles) south of Moscow. They chose samples from layers where very old Upper Paleolithic tools were found. Upper Paleolithic refers to the tools and other artifacts made by modern human beings before 12,000 years ago. In contrast to earlier tool traditions, the Upper Paleolithic includes art, jewelry, and tools made from bone, horn, and ivory.

Anikovich and his team used radiocarbon and optically stimulated luminescence dating to determine that the oldest Upper Paleolithic layers are at least 43,000 and as much as 45,000 years old. They seem to represent the regular presence

of modern human beings during a period of climatic fluctuations in the last ice age. Animal remains show that these modern human beings were hunting small mammals like hares and foxes in addition to the larger reindeer and wild horses. Their artifacts include bone points, antler chopping tools, and perforated shells (for jewelry). The people traveled up to 150 kilometers (90 miles) to get the best stone for their tools, which is another hallmark of modern human groups.

The authors stressed that there was no apparent transition from artifacts of the earlier Middle Paleolithic, made by Neandertals, to the newly described artifact collection. That fact is important because it suggests that modern human beings appeared on the scene rather abruptly, bringing their new technology with them. Anikovich noted, however, that some previously known sites that were thought to be Middle Paleolithic (inhabited by Neandertals) might instead represent specialized big-game hunting camps created by modern human beings.

The fact that modern human beings may have arrived in the Central European Plain by at least 43,000 years ago means that they were able to adapt culturally to extreme environments. Earth was gripped by an ice age at that time, and the climate in eastern Europe was cold and harsh. The new findings also may help to explain the disappearance of the Neandertals, who now seem to have disappeared within 2,000 or 3,000 years of the arrival of modern human beings.

Late survival of Neandertals in Gibraltar. The Neandertals disappeared as modern human beings spread throughout Europe, and anthropologists thought they were completely extinct by about 30,000 years ago. New evidence, however, shows that small numbers of Neandertals survived thousands of years longer in Gibraltar, in southern Spain. Clive Finlayson, of the Gibraltar Museum, published the information in December 2006. A large team of international experts contributed to the study.

Finlayson and his colleagues analyzed newly recovered artifacts and other samples from deposits deep within the site of Gorham's Cave, on Gibraltar's Mediterranean coast. The outer parts of the cave were excavated in the 1940's and 1950's. At that time, the youngest date obtained for Neandertals was about 32,000 years ago, but problems with contamination of the samples caused scientists to question those results. The newly excavated deposits are more intact, and they include a sequence of hearths from which good datable

ANTHROPOLOGY continued

samples of charcoal were obtained. Accelerator mass spectrometer (AMS) radiocarbon dating of charcoal samples from the hearths suggests that Neandertals survived on Gibraltar until at least 28,000 years ago and possibly as recently as 24,000 years ago.

Two factors apparently allowed Neandertals to survive on Gibraltar long after they had disappeared from the rest of Europe. One was the presence of a variety of mild microenvironments that formed a refuge from the bitter conditions of ice-age Europe. Neandertals collected food from nearby plains, shrublands, wetlands, cliffs, and beaches. Gorham's Cave was a favored site because daylight reaches far into the cave and a high ceiling helps ventilate smoke. Superimposed hearths show that Neandertals visited the cave off and on over thousands of years.

The other factor that apparently helped the Neandertals survive so long on Gibraltar was that modern human beings did not visit the area frequently until some thousands of years later. Artifacts attributed to modern human beings appear as early as 32,000 years ago, but the evidence suggests that they were made by small, pioneering groups. Those groups evidently did not remain permanently and rarely interacted with the Neandertals. Thus, both species exploited the same region for several thousand years until the Neandertals finally vanished. Their disappearance may have been caused by deteriorating climate or by the arrival of larger numbers of modern human beings.

Controversy dogs "hobbits." The most heated debate in contemporary paleoanthropology revolves around a population of tiny people who lived on the Indonesian island of Flores until about 18,000 years ago. The official scientific name for these people is *Homo floresiensis* (*Flores man*), but both scientists and the press have taken to calling them "hobbits" after the furry-footed heroes of J. R. R. Tolkien's *Lord of the Rings*. These Indonesian people stood about 1 meter (3.3 feet) tall and had small skulls containing brains about the size of a grapefruit. Nevertheless, they made stone tools and hunted a small, now-extinct elephant.

So much about the "hobbits" is unusual that scientists disagree whether they represent a separate species of *hominin* (a human or human ancestor) or a population of diminutive modern humans. At the center of the disagreement is

whether a hominin with a brain so small could have made the stone tools that have been found with the remains. Although the remnants of at least seven individuals have been found, confirming that they were all very small, only one skull has been recovered. The discoverers and their supporters, led by Michael J. Morwood of the University of New England in Armidale, Australia, argue that the skull is similar to—albeit smaller than—that of *Homo erectus*, a group that lived in Asia until less than 30,000 years ago. The doubters contend that the skull is that of a modern human who suffered from *microcephaly*, a rare pathological condition in which an individual has a small head or cranial capacity and the brain does not develop normally.

Researchers continued the debate in four studies published in 2006 and 2007. In May 2006, anatomist Susan G. Larson presented a paper at the meeting of the Paleoanthropology Society claiming that the shoulder of *H. floresiensis* was more like that of *H. erectus* than that of modern human beings. Larson, of Stony Brook University in New York, said that the upper end of the "hobbit" humerus (upper arm bone) was more nearly at right angles to the elbow than it is in modern human beings. The upper joint surfaces of modern human beings' humeri are turned so the elbows face inward; when people bend their arms at the elbows, their hands come together in front of them. *H. floresiensis* would have had to rotate the shoulders forward to bring the hands together. In fact, Dr. Larson suggested that the "hobbit" shoulders were hunched compared to those of modern human beings, but this would have been a disadvantage only for overhand throwing. Anatomical differences like this are consistent with the "hobbits" being a different species from *H. sapiens*.

Another study, this time involving the stone tools made by *H. floresiensis* and their likely predecessors on Flores, supported the view that the "hobbits" were a species of premodern human beings descended from *Homo erectus*. Anthropologists and archaeologists from Australia and Indonesia, led by Adam Brumm of Australian National University in Canberra and Fachroel Aziz of Indonesia's Geological Survey Institute in Bandung, studied 507 artifacts from the site of Mata Menge. They also examined the stone tools from Liang

Bua, where *H. floresiensis* was discovered in 2003. Mata Menge dates to 800,000 or 900,000 years ago, and the stone tools are fairly typical of those made by *H. erectus* at that time. They are mostly medium-sized flakes of stone removed from small blocks or cobbles. The toolmakers could get five or six flakes from a single cobble. Usually, the tool handlers used the flakes as they were, but sometimes modified them to give them a more durable edge. *H. erectus* made their tools from low-quality stone that they found nearby. Only rarely did they travel any distance to get better stone.

Brumm, Aziz, and their colleagues said that the Mata Menge artifacts are very similar to those that *H. floresiensis* made at Liang Bua more than 700,000 years later. The similarities include the ways that flakes were removed from the cores of stone (often working around the edge of the core, leaving a radial pattern), the size of the flakes, the maximum size of the flake scars, and the proportion of tools made of locally available stone. According to the authors, some of the radially flaked cores from the two sites are virtually identical. The authors used their data to rebut an earlier claim that the stone tools from Liang Bua were too sophisticated to have been made by descendants of *H. erectus*. On the contrary, they said, the similarities between the stone artifacts from Mata Menge and Liang Bua show an unbroken tradition of stone tool-making going back more than 700,000 years.

In September 2006, however, the leading critic of the separate-species perspective, Teuku Jacob of Gadjah Mada University in Yogyakarta, Indonesia, published a paper in which he and his colleagues vigorously argued that the "hobbits" were modern human beings (*Homo sapiens*). The researchers repeated the claim that the one skull discovered so far is that of a microcephalic individual. They pointed to deformation of the skull and details of the limb bones as further evidence of pathology. Jacob and his colleague at Gadjah Mada University, Etty Indriati, supported their argument with data on 76 Rampasasa pygmies who live on the island of Flores today. *Pygmy* is used to refer to human populations in which typical adult height is shorter than about 1.5 meters (5 feet). Jacob and his colleagues asserted that all the characteristics claimed to be distinctive for *H. floresiensis*, such as a weak chin on the jaw, are also present in the Rampasasa. In fact, the researchers claimed that, except for the very small brain, all the measurable features of the *H. floresiensis* fossils fall within the range of modern Australomelanesian peoples. They concluded

that the "hobbits" were simply the pygmy ancestors of the present Rampasasa and that the fossil skull is that of a diseased individual.

A rebuttal to Jacob's paper was published in February 2007 by a team of anatomists and radiologists led by Dean Falk of Florida State University in Tallahassee. In 2005, Falk had published a study of a microcephalic modern human skull that she said was not a good match for the skull from Flores. In the new paper, Falk and her colleagues described their analyses of the brains of 9 modern human microcephalics, including 4 children, along with those of 10 normal humans. The team used three-dimensional CT (computerized tomography) scans of the skulls to reconstruct the shapes and sizes of the brains.

According to Falk, microcephalic brains differ from normal brains in two main areas. One is that the cerebellum, located in the bottom rear of the brain, is oddly broad and protruding in the brains of microcephalics. The second is that the frontal part of the brain in microcephalics is unusually narrow and flattened above the eyes.

Falk and her colleagues attributed the deformation of the Flores skull to compression by the sediments that covered the skull after it was buried in the cave and not to a pathological condition. However, although the brain of *H. floresiensis* sorts with those of modern human beings in terms of overall shape, there remain differences that point to *H. floresiensis* as a separate species.

The critics are still not satisfied, although there is evidence that anthropologists in general are leaning toward recognizing *H. floresiensis* as a distinct species. Both critics and supporters of the separate-species view are in the midst of additional studies, and new excavations are underway at Liang Bua Cave. The best chance of resolving the dispute is for excavators to recover additional skulls. Only then can scientists be sure if the Flores skull was typical of its kind or belonged to an individual with severe pathologies.

Primates communicate with gestures. In May 2007, primatologists Amy S. Pollick and Frans B. M. de Waal, of the Yerkes National Primate Research Center in Atlanta, Georgia, announced that chimpanzees and bonobos use gestures to communicate with each other. Although captive apes have been taught to use sign language with human beings, this finding is the first proof of meaningful gesturing among untrained apes. It means that signing is

ANTHROPOLOGY continued

SIGNING CHIMPS

A chimp extends its hand to communicate with other chimpanzees. Primatologists at the Yerkes National Primate Research Center in Atlanta, Georgia, reported in May 2007 that chimps, as well as other primates called bonobos, use gestures to communicate with one another. The scientists speculated that the first human language may have been a signed rather than a spoken one. According to the researchers, an upturned palm means "I would like some of that food" if used with a chimp that is eating. It may also mean "Please help me" if used during a fight.

shared in common by human beings and apes, and it suggests that the first human language might have been signed rather than spoken.

Chimps and bonobos (formerly called "pygmy" chimpanzees) became different species about 3 million years ago, 3 million to 4 million years after the human lineage separated from theirs. Abilities that are shared by chimps, bonobos, and people—including toolmaking and flexible communication—were probably inherited from a common ancestor.

Pollick and de Waal studied hundreds of hours of video of chimpanzees and bonobos in their day-to-day interactions. Like people, both chimps and bonobos use facial expressions and vocalizations (such as cries, grunts, and hoots) to communicate. However, these forms of communication are pretty closely tied to specific emotions and do not vary much from group to group. Pollick and de Waal found that the apes use gestures more flexibly and that the use of gestures differs somewhat from one group to another. Since each group has its own gestural repertoire, anthropologists view signing as a cultural behavior.

Apes use the same side of their brains (the left side) to produce and process gestural information that human beings use to process language. Pollick and de Waal thus see continuity from gestural communication to vocal communication. It seems that human beings may have signed with each other before they spoke.

Chimps use tools. Since the 1960's, chimps have been observed using sticks, stones, twigs, and other objects as tools. Chimps are also known to kill and eat monkeys. In March 2007, primatologists announced the first evidence of chimps using tools to hunt live game. The finding provides new insights into how human beings' ancient ancestors might have started hunting.

Anthropologist Jill D. Pruetz of Iowa State University and graduate student Paco Bertolani of the University of Cambridge, England, made the discovery at a research site in Fongoli in the West African nation of Senegal. They observed 10 different chimps, including juveniles and females, making spears and using them to stab at *bush babies* hiding in holes in the trees. Bush babies are small, *nocturnal* (active at night) primates that are distantly related to monkeys and apes. During the day, they sleep in holes that are too small for the chimps to reach into.

To hunt the bush babies, chimps break off slender, green saplings, sometimes sharpening the sticks using their teeth. Then the chimps jab the spears into the holes, killing or injuring the bush babies and pulling them out to eat. The chimps at Fongoli are the only ones ever observed using weapons, but the finding suggests that humanity's most ancient ancestors might also have used weapons to hunt small mammals long before they began hunting larger ones. ■ Richard Milo

See also **ARCHAEOLOGY.**

ARCHAEOLOGY

The mysteries of the great stone circle known as Stonehenge have led to centuries of debate about who built it, how it was constructed, and how it was used. Located on Salisbury Plain in southern England, Stonehenge consists of 90 huge stone slabs erected between 2840 and 2640 B.C. Most still stand today, forming a rough circle, with the upright stones capped by *lintels* (large horizontal stones that join the uprights). While theories abound as to the function of this great stone circle, much research points toward its use as a huge calendar by which its builders could recognize the *midwinter solstice.* The midwinter solstice, which occurs on or about December 21 every year, represents the sun's greatest declination in the northern sky.

The construction of this huge monument involved hundreds of workers and considerable engineering skill. Some of the laborers quarried the multiton stones and dragged them great distances to the Stonehenge site. There, additional workers raised the slabs and put them into place. The building of Stonehenge was a great accomplishment of native Britons during the Neolithic (New Stone Age) Period.

In January 2007, archaeologist Michael Parker Pearson of Sheffield University in England announced that remains of 8 houses had been found, part of a large community of at least 30 to 40 houses, near Stonehenge. Excavations revealed that the site of Durrington Walls, combined with the Stonehenge monument 3.2 kilometers (2 miles) away, was part of a much larger ritual and funeral complex around 2600 to 2500 B.C.

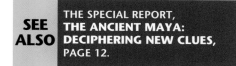

SEE ALSO THE SPECIAL REPORT, **THE ANCIENT MAYA: DECIPHERING NEW CLUES,** PAGE 12.

The excavated houses measured about 5 meters (16 feet) on each side. Originally, they had been built with timber frames, and each had a clay floor with a single, central fireplace. The floors were covered with human debris, including fragments of pottery, flint, stone arrow points, remains of domesticated pigs and other animals, and fragments of wooden bed boxes and cupboards. The archaeologist believes that the pig bones were left after feasts, with the half-eaten remains tossed on the house floors. Detailed analysis of the bones indicates that they are from pigs that had been butchered in midwinter, which was thus the time of year when the houses were used for feasting.

Major questions remain to be answered. Did the labor force that actually constructed Stonehenge live in this village at Durrington Walls, perhaps on a seasonal basis, and were the feasts related to their work? Or was this village integrated into a larger ritual and funeral pattern, involving cremation of the dead, disposal in the nearby River Avon—which flows toward Stonehenge—and, finally, the burial of select members of the community at Stonehenge itself?

The ritual pattern is supported by the archaeological evidence. In 1967, the remains of a large wooden monument, very similar to

STONE AGE HOUSES

The remains of ancient houses lie uncovered at a site called Durrington Walls on the Salisbury Plain in Wiltshire, southwestern England. In January 2007, archaeologists reported the discovery of eight such houses, located 3.2 kilometers (2 miles) from Stonehenge, an enormous stone monument erected by native Britons about 2600 to 2500 B.C. The researchers speculated that the workers who constructed Stonehenge may have lived at Durrington Walls. The site may also have been used for funerals and other rituals.

ARCHAEOLOGY continued

Stonehenge, were discovered at Durrington Walls. Researchers found that while Stonehenge marks the midwinter solstice sunset, the "woodhenge" was arranged to measure the midwinter solstice sunrise. The monuments were thus complementary. Together, they provided the focus for midwinter solstice feasting and rituals involving the disposal of the dead.

Major Aztec discovery. In October 2006, archaeologists Eduardo Matos Moctezuma and José Álvaro Barrera Rivera, both of Mexico's National Institute of Anthropology and History in Mexico City, announced a significant new Aztec find. The excavations focused on an area near the Templo Mayor, a pyramid that was the principal center for Aztec religious rituals and for the burial of the cremated remains of the Aztec emperors. (The Aztec were American Indians who controlled a vast empire in Mexico from the 1200's until the Spanish conquered them in 1521.) After the Spanish destroyed the temple, the center of Mexico City grew up over it. Since the late 1970's, archaeologists have made many, usually minor discoveries around the pyramid. City construction projects have exposed parts of the lower stairway of the Templo Mayor.

This newest excavation was the result of work on a modern pedestrian walkway near the Templo Mayor stairway. Not far below the surface, the archaeologists exposed an enormous, monolithic, sculptured monument. The slab—13 feet (4 meters) long on its longest side—covers 4.3 square meters (46 square feet) and is estimated to weigh at least 11 metric tons (12 tons).

As the archeologists brushed the earth from the monument's surface, they revealed elaborate carvings representing the Aztec earth *diety* (god or goddess), Tlaltecuhtli. The Aztec believed that Tlaltecuhtli, usually portrayed as a

AZTEC DISCOVERY

The stone carving of an Aztec figure is revealed on the surface of a monument discovered in October 2006 at the archaeological site of Templo Mayor in Mexico City. Templo Mayor, a pyramid that was the site of Aztec religious rituals and burials until the 1500's, was covered over as Mexico City grew. Archaeologists believe the newly discovered monument may protect the tomb of an Aztec emperor. If so, it would be the first Aztec tomb ever found.

woman, consumed the dead and brought them to life again. On this monument, the blood-drinking goddess is shown giving birth while squatting. One of her massive claws holds an Aztec glyph of a rabbit and 10 dots. This glyph, 10 Rabbit, represents the year 1502, when the Aztec emperor Ahuitzotl died. His reign was from 1486 to 1502, and he was the father of Emperor Moctezuma, defeated by the Spanish in 1519.

Archaeologists believe that the slab probably covers the tomb of Ahuitzotl. It was first paved over by the Aztec and then hidden by buildings of the Spanish era. The researchers will not know if the ashes of Ahuitzotl, accompanied by grave offerings, are beneath the stone until further excavation is done. If this is Ahuitzotl's tomb, it would be the first imperial Aztec tomb ever found.

Archaeology of slave life. In March 2007, Mark P. Leone, archaeologist for the Archaeology at Annapolis project of the University of Maryland, announced some of the results of long-term excavations of African American slave quarters in Maryland. Near the town of Easton, the archaeologists excavated three structures at the Wye House Farm. These buildings were part of a village inhabited by 1,000 slaves who worked on agricultural and cattle-raising operations for the Lloyd family, owners of the 17,000-hectare (42,000-acre) plantation.

The greatest significance of the Wye House Farm excavations is that famed writer and *abolitionist* (an activist that worked to end slavery) Frederick Douglass briefly lived there in the 1820's. In an 1881 autobiography, Douglass wrote in some detail about the slave settlement. He described a low, poorly built wooden structure known as the long quarter and, nearby, a dilapidated, two-story brick building in which his family lived. Various small houses and huts were scattered in this area, the Long Green, which was roughly 1,600 meters (5,300 feet) long and 90 meters (300 feet) wide.

The archaeological team found remnants of the brick house described by Douglass, as well as the nearby long quarter and another small house or lean-to. From these slave quarters came broken farm tools and a great variety of household goods, including pieces of stoneware and porcelain pottery, a knife blade, clothes, buttons, and a thimble. The archaeologists also found the bones of animals used for food—pigs, cows, and chickens, as well as rabbits, turtles, fish, and even deer hunted or collected by slave families.

While most of the items owned by the slave families, such as pottery vessels and tools, were handed down to them from the plantation's owners, there were some buttons, beads, and other decorations that the archaeologists felt were out of place. They advanced a theory that a secret trade network involving Wye House Farm and other slave communities in the region had obtained some of these goods.

Frederick Douglass escaped from slavery in 1838, fleeing to New York. Within a few years, he joined the abolitionist movement. He also became well known as a spellbinding orator, a scholar, and a diplomat. Although none of the artifacts from the Wye House Farm slave quarters can be directly linked to Douglass, they reflect the nature of slave life in the early 1800's.

Ancient Syrian skulls. The prehistoric Syrian site of Tell Aswad is located about 35 kilometers (22 miles) from the present capital of Damascus. Tell Aswad was a lakeshore village dating back to the earliest part of the Neolithic Period in the Middle East, at least 9,500 years ago. Since the 1980's, archaeologists excavating in the village have exposed houses with round floors, typical of the Neolithic in the region. Researchers also uncovered evidence of some of the earliest agriculture, involving domestic wheat, lentils, and peas. These remains may push the village's origin back even farther in time—to the Pre-Pottery Neolithic A, about 10,500 years ago.

In September 2006, Danielle Stordeur, an archaeologist with Université de Lyon in Lyon, France, reported the discovery of five human skulls that were decorated with plaster faces and were painted to show facial features. The skulls were found at a cemetery outside Tell Aswad and were uncovered under the bones of an infant, though they were probably from an earlier burial, dating as early as 9,500 years ago. The skulls were so tightly clustered, they touched each other. The facial features display eyes that are closed, underlined with black paint. The noses are carefully shaped, including the nostrils, yet the mouths are shown only as a slit.

Although the decorated skulls are not unique in the Middle East, similar ones having been found in early deposits at Jericho and a few other locales, the Tell Aswad discovery provides new clues as to their occurrence. Stordeur believes that the modeled faces on these skulls, and their placement together, are indicative of important residents of the village, perhaps members of a social or religious elite.

ARCHAEOLOGY continued

Battleground in old San Antonio. The Spanish established the city of San Antonio, Texas, in the early 1700's. It was the scene of a number of battles, including the famous Battle of the Alamo in 1836. But beneath the streets and building foundations of the city are found occasional reminders of other struggles.

Archaeologist Mark H. Denton, of the Texas Historical Commission, announced in April 2007 that workers opening up a route for a storm-water drainage line uncovered the remains of a fortification trench. The location is a block southeast of the historic Main Plaza of San Antonio, built about 1735 and the center of town life in the late 1700's and early 1800's. Archaeologists working for the city of San Antonio excavated the preserved segment of the trench. It was about 2 meters (6 feet) wide and 1 meter (3 feet) deep, dug into bedrock and lined with embankments formed by dirt and refuse.

The trench's location clearly shows that it was part of fortifications placed around the Main Plaza in 1835, several months before the Battle of the Alamo. These fortifications were constructed at the entryways to the plaza by the Mexican general Martin Perfecto de Cos. From October to December, General Cos and his Mexican soldiers were under siege by a group of 300 volunteers who were fighting for Texan independence (at the time, Texas was a part of Mexico). Led by Ben Milam, these troops had the goal of taking over San Antonio. On December 5, Milam's men pushed into the town and, after a bloody battle, captured General de Cos and his men. They released the Mexicans after they pledged never to return to Texas. Milam himself was killed by a sniper and buried in a nearby cemetery.

The fortification trench, which gives a brief glimpse into this little-known historical episode, contained gunflints (for flintlock muskets), a broken sword tip, lead musket balls, and other military items. Interestingly, an abundance of pottery fragments and other household debris was also contained in the trench fill. It had obviously been used as a convenient trash dump in the cleanup after the battle.

Earliest shell ornaments. In June 2006, Marian Vanhaeren, an archaeologist at University College, London, reported that small marine shells were perforated and used to make necklaces as early as 100,000 years ago. This new information comes from old collections.

Vanhaeren and her colleague found the specimens in the Museum of Man in Paris. Some came from the site of Skhul in Israel and others from Oued Djebbana in Algeria. Both sites date to the Middle Paleolithic, spanning the period roughly 250,000 to 50,000 years ago.

To date these shell artifacts, a chemical analysis was done on the bits of dirt adhering to them. The results linked the Skhul specimens to a deeply buried cultural layer at that site that is more than 100,000 years old. At Oued Djebbana, the ornaments were linked to excavated deposits about 90,000 years old.

Because of the specimens' great age, the archaeologists had to examine the holes in the shells very carefully. It is possible for such holes to be formed naturally or through deterioration of the shell. But almost all the shells showed convincing evidence that they had been drilled or intentionally perforated so they could be strung on a necklace. Also, the shells were a long way from their original Mediterranean home, where shells of their type are still found today in shallow water in the central and eastern parts of the Mediterranean Sea. Oued Djebbana is more than 240 kilometers (150 miles) distant, clearly showing that the specimens reached these sites through trade.

These artifacts appear to be among the earliest evidence of personal ornaments or decoration. They were used and made by early peoples prior to the appearance of modern human beings (*Homo sapiens*) about 50,000 years ago.

New discoveries at Saqqara. South of Cairo, Egypt, on the west side of the Nile River is a vast expanse of desert that the Egyptians once used as a *necropolis* (city of the dead, or cemetery) for thousands of years. Most visible are the ruins of small pyramids, dominated by the Step Pyramid of Djoser, which is older than the famous pyramids of Giza, also in Egypt. Although archaeologists have been excavating at Saqqara for nearly 150 years, perhaps 70 percent of the site is still unstudied, and significant new discoveries continue to be made.

In February 2007, archaeologists from Macquarie University in Sydney, Australia, uncovered an important tomb from the Fifth Dynasty, (from about 2465 B.C. to 2325 B.C.). The discovery was announced by Zahi Hawass, secretary-general of the Supreme Council of Antiquities in Egypt.

Like other tombs from Saqqara, this example is a largely subterranean *mastaba* (rectangular tomb) made of mud bricks. It has many unusual features. First, the archaeologists uncovered a finely carved wooden false door (it depicted an opening, but was not the actual entryway). Upon opening the tomb, the archaeologists found a chapel-style corridor containing two wooden tables, along with five carved wooden statues. These are life-sized depictions of men with their arms extended at their sides. There was also a remarkable wooden sculpture of a seated man and woman. They were identified as the tomb owner, Kahai, and his wife, Seperiankh. Hieroglyph inscriptions revealed that Kahai was a major official of the period, serving as the scribe of the sacred archives.

The wooden statues are unusual in that the Egyptians generally preferred stone, such as limestone or granite, for such sculptures. Even more surprises may await the excavators as the actual burial place of Kahai, and perhaps his wife and other family members, is likely to be found in a deep shaft underneath the rooms of the mud brick tomb.

In another part of Saqqara, archaeologists from Leiden University in the Netherlands, are excavating a much later tomb. Maarten J. Raven, director of the Leiden research program, announced in February 2007 that this tomb dates to about 1350 B.C. and is believed to be the tomb of Ptahemwia, a royal butler who lived during the reign Akhenaten, (from 1353 B.C. to 1335 B.C.). Akhenaten made his capital at Amarna, along the central Nile, and was considered a heretic because he introduced Egypt to *monotheism* (worshipping only one god). Ancient Egyptians traditionally worshipped many gods.

The tomb's mud walls stand 2 meters (6.5 feet) high, representing a temple structure that can be entered through a gate and then an inner courtyard. A shaft also provides access to underground chapels and burial areas.

Limestone slabs lining the inner mud brick walls are nicely sculpted and painted, with vivid depictions of daily life. Relief

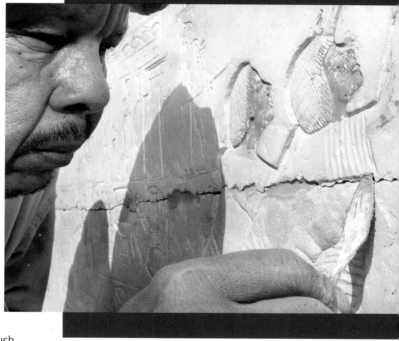

A BUTLER'S REST

An antiquities restorer works on figures engraved on a 3,350-year-old limestone tomb belonging to a royal butler named Ptahemwia. The tomb was discovered in February 2007 near the Step Pyramid—Egypt's oldest pyramid—in Saqqara.

sculptures show images of Ptahemwia, his wife, and an assortment of priests, officials, musicians, and servants. The hieroglyphs on these panels describe Ptahemwia as "Royal Butler, Clean of Hands," indicating a close relationship with Akhenaten. However, he is buried at Saqqara, not at Akhenaten's capital of Amarna.

The tomb is unfinished, suggesting that the royal butler died early or fell out of political favor with the pharaoh. Archaeologists found glyphs showing that the name *Ptahemwia* literally means *sitting in the boat of Ptah*. Ptah was the city god of Memphis, the nearby capital of Egypt until Akhenaten's reign. Perhaps Ptahemwia remained somewhat too loyal to this Ptah, rather than acknowledging the sun god, Aten, the only god who was allowed to be worshipped during Akhenaten's reign. ■ Thomas R. Hester

See also **ANTHROPOLOGY.**

Reconstructing the Antikythera Mechanism

Although computers did not exist in ancient Greece, an archaeological discovery reported in November 2006 revealed a sophisticated, computerlike calculating technology that was used in Greece more than 2,000 years ago.

The corroded fragments of the Antikythera Mechanism, a machine made of bronze and wood, were discovered in 1900 in a Roman shipwreck off the coast of the Greek island of Antikythera. The device was used to calculate the complex movements of the moon, the sun, and other celestial bodies. For about a century, the device remained a mystery—until scientists examined it using modern, high-resolution imaging technology. This technology allowed the researchers to date the mechanism to about 100 B.C. The Antikythera Mechanism provides proof that technology and astronomical knowledge were remarkably advanced in ancient Greece. In fact, the complexity of the mechanics of the device was not matched until the A.D. 1600's, when mechanical calculating machines reappeared in Europe.

An international team of scientists worked on the Antikythera Mechanism Research Project, based at the National Archaeological Museum in Athens, Greece, where the Antikythera Mechanism is housed. Astronomer Mike Edmunds of Cardiff University in Wales, United Kingdom, led the academic component of the project. Scientists from Hewlett-Packard's Mobile and Media Systems Laboratory of Palo Alto, California, contributed a high-resolution imaging technique based on capturing multiple views of difficult-to-see surface inscriptions under different lighting conditions and then clarifying these images with computer software. In addition, an advanced type of *computed tomography*—a three-dimensional X-ray system best known for its use in medicine—was used to study the inside parts of the device under high magnification.

The researchers discovered that the ancient Greek machine—when in its original condition—contained a complicated arrangement of at least 30 hand-cut bronze gears. The gears were operated by turning a knob on the side of the device. The mechanism also had movable dials on its front and back.

The main dial on the front was marked with divisions of the Egyptian calendar, while a smaller dial, inside the main dial, bore the symbols of the Greek *zodiac* (a band-shaped section of the sky with 12 constellations). Three clocklike hands on the main dial represented the date and the positions in the sky of the sun and moon. The dials on the back of the device indicated the annual cyclic movements of the sun, the moon, and Earth. *Glyphs* (carved symbols) on the lower back dial provided information about solar and lunar eclipses.

The investigators explained that the gear-and-dial system could be used to calculate the movements and relative positions of the moon, sun, planets, and stars throughout the year. The researchers noted that the planets were modeled not as *geocentric orbits* (with the sun and planets orbiting Earth, as some people believed during ancient times) or as *heliocentric orbits* (with the planets orbiting the sun, as we know today), but rather as the planets would have appeared in the sky to an observer on Earth.

The Antikythera Mechanism would have allowed ancient astronomers to accurately predict the locations in the sky of the known planets (at that time, Mercury, Venus, Mars, Jupiter, and Saturn), the rising and setting of certain stars, and the likely occurrences of solar and lunar eclipses at particular times of the year. The knowledge obtained through the mechanism would have been useful to the ancient Greeks not only in astronomy, but also in the realms of spirituality and society. For example, many people in ancient Greece considered eclipses powerful *omens* (predictions of future events), so knowing when eclipses would happen would have allowed officials to prepare important rituals or other appropriate activities. The mechanism may have also been used as a navigation instrument and as a teaching aid.

The movable metal parts of the mechanism were housed in a wooden case carved with ancient Greek inscriptions. The researchers who deciphered the inscriptions concluded that text provided information on planetary movements and detailed instructions on how to use the mechanism.

Understanding how the Antikythera Mechanism worked allowed the researchers to determine that the device reflected many of the ideas of Hipparchus (180 B.C.?–125 B.C.?), a Greek astronomer credited with improving scientific models of lunar, solar, and planetary movement. Thus, the researchers speculated that Hipparchus or someone associated with him might have designed the machine. The mechanism appeared to take into account a number of actual astronomical phenomena, including irregularities in the motion of the moon caused by its *elliptical* (oval) orbit around Earth.

The Antikythera Mechanism demonstrates that the astronomical and mathematical knowledge and technological capabilities of the ancient Greeks were highly advanced. However, much of the knowledge of the ancient world was lost during the so-called Dark Ages, a period lasting roughly from the A.D. 400's to 900's when Europe did not value learning and scientific development as highly as was done in ancient Greece, Rome, and Egypt.

Ancient artifacts such as the Antikythera Mechanism have scientists speculating that perhaps people thousands of years ago produced other advanced technologies that remain to be discovered. As Mike Edmunds, admiring the beauty of the design of the Antikythera Mechanism, aptly noted, if the ancient Greeks "can do that, what else could they do?" ■ Alfred J. Smuskiewicz

ANCIENT COMPUTER
A corroded fragment (above) of the Antikythera Mechanism on display at the National Archaeological Museum in Athens, Greece, shows how the artifact looked when it was discovered in 1900. Visitors to the museum (below) also can view a tentative reconstruction of the bronze system of wheels and cogs that allowed this device to compute complex astronomical movements.

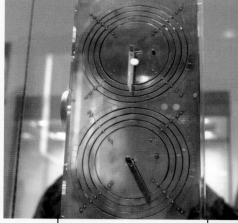

ASTRONOMY

Saturn's giant moon Titan has lakes of organic molecules near its North Pole. Writing in the Jan. 4, 2007, issue of *Nature,* Ellen R. Stofan of University College, London, and the Cassini radar team reported the discovery of these features using a radar system aboard the American-European Cassini Orbiter space probe. The Cassini Orbiter, launched in October 1997, has been in orbit around Saturn since July 2004.

When the American Voyager 1 spacecraft flew by Titan in November 1980, it discovered that the bulk of Titan's atmosphere is made of molecular nitrogen—just like Earth's atmosphere—with methane, previously discovered by telescope, as the next most abundant gas. Methane is the simplest *hydrocarbon* (organic carbon-hydrogen) molecule, and it occurs in Earth's atmosphere as well but in very small amounts.

Titan, a body larger than the planet Mercury, is made of rock and water ice. The atmosphere is tightly bound by gravity, but the methane is chemically unstable. Ultraviolet light from the sun breaks it apart to form other hydrocarbon molecules and, with nitrogen, a different class of organics called nitriles. All the products of methane chemistry form hazes that impede scientists' view of the surface. The methane products are thought to be continuously raining out of the atmosphere, which is very cold because Titan is so far from the sun. The surface temperature is –179 °C (–290 °F).

Scientists believe that the destruction of methane is rapid enough that all the methane in

SEE ALSO THE SPECIAL REPORT, A COSMIC ASSIGNMENT, PAGE 26.

Titan's atmosphere since the birth of the solar system should have been gone by now. Hence, since the Voyager measurements came to Earth, scientists have been searching for the source of methane on Titan. One of the primary goals of the Cassini mission is to find that source.

Earlier Cassini radar images and other images made by an instrument that detects *infrared* (thermal) radiation ruled out the possibility of global seas of methane on Titan's surface. In the equatorial region, dunes made of solid organic particles seem to predominate. Yet both instruments have detected river channels in many places on Titan's surface. Furthermore, the European Huygens probe, which was deployed from Cassini and landed on Titan's surface in January 2005, detected methane vaporizing out of the ground at the landing site near the equator. So it seems that there is more methane present on Titan than the amount in the atmosphere.

The radar images reported in January 2007 cover a region near the North Pole of Titan. Dark, irregularly shaped areas ranging from 1.6 to 160 kilometers (1 to 100 miles) across look like bodies of liquid flooding a terrain cut here and there by channels. Although no definitive proof exists that the dark areas are liquid, various lines of evidence point to this assumption. Given the abundance of methane in the atmosphere, the Cassini radar scientists concluded that the lakes are filled with methane, a liquid under Titan's bitterly cold conditions.

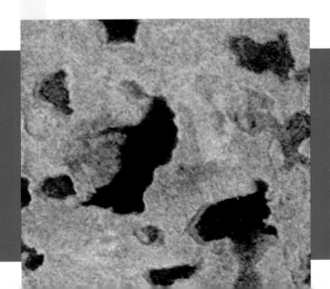

TITAN SEAS

Sea-sized bodies of what scientists believe may be liquid methane dot the surface of Saturn's largest moon, Titan. The bodies vary in size from 1.6 to 160 kilometers (1 to 100 miles). The radar image, captured by the Cassini Orbiter as it circles Saturn, was released in March 2007.

In a companion paper published in *Icarus* in January 2007, Giuseppe Mitri of the National Aeronautics and Space Administration's (NASA) Jet Propulsion Laboratory (JPL) at the California Institute of Technology in Pasadena and his colleagues show that such lakes of methane are expected to be concentrated at the polar regions since temperatures there should be a few degrees colder than at the equator. The scientists also argue that the lakes are more stable if they contain not only methane but also a similar hydrocarbon named ethane, which comes from methane in the upper atmosphere under the action of sunlight.

The coverage of lakes in the Northern Hemisphere, based now on several radar passes over the region, turns out to be sufficient to supply the entire atmosphere with methane and may explain why Titan's atmosphere, even at the equator, has a fairly high abundance of methane—equivalent to a methane "humidity" of almost 50 percent. However, the lakes are almost certainly not deep enough to provide a storage reservoir for methane over billions of years of Titan's history, so the search for the ultimate source of methane on Titan continues.

Testing whether the lakes really are filled with methane and ethane will require waiting for spring to progress in Titan's north. Then other instruments on Cassini can use the extra sunlight to try to detect the characteristic colors of liquid methane at infrared wavelengths. A year on Titan (and its parent planet, Saturn) is 29 Earth years, so it may be 2008 or later before the region is sufficiently illuminated to test the idea that the lakes of Titan are liquid.

Water ice on Mars. The South Pole of Mars may hold a cap of water ice more than 3.7 kilometers (2.3 miles) thick. Writing in the April 6, 2007, issue of *Science,* JPL planetary scientist Jeffrey J. Plaut and an international team of researchers analyzed data from the radar system aboard the European Mars Express Orbiter. Mars Express arrived at Mars in December 2003 carrying a suite of instruments designed to determine where water is present today on Mars. This includes water in ice and bound into minerals on the Martian surface. Mars Express will also attempt to determine how much water might have been present on Mars in the past. This information is essential in order to gauge whether Mars might have had life in the past, whether life was widespread at the time, and whether life might exist there today.

The poles of Mars are known to contain caps of water ice that are present year-round and thinner layers of carbon dioxide ice (the frozen form of the main Martian atmospheric gas) that wax and wane with the seasons. The permanent ice deposits display fine layers that may reflect variations in the amount of dust contained in the ice, thus displaying a history of climate change on Mars. Understanding the total thickness of the caps allows for an estimate of the minimum amount of water that was present on Mars in the past—some of which may have been lost to space.

By mapping the variation in the thickness of the polar cap at the South Pole of Mars, the Mars Express scientists could calculate the depth of a liquid ocean that might have once existed

MAGNETIC SUN

Part of the solar magnetic field erupts from a sunspot in an image captured by the Hinode spacecraft. Sunspots are dark features on the surface of the sun that form where magnetic field lines from the solar interior break through. Hinode, launched in September 2006, is a joint mission by Japan, the United Kingdom, Europe, and the United States to study the sun's magnetic field. Dramatic images taken by Hinode have revealed that the magnetic field is much more turbulent than scientists previously thought.

ASTRONOMY continued

on Mars if its remnant today is the polar cap. Spread out over the whole Martian surface, the ice in the polar cap would make a liquid water ocean 11 meters (36 feet) deep. While this seems very shallow compared to Earth's oceans, it represents the lower limit of the amount of water, as large amounts may be or have been present in the north polar region, some is bound to minerals elsewhere on Mars, and some has escaped to space.

If Mars was once much warmer than today, as suggested by dried channels on the surface, the water in the polar caps alone would have been more than enough to host ecosystems across widespread regions of the surface. NASA plans to send a lander to the north polar regions of Mars in 2008 to sample some of the ice there. The two rovers Spirit and Opportunity, which landed on Mars in January 2004, continue to find evidence that water once existed as liquid much closer to the equator. Ultimately, more ambitious missions will tackle the most difficult challenge: the search for evidence of Martian life itself.

Exoplanets examined. Since the discovery of the first extrasolar planet (now called exoplanets by most astronomers) in 1992, the detection dominated news about these planets. In May 2007, astronomers announced the discovery of 28 new exoplanets. These discoveries, coupled with those before 2007, bring the total number of known planets orbiting other stars to 236. This is enough to begin taking a census of their properties, including their size, their distribution across the galaxy, and their atmospheric composition and temperature variations.

Astronomers in 2006 found the nearest exoplanet yet, a body orbiting the star Epsilon Eridani, only 10.5 *light-years* away. A light-year is the distance light travels in one year, approximately 9.5 trillion kilometers (5.9 million miles). Like most of the other exoplanets discovered so far, Epsilon Eri b was first noticed indirectly, by its effect on the motion of its parent star. Careful observations of tiny shifts of the spectrum of the star revealed the planet in 2000, but now the motion of the star has been seen more directly by the Hubble Space Telescope. The Hubble's incredibly accurate pointing system revealed the star's motion in the sky with respect to the other stars. Combined with the spectral shifts, that information enabled a group led by astronomers G. Fritz Benedict and

Barbara E. McArthur of the University of Texas in Austin to fully analyze the orbit. They found a 6.9-year orbit for Epsilon Eri b. Perhaps more interestingly, the planet should be seen directly by the Hubble Space Telescope late in 2007, when the planet will be closest to the star and therefore reflecting more light than it does in other parts of its orbit.

Going to the other extreme, astronomers have detected the most distant exoplanets found so far, near the galactic center about 26,000 light-years away. Again, the Hubble was used, this time to observe regular transits as orbiting exoplanets crossed in front of the stars. When the orbital plane of the planet happens to lie in Earth's line of sight, astronomers can observe the tiny dip in the brightness of the star when the planet crosses in front of it. Kailash C. Sahu of the Space Telescope Science Institute in Baltimore led a group of astronomers who located 16 exoplanets this way. A NASA space observatory called Kepler, to be launched in late 2007, will employ the same method to search for more exoplanets, with the hope of finding planets as small as Earth. The exoplanets detected so far have all been very large, comparable in diameter to gas giants closer to home, such as Jupiter and Saturn.

The least massive exoplanet found to date, equal to five Earth masses, was also discovered in 2006. A group of astronomers led by Jean-Philippe Beaulieu of the Institute d'Astrophysique in Paris used gravitational lensing, in which a background star's light is bent by a foreground star's gravity, causing the background star to become temporarily brighter than normal. If the foreground star has a planet, the planet can cause a brief flare-up in the already enhanced light of the background star. The duration of the brightening tells the astronomers the mass of the intervening body.

A number of the exoplanet studies reported in 2006 used the Spitzer Space Telescope, an orbiting *infrared* observatory. Planets emit most of their light at infrared wavelengths.

Three teams of astronomers published the results of Spitzer observations aimed at analyzing the atmospheres of exoplanets, using transits to observe the spectrum of a star when the planet was shielded from view by the star and then when the planet transited the star. By subtracting the two spectra, the astronomers could deduce the spectrum of the planet alone. The three

groups, led by Mark R. Swain of Boston University; Carl J. Grillmair of the Spitzer Science Center at the California Institute of Technology in Pasadena; and L. Jeremy Richardson of NASA's Goddard Space Flight Center in Greenbelt, Maryland, attempted to determine the compositions of the planetary atmospheres by examining the infrared spectra. None of the three groups found evidence of any specific emissions (such as oxygen and hydrogen, which are found in Earth's atmosphere) in the spectra. This likely means that clouds cover the planetary surfaces. A fourth Spitzer study of transiting exoplanets, published in 2006 by Joseph Harrington of the University of Central Florida in Orlando and several colleagues, was able to measure the temperature variations of an exoplanet from day to

night. The variations were extreme because the planet faces its star perpetually, just as the moon always faces Earth.

Finally, again by observing transiting exoplanets, a group of astronomers led by David Charbonneau of the Harvard-Smithsonian Center for Astrophysics was able to obtain the most accurate measurements yet of the diameters of exoplanets by timing the duration of the transits and combining them with the known orbital speed. Charbonneau and his team used this method to show that some exoplanets are "puffed up," meaning that they are too big to be easily explained by theoretical models. Theorists think that this is an effect of the high temperatures of these atmospheres due to the proximity of the stars.

ASTRONOMY continued

A star goes nova. Historically, astronomers distinguished a nova from a supernova by differences in *luminosity* (rate at which a star sends light and related forms of energy into space). Later, astronomers distinguished the two types of stellar explosions by the radically different mechanisms by which they occur. Now, astronomers are closing in on a more complete understanding of how the two are related by observing a nova that may be developing into a supernova.

A nova typically reaches a luminosity of some 100,000 to 200,000 times that of the sun. Some novae are recurrent; they go off repeatedly, on a time scale of decades or longer. Astronomers have long known that novae occur in binary star systems that have a *white dwarf* as one of the two stars and a *red giant star* as the other. A white dwarf is a compact, superdense stellar remnant left when a sun-sized star runs out of fuel and reaches the end of its nuclear reactions. A red giant star is nearing the end of its life also, shedding mass through a stellar wind. A nova occurs when some of this mass trickles onto the white dwarf, triggering a temporary outburst as the new material undergoes surface nuclear reactions. Astronomers think that a supernova can occur if the white dwarf accumulates enough new mass to exceed the limit for stability, which is 1.44 times the mass of the sun. When the white dwarf goes over this limit, a supernova explosion results, literally blowing up the entire white dwarf. This is a Type I supernova. A Type II supernova takes place when a very massive star reaches the end of its nuclear reactions and violently collapses, ripping off its outer layers as it does so.

A nova that occurred in February 2006 was observed with several different kinds of telescopes and interpreted by several different groups of astronomers. The star that underwent the nova is called RS Ophiuchi, and it had been observed to flare up several times previously. But now, with optical, infrared, radio, and X-ray telescopes available to observe the outburst, astronomers learned more about the details. Teams led by John D. Monnier of the University of Michigan in Ann Arbor and Phillip A. Evans of Keele University in Staffordshire in the United Kingdom interpreted their infrared data, obtained at several telescopes, as being due to an asymmetric shock wave that traveled outward from the star. Another team, led by Timothy J. O'Brien of the University of Manchester, U.K.,

observed the nova using a radio telescope and confirmed its asymmetry. The shock wave was created when the high-speed gas ejected from the white dwarf ran into the stellar wind from the red giant, and the wind material, which encapsulates both stars, was itself asymmetric. This implies that the stellar wind is not global, but is confined to the equatorial plane of the red giant, something previously suspected but not proven.

The X-ray observations made during February's nova, obtained with two different satellite observatories especially designed for rapid responses to unpredictable events as such novae, confirmed not only the shape of the shock, but also its velocity and its density. One team, led by Jennifer L. Sokoloski of the Harvard-Smithsonian Center for Astrophysics, used the Rossi X-Ray Timing Explorer to obtain its data, and the other group, led by Michael F. Bode of Liverpool John Moores University, U.K., used the Swift satellite, which has both X-ray and gamma-ray detectors aboard. Based on the interval between nova outbursts, the white dwarf is inferred to be rapidly approaching the mass limit at which a Type I supernova will occur. It is impossible to predict just when the stellar explosion will take place, though probably, within a few hundred thousand years, the astronomers of the future will observe a supernova remnant where RS Oph used to be.

The history of dark energy. One of the biggest news stores in astronomy has built up since 1998, when researchers announced that the expansion of the universe is speeding up, not slowing. According to traditional cosmological theory, universal expansion should be slowing down because of gravity. *Dark energy* is the name astronomers have given to the mysterious force that is pushing the galaxies throughout the universe away from each other. Now astronomers know that dark energy, which comprises over 70 percent of the energy of the universe, has been present at least as far back as when the first galaxies and stars were forming. This discovery was made possible by observing Type I supernovae.

Supernovae of this class can be used to measure distances to the most remote galaxies because they have the same power output wherever and whenever they occur. By observing the apparent brightness of a Type I supernova, astronomers can calculate its distance from Earth. Other classes of stars and phenomena are also used as "standard candles" in this way, but only supernovae are so bright that they can be seen across the universe.

The expansion speed of a distant galaxy is determined by its *redshift,* which is the fractional shift of its spectrum due to the motion of the galaxy away from us. Soon after astronomers agreed on the current expansion rate by observing Type I supernovae and their redshifts, the acceleration of the expansion became apparent. By 1998, astronomers had been able to measure the speeds and distances of enough galaxies to realize that the expansion was speeding up, not slowing down, as theory suggested it should be.

Because of the time that light takes to travel, looking at ever-increasing distances means that astronomers were looking farther and farther back in time. As a result, viewing the most distant Type I supernovae had revealed an increasing rate of expansion, leading to the first realization that something was pushing the galaxies apart. Starting around 5 billion or 6 billion years ago,

the dark energy became stronger than the gravity pulling galaxies together, and the acceleration started. Before that time, gravity had prevailed, and the universe had been slowing down.

In hopes of finding out how long the dark energy has been operating in the universe, Adam G. Riess of Johns Hopkins University in Baltimore and his colleagues observed supernova redshifts at unprecedented distances— more than 9 billion light-years. Even though the expansion was slowing 9 billion years ago, Riess and his team found evidence for dark energy even then. The expansion was not slowing down as rapidly as expected, and the difference was attributed to dark energy. Riess and his team published their results in early 2007. Now, astronomers know that the mysterious force pulling the universe apart has been present almost from the beginning of the universe.

■ Jonathan Lunine and Theodore Snow
See also **PHYSICS; SPACE EXPLORATION.**

A PEEK AT THE DARK SIDE

A hazy ring of dark matter is revealed in a set of composite images captured by the Hubble Space Telescope and released in May 2007—the strongest evidence to date that dark matter exists. Dark matter is an invisible substance that makes up most of the matter in the universe. It cannot be detected directly because it does not give off, reflect, or absorb visible light, radio waves, X rays, or any other kind of electromagnetic energy. However, astronomers have long inferred its presence because of the gravitational effects that it exerts. Astronomers believe that the dark matter captured by Hubble was the result of a collision between two galaxy clusters 5 billion light-years from Earth. (A light year is the distance light travels in a year, 9.46 trillion kilometers [5.88 trillion miles]).

ATMOSPHERIC SCIENCE

The World Meteorological Organization and the United Nations Environment Programme established the Intergovernmental Panel on Climate Change (IPCC) in 1988 for the purpose of addressing the scientific, technical, and socioeconomic aspects of global climate change. The IPCC is charged with periodically conducting a comprehensive assessment of the best available knowledge about global climate change. The IPCC carries out its tasks by means of three working groups and a special task force, each consisting of hundreds of experts from around the world. After reviewing many scientific and technical publications, the working groups present the results of their efforts in assessment reports for the world's leaders and the global scientific community. Reports have been published in 1990, 1995, and 2001.

In February 2007, the IPCC began releasing parts of its Fourth Assessment Report, *Climate Change 2007*. These reports paint a picture of human-induced climate change that is at once challenging and controversial.

Many climate experts found the IPCC's reports very believable. For example, Martin Rees (Lord Rees), president of the Royal Society of London noted, "This report makes it clear, more convincingly than ever before, that human actions are writ large on the changes we are seeing, and will see, to our climate. ... We need both to reduce our emissions of greenhouse gases and to prepare for the impacts of climate change. Those who would claim otherwise can no longer use science as a basis for their argument."

Climate Change 2007 represents the best available scientific knowledge as of the end of 2006, summarized and synthesized by the IPCC. The IPCC began the Fourth Assessment Report with the release of its "Summary for Policymakers" on Feb. 2, 2007, in Paris. The main findings were that the "warming of the climate system is unequivocal," with an increase of about 0.74 °C (1.3 °F) in the 100 years ending with 2005, and that "most of the observed increase in globally averaged temperatures since the mid-20th century is very likely due to the observed increase in anthropogenic [human-related] greenhouse gas concentrations." Looking to the future, the IPCC projected that the increase in global average temperatures will be in the range of 1.8 °C to 4 °C (3.2 °F to 7.2 °F) by

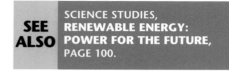

SEE ALSO SCIENCE STUDIES, RENEWABLE ENERGY: POWER FOR THE FUTURE, PAGE 100.

the end of the century, while the rise in sea levels around the globe will be in the range of 28 to 43 centimeters (11 to 17 inches).

The IPCC also found strong evidence that major changes are underway in atmospheric composition, global temperatures, and weather phenomena. The atmospheric concentrations of carbon dioxide, methane, and nitrous oxide—all greenhouse gases—have increased dramatically since 1750 as a result of human activities. The primary source of the observed increase in carbon dioxide was judged to be the burning of fossil fuels, with land-use changes making an important contribution.

Heat waves are occurring more frequently. In the 12-year period from 1995 to 2006 eleven of the years rank among the top 12 warmest years since 1850, when systematic temperature measurement began. Perhaps most worrisome, the IPCC noted, "Average Arctic temperatures increased at almost twice the global average rate in the past 100 years." The IPCC says there is a greater than 50 percent chance that people have contributed to increases in hurricane intensity, and a greater than 66 percent probability that there will be further increases in average hurricane intensity in the 2000's.

Another part of the Fourth Assessment, released on April 6, 2007 in Brussels, Belgium, is the most comprehensive summary yet produced of research into the effects and impacts of climate change. The IPCC found that climate change is very probably already having significant impacts on Earth. The report shows that climate change is affecting the incidence of extreme weather events, such as hurricanes and droughts. "It is impossible to say with certainty that climate change is the cause of any single hurricane, heat wave, flood or drought," says Saleemul Huq, one of the report's lead authors and head of the climate-change group at the International Institute for Environment and Development in London. "But taken together, the increase in frequency and intensity of such events during the last decade of the twentieth century provides strong evidence that climate change is already occurring and is no longer a problem of the future."

A third part of the IPCC's assessment is responsible for evaluating strategies for reducing greenhouse gas emissions and suggesting other options for mitigating climate change. This report was released on May 4, 2007, in Bangkok, Thailand. Other, more detailed publications were scheduled for May, June, and October 2007.

A quiet Atlantic hurricane season. By its June 1 opening, the hurricane season for 2006 was expected to be another active one like those of 2004 and 2005, when almost a dozen devastating storms made landfall in the United States. However, when the season closed on Nov. 30, 2006, it was regarded as the quietest season in years—only three tropical storms had made landfall in the United States. The month of October, historically one of the most active months, was nearly free of Atlantic tropical cyclones.

This sense of quiet was misleading when the central and western Atlantic is considered. Overall, activity in the 2006 season nearly matched the historical average, with nine named tropical storms, five of which reached hurricane strength, and two of which were major hurricanes. However, 2006 began with a carryover storm from 2005: Tropical Storm Zeta formed in December 2005 and continued into early January 2006—only the second time on record that a storm continued into January.

In the first part of the official 2006 hurricane season, Tropical Storm Alberto (June 10 to 14), the only storm to enter the Gulf of Mexico in 2006, came ashore June 13 in Florida's Big Bend region (resulting in two deaths). The storm then moved north through Georgia and South Carolina. Tropical Storm Beryl (July 18 to 21) brushed Cape Cod, Massachusetts. Tropical Storm Chris (July 31 to August 6) passed over Puerto Rico and Cuba, dropping heavy rain. Tropical Storm Debby (August 21 to 26) formed off the west coast of Africa, but then drifted north and dissipated.

Tropical Storm Ernesto (August 24 to September 1) reached hurricane strength for a short time on August 27. It subsequently crossed Florida on August 30, entered the Atlantic, and then made a final landfall along the North Carolina coast on August 31. Ernesto resulted in at least seven deaths in Haiti, Cuba, and the United States.

After Ernesto, four more tropical storms formed and reached hurricane strength: Hurricanes Florence (September 3 to 12); Gordon (September 11 to 20); Helene (September 12 to 24); and Isaac (September 27 to October 2). Gordon and Helene were by far the season's two strongest storms. In Gordon, the maximum sustained winds reached about 190 kilometers per hour (120 miles per hour), while in Helene, they reached about 200 kilometers per hour (125 miles per hour). Both storms were classified as

THE SOUND OF THUNDER

Images taken by the Tropical Rainfall Measuring Mission (TRMM), a satellite launched by NASA and NASDA (the Japanese National Space Development Agency) in 1997, capture thunderstorms that spawned at least 65 tornadoes in Kansas, Oklahoma, and Texas in late March 2007. An instrument aboard TRMM—the Precipitation Radar—measured rainfall as heavy as 50 millimeters (2 inches) per hour (red area in main image) in central Texas on March 29. The radar also produced a three-dimensional image indicating the heights of rain cells within the storm (inset). TRMM, which was to end its mission in 2007, has provided scientists with a better understanding of climate, to help them judge the effects of global warming.

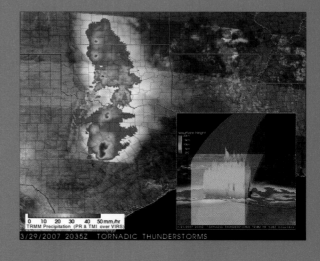

ATMOSPHERIC SCIENCE continued

Category 3 on the Saffir-Simpson scale, which rates the intensity of storms from Category 1 to 5.

What was different between 2004 and 2005 (very active years) and 2006 (the so-called quiet year)? The answer was the rapid appearance of a weak El Niño event in the eastern and central Pacific (El Niño is an interaction of the Pacific Ocean and atmosphere that results in greater rainfall along the coasts of Central and South America.) Other factors included a high-pressure region around Bermuda in the central Atlantic and the spread in the atmosphere of dry, dusty air from the Sahara Desert over the tropical Atlantic. Winds circulating around the high-pressure area over Bermuda tend to pull tropical systems north in the western Atlantic. A layer of dry, dusty air tends to cool the surface waters by absorbing or deflecting incoming sunlight. The dry air also tends to evaporate clouds that penetrate to mid-levels in the atmosphere, 1,830 to 7,620 meters (6,000 to 25,000 feet) up.

El Niño surprise. The rapid onset and development of the El Niño event in mid-August caught global forecasters by surprise; even sophisticated computer models did not see its formation until it was underway. "It turns out that El Niño developed more rapidly than expected, and the atmosphere responded quickly," said Gerry Bell of the National Oceanic and Atmospheric Administration Climate Prediction Center of Camp Springs, Maryland. "So that really helped to offset the overall favorable conditions [for hurricanes] that we've had in place for more than the last decade."

In an El Niño event, the trade winds in the tropical eastern and central Pacific, which normally blow strongly from east to west, weaken and even vanish. As a result, the ocean surface layer warms significantly in this region and stays warm until the trade winds return. The onset of an El Niño signals changes in atmospheric circulation all around the globe. One of these changes is a strengthening of the winds that blow from west to east in the subtropical Atlantic. Such winds work against the ability of tropical storms to grow in intensity and tend to push such storms north and east, away from the U.S. Atlantic coast. This behavior could be seen in the storms named Florence, Gordon, Helene, and Isaac. These storms started in the central Atlantic, moved westward toward the United States, and then turned out into the northern Atlantic, where they dissipated.

With the rapid demise of El Niño in February 2007, the return of more normal conditions in the Pacific, and the possibility of a La Niña developing in the Pacific, the 2007 hurricane season promises to be very active. During La Niña events, Pacific Ocean waters are unusually cold. These conditions usually result in greater rainfall across the Pacific Northwest of the United States and warmer and drier conditions across southern portions of North America. These conditions in the southern United States, Central America, and Mexico are ideal for hurricane formation.

From 1995 to 2005, the yearly average has been 15 named storms and 8 hurricanes—4 of them major. This level is well above historic values. Long-range forecasters are already warning of many storms for late summer and fall of 2007. This period of enhanced hurricane activity might persist for the next 10 to 20 years.

■ John Snow

See also **AGRICULTURE; OCEANOG-RAPHY.**

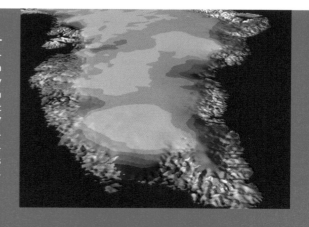

ICE MELT

The ice sheet covering Greenland is thinning around the edges and thickening in the middle in an image captured by NASA's Ice, Cloud, and Land Elevation satellite (ICESat). Scientists with the Arctic Ice Mapping Project reported in May 2007 that the net effect of the changes in thickness was a significant loss of ice. In addition, the speed of glacial melting has increased over the years. Both of the conditions may be related to global warming.

Findings of the Intergovernmental Panel on Climate Change

In the first half of 2007, the Intergovernmental Panel on Climate Change (IPCC) released three different reports on climate change that explained a serious problem, but one with possible solutions. The reports prompted many policymakers and scientists to declare that climate change was undisputable. However, political debate continues.

The IPCC was created in 1988 under the World Meteorological Organization (WMO) and the United Nations Environment Programme (UNEP). The WMO and UNEP established the IPCC because a large number of scientists were concerned that human activities were causing an increase in *greenhouse gases* that was leading to changes in climate with negative effects. (Greenhouse gases, such as carbon dioxide, trap heat in the atmosphere.) In fact, in 1985, an international meeting of scientists had concluded that "as a result of the increasing greenhouse gases it is now believed that in the first half of the next century [the 2000's] a rise of global mean [average] temperature could occur which is greater than any in man's history."

This early concern resulted in initial plans for a new body, with two missions: first, to assess scientific knowledge on climate change, and second, to establish practical responses for decision makers, such as the governments of the world, to consider. When the IPCC was eventually created, it added a third focus—the impact of climate change on the well-being of the environment and society.

Soon thereafter, the UN General Assembly requested an assessment report to be delivered in 1990 as background for the UN Conference on Environment and Development in Rio de Janeiro, Brazil, in 1992. The conference led to the development of the Framework Convention on Climate Change, which was later amended by the 1997 Kyoto Protocol. The Kyoto Protocol amendment requires nations committed to the protocol to contribute to the reduction of the world's greenhouse gases so they reach levels that are 5 percent less than they were in 1990. Those measures are to be in place between the years of 2008 and 2012.

Since its first major assessment report in 1990, the IPCC has produced three other major assessments (1995, 2001, and 2007). The 2007 assessment was released in stages, and summaries were made available during the first half of the year. These summaries focused on climate science (temperature and weather changes); adaptation and vulnerability of systems, such as environments and ecosystems; and the need for changes in energy policies in order to reduce greenhouse emissions.

The "Summary for Policymakers," issued in February by Working Group I of the IPCC, was the first report from the 2007 assessment. The report focused on how climate change is already affecting environments. The IPCC concluded, "Warming of the climate system is unequivocal, as

BANGLADESH CLIMATE CHANGE

A boy fishes with a net on the shore of one of thousands of small islands along the coast of Bangladesh. Scientists predict that such changes in the global climate as more coastal storms and a rise in sea level could cause a catastrophic loss of farmland and increased hardship for the 150 million inhabitants of Bangladesh, already among the poorest nations in the world.

is now evident from observations of increases in global average air and ocean temperatures, widespread melting of snow and ice, and rising global average sea level." The IPCC further stated, with 90 percent certainty, that these events were occurring mostly as a result of the emission of greenhouse gases produced through human activities.

The IPCC predicted that the increase in average temperatures around the world will be in the range of 1.8 °C to 4 °C (3.2 °F to 7.2 °F) by the end of the 2000's. The results of this increased warming, the IPCC projected, would include the continued rise of sea levels, an increase in maximum high and low temperatures, greater *heat indexes* (how hot the air feels) in parts of the world, higher precipitation in some areas, and increasing drought in others.

In April, the second summary from the 2007 assessment was issued by Working Group II. This report assessed which systems are vulnerable and how well they would be able to adapt to climate change. The group concluded that since 1970, many observed changes in *physical systems* (snow, ice, frozen ground, water cycle, and ocean waves and currents) and *biological systems* (living environments on land, in oceans, and in lakes and streams) have probably been related to human-caused global warming. These changes include a greater number of glacier lakes and expansions in size of existing lakes, both due to ice melt, and early bird migration and egg laying, signaling an earlier start to seasonal changes.

The report acknowledges that it is difficult, at this point, to isolate the large-scale impact of climate change and distinguish it from the many other factors that can cause such change. However, as Earth warms, the IPCC predicts that events such as reduction in permafrost, increased beach erosion, and species extinction will have direct connections to human-caused climate change. Regardless of the scenario, the report concluded that adaptation to future climate changes would be necessary. It argued that a focus on making communities more resilient to the effects of climate change, while also improving energy policies, would have the best prospects of diminishing future risks.

The final summary, from Working Group III, was released in May 2007 and focused on *mitigation*—that is, efforts to reduce the human-caused emission of greenhouse gases into the atmosphere. The report discussed opportunities to reduce emissions across a wide range of economic sectors, such as transportation, buildings, agriculture, and industry. The report concluded that decision makers have a wide range of options available to them right now for reducing greenhouse gas emissions. These options include switching from coal fuel to renewable sources, such as water, solar, and wind power. Other fuel-switching options are nuclear power and natural gas. Reducing deforestation and promoting reforestation would reduce carbon dioxide levels in the atmosphere, as trees use this gas for photosynthesis. Industry can contribute to the reduction of greenhouse gases by controlling emission releases and instituting more efficient use of electric power (especially electric energy that comes from fossil fuel sources). The IPCC also recommended lifestyle changes that allow individuals to contribute to the mitigation—for example, consumers could become more educated about climate change, use products that limit carbon emissions, and use public transportation in order to reduce the number of carbon-emission vehicles on roadways.

The IPCC also provided recommendations for the near future—up to 2030—and for the long term—2050 and beyond. These included broader use of and more efficient sources for solar, tidal wave, and wind energy; the construction of "smart" buildings that are capable of monitoring and controlling emissions; and more advanced electric and *hybrid* (running on gasoline and electric energy) vehicles that have stronger and longer-lasting batteries.

Leaders of many developing countries believe that human-caused climate change is a problem caused by wealthier, developed countries, which should be the first to address it. However, much of the future growth of greenhouse gas emissions is projected to come from China and India, which are rapidly developing industry. Most experts argued that the entire world would have to pay the costs of mitigating climate change.

The IPCC concluded that while there are many uncertainties about the future costs and benefits associated with reducing greenhouse gases, aggressive mitigation could cost up to 3 percent of one year's global gross domestic product (GDP), a measure of global economic activity, by 2030. Although this cost is steep, the IPCC makes it clear that it is still cheaper than inaction. The IPCC projects that these same attempts would cost as much as 5.5 percent of the GDP by 2050.

In recent years, there has been increasing emphasis on global warming in the media and an upswing of support for mitigating climate change, thanks in part to former Vice President Al Gore's 2006 movie, *An Inconvenient Truth*. However, the IPCC has not been without its critics, especially regarding the role of politics in its activities. In 2007, *Der Spiegel*, a leading German newspaper, commented that because the IPCC is "a scientific institution and panel of experts," it should impart results and

TOO-RAPID GROWTH

A chemical processing plant emits greenhouse and other types of gases into the atmosphere in Baokang, China. Although the Chinese government set a goal to reduce industrial emissions and energy consumption by 2010, international experts predicted that because of the rapid growth of the Chinese economy, the country would overtake the United States as the greatest emitter of greenhouse gasses before the end of 2007.

analyses in an unbiased manner. Other critics believe that IPCC leaders have a moral obligation to advocate for action on climate change, given their views on the immediacy and seriousness of the problem.

Another concern is that the IPCC is "policy neutral, but policy relevant." What this means is that the IPCC does not present explicit policy options—instead, it makes broad-reaching recommendations. Of course, because the IPCC seeks to be relevant to policymakers, it must apply some criteria to judge the relevance of national policies, but these criteria are not explicit. The IPCC and its assessments thus do not provide specific guidance on practical options for policymakers who are trying to mitigate climate change. Also hampering policymakers are differences in the definition of climate change used by the Framework Convention on Climate Change and the IPCC. The Framework Convention defines climate change narrowly: "only those changes to climate that result from human emissions of greenhouse gases." In contrast, the IPCC definition includes any "change in climate, regardless of cause." These two interpretations can cause problems because climate changes for many reasons beyond human influence, and climate impacts occur for reasons beyond climate changes. If a nation's leaders want to receive international funding in order to lessen the effect of climate change as defined by the IPCC, they have to fulfill the provisions of the Framework Convention. But as the IPCC Working Group II indicates, applying this standard is often very difficult in practice.

Despite its faults, the IPCC stands as a testament to the influence of scientists in the political debate on climate change. Whether the 2007 reports will be looked back on as marking the end of scientific debate on climate change or simply as a milestone in the evolution of that debate remains to be seen. But what is already clear is that the political terrain of climate change remains contested, ensuring a constant demand for expert input on policy. The IPCC will continue to sit at the intersection of climate science and politics, and its future effectiveness and influence will depend a great deal on how it chooses to evolve to meet the information needs of policymakers. The next challenge for the IPCC will be not to convince people of the reality of climate change, but to help world leaders shape expert knowledge into concrete action. ■ Roger Pielke

BIOLOGY

For the first time, biologists in 2007 showed that a plant can grow toward a scent. After being exposed to a tomato plant's scent, a type of dodder vine sent out a long skinny shoot toward the nearby tomato. This was the conclusion of tests reported in September 2006 by researchers at Pennsylvania State University in University Park.

Botanists have known that plants can direct their growth toward—or sometimes away from—light, gravity, and even touch. However, the Penn State research was the first demonstration that a plant could follow airborne chemicals, said lead researcher Consuelo M. De Moraes.

The type of dodder studied by the researchers looks more like a pile of living, orange spaghetti than like a green, leafy plant. Dodder vines do not contain *chlorophyll* (the green pigment that plants use to convert sunlight to energy). Instead, dodders send out shoots that twist and tangle around other plants and steal nutrients from them.

Dodders annoy farmers by stunting crops and reducing harvests. They do an estimated $4 million worth of damage a year just in California's tomato fields, and they attack other plants as well. The United States Department of Agriculture has ranked dodders among the 10 most destructive weeds in the country.

The Penn State researchers conducted a series of experiments in which they set out possible lures to see what made young dodder vines grow in a particular direction. In the most dramatic test, they put dodder seedlings in a container connected by a pipe to another container holding tomato extract. The scent alone was enough to send the dodders growing toward the pipe.

By trying the scents of other plants, the researchers found that wheat odors repel dodder. The experiments opened up new areas of research in the biology of plant growth. As a bonus, they might inspire new ideas for repellents to protect crops, say the researchers.

Fast evolution. Two small groups of animals changed so fast biologically that people had a rare chance to see the workings of vertebrate evolution in real time. The fast changes occurred in a kind of field cricket and a type of lizard.

The change in the crickets took place on Kauai, one of the Hawaiian Islands. In the space of about five years, most of the male *Teleogryllus oceanicus* crickets there lost their power to

 SEE ALSO THE SPECIAL REPORT, **THE LATEST BUZZ ABOUT HONEY BEES,** PAGE 42.

chirp, said Marlene Zuk of the University of California at Riverside. She and her colleagues reported the finding in September 2006.

These crickets had spread to Hawaii from Australia and the islands of the western Pacific. In Hawaii, however, they met another invader: a fly from North America. Females of the fly *Ormia ochracea* are about the size of house flies and have red eyes. At dawn and dusk, the females hunt for crickets by following the sounds of their chirps. That sound leads them to male crickets advertising for females. When a female fly finds a noisy cricket, she deposits her young on him. The little fly larvae burrow into the cricket's body and nibble on him as they grow. The flies are well fed, but the cricket eventually dies.

During the 1990's, Zuk found that the flies on Kauai were attacking a lot of crickets—at least one-third of those she sampled. Crickets were getting scarce. By 2003, cricket numbers were rising again, but most males no longer chirped.

A normal male cricket makes noise by rubbing together special structures on his wings. Zuk found that the silent males on Kauai had deformed wings that could not make noise. Through breeding experiments, her lab found that the deformed wings came from mutations in only one or two genes. As the flies killed off many chirping males, these silent mutations spread though most of the population on Kauai in about 20 cricket generations, Zuk calculated.

The silent males now have a different problem, since they cannot make the noise that lets females find them. For now, the silent males seem to cluster around any remaining chirper as if they are using him to attract females to the right place. What will happen to the mutation now is not clear, Zuk said.

Another research team not only saw natural selection working fast, but also provoked it. (Through the process of natural selection, individuals with less useful traits die off or fail to reproduce. Those with more useful traits thrive.) The research involved small brown lizards *(Anolis sagrei)* on six tiny islands in the Bahamas.

BIOLOGY continued

Jonathan B. Losos from Washington University in St. Louis and his colleagues carefully measured the *Anolis* populations and then introduced predators, curly-tailed lizards *(Leiocephalus carinatus),* onto some of the islands.

After six months, the researchers carefully measured the *Anolis* lizards again. Those that had survived tended to have longer hind legs than the ones that were killed. The survivors were the faster ones, better able to run away from the new predators. The predators tend to hunt mostly on the ground, however, and Losos predicted that, eventually, the *Anolis* lizards that survived would be the ones that climbed up into the shrubbery.

In another six months, the researchers returned to measure the surviving *Anolis* lizards again. This time the trend had shifted, favoring shorter hind legs. The surviving lizards were those that could dart around on twigs, where short legs worked well. Losos and his colleagues reported their findings in November 2006.

Overlooked antique plants. Until 2007, not even botanists paid a lot of attention to the little water plants in the plant family called Hydatellaceae. The 10 or so species are scattered in New Zealand, Australia, and Asia. The plants grow narrow leaves like blades of grass and bloom with little clusters of pinhead-sized flowers. Botanists used to classify them as relatives of the grasses, which are not a particularly old group of plants.

FAST-TRACK LIZARDS

An *Anolis* lizard clings to a twig. Researchers reported in November 2006 that *Anolis* lizards can evolve within a few months rather than over thousands or millions of years, as previously thought. The scientists, from Washington University in St. Louis, observed that *Anolis* lizards with long back legs initially survived the introduction of a new predator that hunted on the ground. However, within one year, the balance had shifted to *Anolis* lizards with shorter hind legs that enabled them to better maneuver in trees.

But a new study shows that the Hydatellaceae are cousins of water lilies, reported Sean W. Graham of the University of British Columbia in Vancouver and his colleagues in March 2007. They place the Hydatellaceae almost at the bottom of the family tree of living plant families. In Graham's version of the family tree, the Hydatellaceae and water lilies rank as the second most ancient branch that still has living relatives. Finding these modern descendants of old families offers clues to the early history of flowering plants.

Graham and his colleagues did not start out to study that history. Instead, one of Graham's students, Jeffery M. Saarela, was analyzing DNA from the various grasses and their relatives to understand their family relationships. Surprisingly, the sample from the Hydatellaceae did not look closely related at all. Graham, Saarela, and their colleagues expanded their study to look at more DNA but still found that the Hydatellaceae had been classified incorrectly.

The research team also took a new and very detailed look at the plants' structures, such as their pollen and seeds. These traits also fit the idea that the Hydatellaceae are relatives of water lilies, said Graham.

Meerkats teach their young. Meerkats teach their pups how to handle live scorpions and other prey, according to a report in July 2006. Many animals learn tasks as they grow up, but that does not mean other animals teach them. Teaching means doing a task in a certain way when pupils watch. Only a few studies have identified animals, including a kind of ant, that teach. Studying animal teachers offers clues to how teaching evolved in people, says one of the meerkat researchers, Alex Thornton of the University of Cambridge in England.

The meerkat, a kind of mongoose, lives in groups in dry parts of Africa. All members share the work of raising pups, although only a few of the meerkats, mostly the top-ranked males and females, ever become parents. When pups are about a month old, they start tagging along on the group's daily search for food. At first, pups are terrible at hunting. Mostly, they beg food from older meerkats, who share their catch of small prey, such as lizards or scorpions.

Thornton and Katherine McAuliffe, also of Cambridge, found that older meerkats killed at least one-third of the prey before they gave it to very young pups. That way, dinner could not run away from even the most bumbling pup. The researchers also found that, at least one-third of the time, the older meerkats disabled the prey—for example, removing a scorpion's stinger. One of the scorpion species that meerkats eat can deliver fatal stings.

As pups grew older and more experienced, the adults did not seem to pamper them as much. Pups got more and more of their food alive and with stingers intact. Feeding pups cuts into the efficiency of hunting, the researchers pointed out. Adults give away food they could

COPYCAT MACAQUES

An infant macaque observes a scientist sticking out his tongue, then promptly imitates the action. Researchers led by evolutionary biologist Pier F. Ferrari of the University of Parma in Italy reported this behavior in macaques in September 2006. Previously, scientists believed that only human and chimpanzee infants were capable of such imitation. The researchers suggested that imitating the facial movements of adults helps infant macaques develop social skills.

eat themselves, and they sometimes spend extra time watching the youngster eat. If pups lose control and let prey escape, the adults often bring it back.

To test the effect of pup age, researchers used recordings of begging calls from youngsters of different ages. When meerkats foraged with very young pups, researchers played recordings of older pups begging. The adults changed their behavior and increased the proportion of unharmed, hard-to-handle prey they gave to the pups. The researchers then reversed the situation among meerkat groups with experienced pups. At the sound of recorded calls of much younger pups, the adults increased the proportion of easy-to-handle prey.

To see whether gentle introductions help young meerkats hunt, Thornton and McAuliffe tried some coaching of their own. On each of three days, they gave several pups a dead or merely disabled scorpion. Other pups just got extra bits of cooked egg. On the fourth day, all the pups got a live, stingless scorpion. Those that had confronted live scorpions before did the best and managed to eat theirs. Pups fed cooked egg did the worst, letting the prey escape.

Smart birds. Two research groups report that birds—chickens and scrub jays—can do some things once thought possible only for people. For example, chickens can use sounds to represent things in their environment, much as people use words, reported Christopher S. Evans and Linda Evans of Macquarie University in Sydney, Australia, in November 2006.

The Evans lab has studied chicken sounds before. The researchers found that roosters make a series of "tck, tck" clucks when they find food. When researchers played "tck, tck" recordings to hens, the birds looked down at the ground as if

BIOLOGY continued

trying to find food also. However, this is not over-whelming evidence of wordlike sounds, Chris Evans said. Clucks might just be triggers that set off automatic reactions to look around for food.

As a stronger test for wordlike sounds, the Evanses worked with caged hens. For some of the birds, the researchers scattered corn on the cage floor. They used just a few grains, not enough to spoil the birds' appetites. Other hens got no treat. Then the researchers played "tck, tck" recordings to all the hens. The birds that had already nibbled the corn looked down for about three seconds. The other birds spent more than twice as long looking down.

The difference shows that the "tck, tck" sound is more than just a trigger to look for food, said the Evanses. An automatic trigger should have the same effect on all the birds. Yet hens that had found and eaten the corn did not keep looking for something they already knew about. The other hens looked intently.

The scrub jays' feat took place in the lab of Nicola S. Clayton of the University of Cambridge in the United Kingdom. In February 2007, she and her colleagues reported finding scrub jays that knew how to plan ahead. Many animals do things that might look like planning, said Clayton. They may climb into safe nooks to hibernate for the coming winter or migrate to warmer climates. But such action does not necessarily mean that the animals plan. They might just instinctively be responding to some cue, such as shortening days or dropping temperatures. In contrast, a person can take an imaginary look into the future and make plans accordingly. Seeing in the imagination what the coming months have in store allows a person to plan.

Since animals cannot describe their inner thoughts to people, it is hard to test for planning. However, Clayton said she came up with a way to get a rough idea. She started by giving her birds overnight sessions in a three-room suite. On some mornings, a test bird was enclosed for an hour in a chamber with no breakfast. (The rest of the day, the bird could eat as much as it wanted.) On other mornings, the bird was penned in a chamber at the other end of the suite. There, it was given a breakfast of ground-up nuts. In this manner, the birds had a chance to learn that breakfast was served in one chamber but not in the other.

For the test, the researchers offered the birds an evening treat of whole nuts. The jays could eat what they wanted and could hide nuts in either of the chambers. (In the wild, scrub jays hide nuts to dig up later.) This was the first time in this particular suite that the birds had been offered food that was not ground up and therefore could be hidden.

The eight birds tested did most of their hiding in the chamber where they did not get breakfast, the researchers reported. That, said Clayton, supports the idea that scrub jays perform an action that gives the same result as human planning.   ■ Susan Milius

See also **CONSERVATION; ECOLOGY.**

A NEW BIRD

A bright yellow red-crowned Yariguies brush-finch is presented as one of the newest bird species to be discovered. Scientists announced their finding in October 2006. The Yariguies brush-finch was found in an unexplored Andean cloud forest in Colombia and named in honor of the Yariguies people who once inhabited the area.

BOOKS ABOUT SCIENCE

Here are 12 important new science books suitable for the general reader. They have been selected from books published in 2006 and 2007.

Archaeology. *The Invisible Sex: Uncovering the True Roles of Women in Prehistory* by J. M. Adovasio, Olga Soffer, and Jake Page is a thought-provoking reevaluation of the theory that prehistoric men worked as hunters, cave painters, and toolmakers, while women had secondary roles as bearers of children. Examining evidence from buried tools, cave art, and other remains, archaeologists Adovasio and Soffer, along with science writer Page, demonstrate that women's roles were at least equal to that of men. Women probably hunted, made tools, and painted. Furthermore, it is almost certain that they led in the development of textiles and agriculture. (Collins, 2005, 302 pp., $26.95)

Astronomy. *Postcards from Mars: The First Photographer on the Red Planet* by Jim Bell is a collection of photos of Mars. Since early 2004, two robotic rovers, Spirit and Opportunity, have been crisscrossing the Martian desert, sending back tens of thousands of images from the surface of the Red Planet. Jim Bell, the leader of a team that designed the cameras on the rovers, has selected a small sample of the most spectacular and appealing color photographs of this remarkable world. Before the Mariner 4 spacecraft

flyby in 1964, all that was known of our neighbor planet was what scientists could see through telescopes from Earth, never closer than 64 million kilometers (40 million miles) away. Now, readers can see details as small as grains of sand on the surface of Mars. Thus, the tracks of the rovers in the Martian desert, which appear on the cover photo of this lovely book, mark a great step forward in our exploration of the solar system. (Dutton, 2006, 208 pp., $50.00)

Biology. *Animal Architects: Building and the Evolution of Intelligence* by James R. Gould and Carol Grant Gould surveys the wide variety of structures built by species from ants to elephants. Some, like the nests of falcons, are no more than depressions scraped into the ground, but others, like the hives of bees and the webs of spiders, are intricate and ingenious. Princeton University professor James Gould and science writer Carol Gould pose an intriguing question—do animals have mental concepts of what they are building, or do they construct such complex architecture out of instinct? Instinct may account for some of what animal architects do, conclude the authors, but many structures, like beaver dams and the nests of weaver birds, display a higher order of abstract reasoning and even a sense of beauty and proportion. (Basic Books, 2007, 290 pp., $26.95)

Darwinism and Its Discontents by Michael Ruse affirms that a 150 years after the publication of the *Origin of Species*, Darwin's ideas still stir the emotions of true believers from both the religious and the scientific communities. Ruse, a professor of philosophy at Florida State University in Tallahassee, has been thinking and writing for decades about this controversy, and in this important book he gives an eloquent overview of the issues Darwin raised and the criticisms leveled against him. Most of his critique covers mainstream intellectuals, like the Victorian Darwinist Herbert Spencer, who interpreted evolution as the agent of progress in all fields of human endeavor. Darwin's ideas, Ruse concludes, have been proven sound over and over again, but they are explanations of biological processes, not guides to morality. (Cambridge University Press, 2006, 275 pp., $30.00)

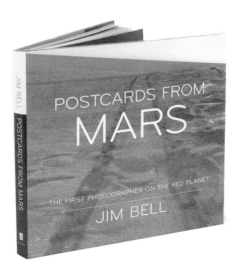

BOOKS ABOUT SCIENCE continued

Ecology. *Aldo Leopold's Odyssey: Rediscovering the Author of "A Sand County Almanac"* by Julianne Lutz Newton is a thoughtful biography of Aldo Leopold that traces the influences on his thought and the influence of his work, from 1909, when Leopold joined the United States Forest Service, through his 15 years teaching and writing at the University of Wisconsin during the heart of the Great Depression. Leopold's collection of essays on ecology, *A Sand County Almanac,* became an instant classic when it was published in 1948 and is today regarded as one of the most eloquent writings of environmentalism. More than a biography, Newton's book chronicles the creation of the environmental ethics movement. (Island Press, 2006, 504 pp., $32.95)

Ethology. *Jane Goodall: The Woman Who Redefined Man* by Dale Peterson tells the life story of the "chimp lady" whose pioneering studies of apes in the wild revolutionized the study of animal behavior. Goodall's life story is almost a classic rags-to-riches tale. In 1957, using money she had saved from a routine job as a secretary, she traveled to Africa, following a passion for adventure. There, she met eminent anthropologist

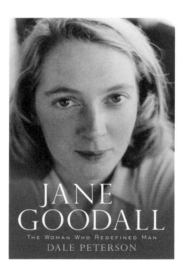

and naturalist Louis S. B. Leakey, who recruited her to do research on the wild chimpanzees of the Gombe Reservation in Kenya. The young Goodall proved a quick learner, and her patience and skill in observing the behavior of the great apes revealed a wide variety of complex activities never before recognized in the wild. Science writer Peterson traces her rapid rise to success and world fame, nicely balancing details of her personal life with descriptions of her work and her writings. This is the first major biography of Goodall and a worthy account of a remarkable woman. (Houghton Mifflin, 2006, 752 pp., $35.00)

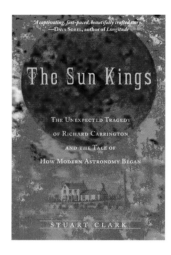

History of Science. *The Sun Kings: The Unexpected Tragedy of Richard Carrington and the Tale of How Modern Astronomy Began* by Stuart Clark tells about Sept. 1, 1859, when British astronomer Richard Carrington, who had painstakingly sketched the appearance of sunspots every clear day since 1853, saw a giant fireball leap across the sun. At the same time, brilliant auroras appeared in the sky even at tropical latitudes, where such things are rare. Telegraph operators worldwide reported a mysterious disturbance that caused sparks to leap from their receiving sets. Stuart Clark shows in this lively, entertaining account how Richard Carrington and his contemporaries were able to connect the solar events and begin what is now modern astronomy. He also reveals the story of the personal scandal that ultimately destroyed Carrington's marriage and his reputation as an astronomer. (Princeton University Press, 2007, 224 pp., $24.95)

Medicine. *The American Plague: The Untold Story of Yellow Fever, the Epidemic That Shaped Our History* by Molly Caldwell Crosby reminds readers that yellow fever was once one of the most dreaded and deadly diseases in the American South, though it is scarcely remembered today by anyone outside the medical profession. Journalist Crosby's account of the yellow fever plague in the 1800's focuses on the personal and economic devastation that it brought to Memphis, Tennessee. She also tells of the work of Walter Reed, the army doctor who went to Cuba to find the cause and cure for the disease. Reed and his coworkers achieved their goal, but only after experimenting on human subjects, including themselves, sometimes with fatal consequences. (Berkley, 2006, 368 pp., $24.95)

Natural History. *The Wild Trees: A Story of Passion and Daring* by Richard Preston reveals that, surprisingly, one of the few remaining unexplored habitats on Earth is in the United States: the high forest canopy of the American Northwest. Since 1992, a group of athletic adventurers has adapted techniques first developed by tree surgeons, cavers, and climbers to scale the heights of tall redwoods and Douglas firs. Richard Preston, known for his best-selling book about the Ebola virus, *The Hot Zone*, has climbed with these remarkable people and listened to their stories. His account of life hundreds of feet from the ground in the California forest, no less riveting than an adventure in the high Himalayas, reveals an aerial ecosystem as rich and exotic as any in the remotest depths of the Amazon. (Random House, 2007, 300 pp., $25.95)

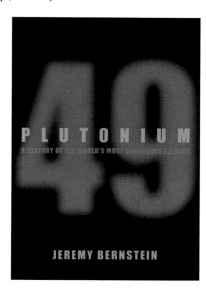

Physics. *Plutonium: A History of the World's Most Dangerous Element* by Jeremy Bernstein is a literate history of a chemical element that is not found in nature and whose only use seems to be the destruction of life and property. Produced in nuclear reactors and used to fabricate the nuclear weapon that was dropped on Nagasaki, Japan, in 1945, ending World War II, plutonium is also highly toxic if breathed or ingested. But chemically and physically, says veteran science writer and

nuclear physicist Bernstein, it is a fascinating substance. For instance, in one of its crystalline forms, it shrinks when heated, unlike most metals. In 1942, shortly after plutonium was discovered, only a few millionths of a gram existed in one government lab. Today, hundreds of tons of plutonium are stored around the world in the form of reactor products and nuclear weapons, and dealing with the threat they pose is a continuing challenge to modern society. (Joseph Henry Press, 2007, 224 pp., $27.95)

Uncertainty: Einstein, Heisenberg, Bohr, and the Struggle for the Soul of Science by David Lindley examines one of the central principles of quantum mechanics, the physical law that governs the behavior of things the size of atoms and smaller—that the positions and speeds of individual particles cannot be known precisely, but can be expressed only as statistical probabilities. Science writer David Lindley's book recounts how this idea took root among the great physicists of the 1920's. His book focuses on a clash of three of the titans of science at this time: Albert Einstein, Werner Heisenberg, and Niels Bohr. Einstein suspected that the statistical nature of quantum mechanics hid a fatal flaw in its ideas, arguing that "God does not play dice with the Universe." But Heisenberg and Bohr thought otherwise, and though quantum mechanics seems weird and unfamiliar even today, it remains one of the most successful theories of modern physics. (Doubleday, 2007, 257 pp., $26.00)

Psychology. *The Lucifer Effect: Understanding How Good People Turn Evil* by Philip Zimbardo was written by the researcher whose experiment on the mentality of repressive power has become famous in the annals of psychology. In 1971, Zimbardo divided a group of Stanford University students into "guards" and "prisoners" and set up a mock penitentiary. Within days, the guards began to practice random acts of cruelty and intimidation, and the prisoners began to exhibit signs of pathological submission. Looking back at those experiments with the perspective of 30 years, Zimbardo describes how organizations, situations, and peer pressure can induce otherwise ordinary people to violate their own moral sensibility, as happened at the Abu Ghraib prison in Iraq. Nevertheless, Zimbardo applies the insights gained from his experiment to explain how good people can manage to resist pressures to do wrong, even in the face of pervasive evil. (Random House, 2007, 592 pp., $27.95) ■ Laurence Marschall

BOOKS ABOUT SCIENCE FOR YOUNGER READERS

These six new books about science are suitable for the young reader. They have been selected from books published in 2006 and 2007.

Anthropology. *Little People and a Lost World: An Anthropological Mystery* by Linda Goldenberg explores one of the most significant anthropological find in decades. In 2003, scientists on Flores Island, Indonesia, found the remains of a prehistoric people so tiny that they were nicknamed "hobbits," after the characters in J. R. R. Tolkien's *Lord of the Rings.* This discovery of people under 1 meter (3.3 feet) tall caused a fierce debate in the scientific community. Clearly written, with many fascinating color photographs, this book describes how these fragile finds were discovered and handled—in some cases, mishandled—and examines the international arguments that this new and surprising find evoked. An extensive resource list is included. (Lerner/Twenty-First Century, 2006, 112 pp. illus., $29.27)

Atmospheric Science. *Hurricane Force: In the Path of America's Deadliest Storms* by journalist Joseph B. Treaster gives readers firsthand knowledge of the fury of Hurricane Katrina. Holed up in New Orleans's City Hall during Hurricane Katrina, Treaster reported about the storm and its aftermath for *The New York Times.* He writes with the intensity of an eyewitness (and uses other firsthand accounts) to describe the terror of the hurricane and the human misery it left in its wake. Photographs and weather diagrams detail this tragedy within an overview of America's hurricane history. (Houghton Mifflin/Kingfisher, 2006, 128 pp. illus., $16.95)

Biology. *Extreme Animals. The Toughest Creatures on Earth* by Nicola Davies investigates animals who live in conditions "that would kill a human quicker than you could say coffin." Although Davis's writing is informal and often funny, her book is well researched and informative. The book introduces mammals, reptiles, even bacteria, that make their homes in the world's most extreme places, such as cold-blooded frogs who turn themselves into "frog Popsicles." Illustrations and cartoons add both information and humor. (Candlewick, 2006, 64 pp. illus., $12.99)

Ecology. *One Well: The Story of Water on Earth* by Rochelle Strauss surprises readers with the information that all water on Earth—raindrops, lakes, oceans, and glaciers—is connected: "the water you drank today may have rained down on the Amazon rainforest five years ago." The author also emphasizes that a water shortage is a global problem. In the brightly colored illustrations, a young girl moves from place to place, showing how water moves around the world and the ways in which it is recycled. The book explains how a system that has worked well for billions of years could be affected by climate change and pollution. The book's afterword suggests things that kids can do to help. (Kids Can Press, 2007, 32 pp. illus., $17.95)

Fossil Studies. *Barnum Brown: Dinosaur Hunter* by David Sheldon introduces readers to young Barnum Brown, who liked exploring around the family farm in Kansas collecting fossils. Parlaying his boyhood hobby into a job at the Museum of Natural History in New York City in the late 1800's, Brown took on the challenge of building the museum's dinosaur collection. His crowning achievement was the discovery of a *Tyrannosaurus rex* that wowed museum visitors. Vivid illustrations capture the size of the dinosaurs and the empty badlands where Brown discovered them. (Walker, 2006, 32 pp. illus., $16.95)

Science and Society. *An Inconvenient Truth* by Al Gore and Jane O'Connor adapts Gore's 2006 book (and the Oscar-winning documentary film of the same name) for kids by putting his theories about climate change in basic language and arguing his case forcefully at a level his audience can understand. Full-color photographs show how climate change is affecting the world, from melting glaciers to rising seas. In his introduction, Gore notes that reading Rachel Carson's *Silent Spring* as a 14-year-old was the catalyst for his lifelong interest in the environment. (Viking, 2007, 192 pp. illus., $23.00)

■ Ilene Cooper

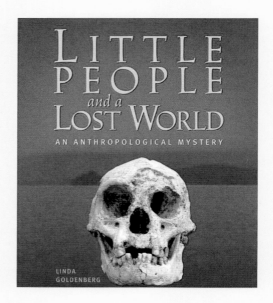

CHEMISTRY

In January 2007, researchers in the United Kingdom unveiled a highly sensitive, laser-based method to detect counterfeit drugs while they are still inside packages. Identifying counterfeit drugs, which usually cost less than the real ones, is difficult because they are often sold in genuine-looking packaging. But the counterfeit products may have incorrect ingredients; their dosages may be too small; or their ingredients may be contaminated with harmful impurities. According to the World Health Organization, counterfeit drugs have become a public health menace, particularly in the developing regions of Africa and Asia.

The new drug detection technology, reported by chemist Pavel Matousek and his colleagues at the government-run Rutherford Appleton Laboratory in Didcot, England, was developed to address this industry need. It uses a special form of *Raman spectroscopy,* an instrumental method of identifying molecules. A Raman spectroscope first beams a laser light onto a sample. The light gets absorbed by the chemical bonds of molecules in the sample and then emerges as a pattern of scattered light. This pattern, picked up by a sensitive light detector on the instrument, identifies the types of molecules present in the sample, just as a fingerprint identifies a person.

Drug manufacturers and distributors have long used Raman spectroscopy as a quality-control tool to analyze the composition of drugs in their plants. But while traditional Raman spectroscopy is good at detecting laser light that has bounced directly off the surface of a drug, it is poor at detecting light coming from a drug encased in a blister pack or plastic bottle. Light reflected from the surface of the packaging drowns out the much weaker light coming from the drugs inside.

To get around this limitation, the Rutherford Appleton group used a new form of Raman spectroscopy called spatially offset Raman spectroscopy (SORS). In SORS, the detector for picking up the scattered signal is placed about 3 millimeters (0.1 inch) off to the side of its usual location. In that position, light reflected from the packaging surface does not interfere with the light signal released by the drug itself. Using their SORS instrument, Matousek and his coworkers found they could detect the molecular fingerprints of several types of packaged

painkillers that would be difficult or impossible to identify with conventional Raman spectroscopy. Encouraged by these results, the researchers suggested that SORS could be the next frontline weapon in the fight against pharmaceutical fakes.

Magnetic water filter. In November 2006, investigators at Rice University in Houston reported a new and potentially low-cost method of removing deadly arsenic from drinking water. The procedure used nanoscale crystals of *magnetite,* a magnetic, rust-colored compound of iron and oxygen, along with a handheld magnet. Nanoscale particles are about the size of one *nanometer*—that is, one-billionth of a meter, or 0.000000001 meter (1/25,400,000 inch). The new purification method promised to meet an urgent need in rural parts of countries such as Bangladesh and India, where arsenic contamination from village wells has spread a trail of disease and suffering.

In high enough doses, arsenic is a lethal poison. Lower doses of this tasteless, colorless metal element are found naturally in well water in many parts of South Asia. People who drink this water often suffer from serious illnesses such as skin cancer, disfiguring skin calluses and discolorations, and stomach pains. Current technologies to remove most arsenic from drinking water usually require pumps and filtration systems that use a lot of electric energy. However, electric power is not common in the impoverished villages with the most serious arsenic contamination. According to the team at Rice, led by chemist Vicki L. Colvin, the new arsenic-removal procedure would be an advantage in such areas because it requires neither elaborate equipment nor electric power.

In their experiments, the Rice group sprinkled arsenic-contaminated water with crystals of magnetite. (They used magnetite because iron compounds are well known to absorb arsenic in a solution.) Soon, nearly all the arsenic was clinging to the magnetite particles suspended in the water. The scientists next placed a magnet near the bottom of the solution container. The magnet pulled the arsenic-coated magnetite particles to the bottom, where they could be removed. The researchers found that as the magnetite particles got smaller, their arsenic-removal efficiency increased. Normally, as magnetite particles grow smaller, they need more and

CHEMISTRY continued

more powerful magnets to remove them from solution. But the Rice team found that as the magnetite particles reached nanometer scale (about the size of viruses), they could be removed with magnets of very modest power, such as the ones used in computer disk drives. Thus, contaminated well water in villages could be purified with handheld magnets.

TREATMENT FOR TAINTED WATER

A woman drinks from a polluted pond in the Rajshani district of Bangladesh. Prolonged exposure to such chemicals as arsenic, often found in polluted water, can cause serious health problems and even death. In November 2006, researchers at Rice University in Houston reported that they had developed a new method of removing arsenic from water. The system involves nanoscale magnetite crystals and a handheld magnet.

New tool for chemists. Chemists usually force molecules to react by applying various conditions—such as heat, light, or electricity—that cause the molecules' bonds to break and rearrange themselves. In March 2007, a group of researchers at the University of Illinois in Urbana-Champaign reported a novel way to induce reactions in molecules—applying mechanical force to their chemical bonds. According to the investigators, putting strain on molecules by stretching them along a *single axis* (in a uniform direction) can cause their bonds to break and reform at very precise locations in their chains of atoms. The resulting products are not normally formed by reaction conditions that use heat or light.

It has always been possible to use force to break chemical bonds, but never before in a predictable way. Put enough pressure on a plastic broom handle, for example, and it will snap in two, but at a random location along the chains of atoms in its molecular structure. The goal of the Illinois team was to remove this unpredictability. To do this, the investigators, led by chemist Jeffrey S. Moore, synthesized *polymers* (compounds formed by linked, smaller molecules) containing weak links that were easily broken. They found they could apply mechanical force in a way that tugged on atoms along the long axis of the polymers, causing only the weak bonds to break and leaving the other bonds undisturbed.

The weak links in the polymer chains were molecules of a compound called benzobicyclobutene, which contain rings of carbon atoms that pop open with even a gentle nudge. To apply force to the long axis of the polymers, the scientists sent ultrasound waves through solutions of the polymers. The sound waves caused microscopic bubbles to form and then collapse. The resulting forces stretched and pulled on the polymer bonds until the rings opened up and formed new molecules. These new molecules were different from the ones formed when the same polymer was broken up with heat or light.

The Illinois researchers believe that the same procedure of designing molecules with weak links and using bubbles in solution to apply mechanical forces could allow chemists to create new and unusual molecules. Outside the laboratory, other applications of the technology may be possible, they say. For example, a parachute cord could be made of a synthetic polymer that would turn red when dangerous strains that could cause failure were building up in it. The stresses would trigger a chemical reaction in any weak polymer linkages in the cord, producing a red dye to warn people not to use the parachute.

Heaviest chemical element found. A joint team of researchers in Russia and the United States reported in October 2006 that they had created the heaviest chemical element yet known. The new element was so weighty because it had a record number of protons and neutrons crowded into its nucleus. (Nearly all the weight of an atom is in its nucleus.) One atom of the new element, which was made in a laboratory, had 118 protons in its nucleus. By contrast, uranium, the heaviest naturally occurring element, has 92 protons in its nucleus.

Like other superheavy elements reported in the past decade, the newly discovered one was unstable, lasting only about one-thousandth of a second before it broke apart. But scientists hailed its discovery as a sign that there are still unknown, extraheavy elements waiting to be created. Chemists are especially intrigued by theoretical calculations showing that some of these undiscovered massive elements might be stable enough to allow researchers to examine their chemical behavior and perhaps make compounds from them.

Physicists at the Joint Institute for Nuclear Research in Dubna, Russia, created the newest element with a U.S. team of researchers from the Lawrence Livermore National Laboratory in Livermore, California. The new element has an *atomic number* of 118. (The atomic number of an element equals the number of protons in its nucleus.) The Dubna-Livermore group has pre-

viously made other superheavy elements, including those with the atomic numbers 113, 114, 115, and 116.

The Russian and American scientists made element 118 by smashing together atoms of lighter elements inside a *particle accelerator*, a machine that speeds up atoms or atomic particles until they collide to form new atoms or particles. The scientists' method was to bombard atoms of a radioactive element called californium, which has 98 protons in its nucleus, with atoms of calcium, which has 20 protons in its nucleus. In a small number of cases, the nuclei of these two types of atoms stuck together, forming the new element, with a nucleus of 118 protons. To verify that they had actually formed element 118, the scientists analyzed the fragments given off by the new element after it *decayed* (broke down into smaller particles). According to physicist Ken Moody, lead investigator in the Livermore group, the number and type of these fragments showed that they could only have come from element 118. (An earlier claim of finding element 118, made in 1999 by scientists at Lawrence Berkeley National Laboratory in Berkeley, California, was later withdrawn when the supporting data could not be verified.)

Element 118 will not be named until other laboratories duplicate the team's findings. Meanwhile, the Dubna and Livermore researchers have set their sights on preparing even heavier elements. Doing so could bring them closer and closer to the "island of stability," a hypothetical region of very stable, superheavy elements that chemists have long believed may exist beyond any elements yet discovered.

HEAVYWEIGHT CHALLENGE

The scientists pictured here are at work in a laboratory of the Joint Institute for Nuclear Research in Dubna, Russia, where the heaviest chemical element—atomic number 118—was created. Russian scientists worked jointly with others at the Lawrence Livermore National Laboratory in California. The new element was created by bombarding the atoms of another element named californium with calcium atoms. Element 118, which has yet to be named, flashed in and out of existence in less than one-thousandth of a second.

CHEMISTRY continued

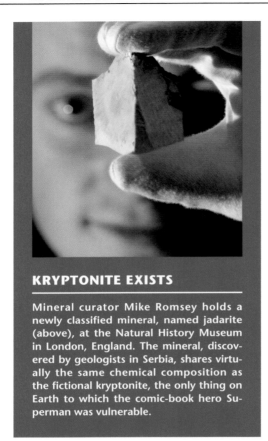

KRYPTONITE EXISTS

Mineral curator Mike Romsey holds a newly classified mineral, named jadarite (above), at the Natural History Museum in London, England. The mineral, discovered by geologists in Serbia, shares virtually the same chemical composition as the fictional kryptonite, the only thing on Earth to which the comic-book hero Superman was vulnerable.

Scientists find the real kryptonite. In April 2007, scientists in the United Kingdom and Canada announced that they had identified a new mineral with a chemical composition almost identical to that of kryptonite, the fictional mineral that robs Superman of his superpowers. Unlike the kryptonite in comic books and films, the real-life version is not made of glowing green crystals, is not radioactive, and is not dangerous to superheroes—or anyone else. Instead, the new material, which will be named jadarite, is white and powdery, with crystals that measure less than 5 *microns* across. A micron is equal to 1,000 nanometers (1/25,400 inch). Mineralogist Chris Stanley of the Natural History Museum in London worked with chemists at the National Research Council of Canada to identify the mineral and its chemical structure, or the arrangement of its atoms.

According to Stanley, the new mineral, which was discovered in a mine in Serbia, has

the formula sodium lithium boron silicate hydroxide. That, he noted, was almost exactly the formula of kryptonite, as described in the film *Superman Returns* (2006). (The only difference was that kryptonite also contained the element fluorine, while jadarite does not.) While jadarite may not be of much use to Superman's archenemy, Lex Luthor, it could be a valuable source of the element lithium, or the silicon-boron-oxygen compound called sodium borate, Stanley said. Lithium, which has many uses, is widely found in batteries, while sodium borate, also known as borax, is a common cleaning agent.

Chemists discover rare form of iron. In a June 2006 report, a team of researchers in Germany and the United States disclosed that they had discovered a compound containing a very uncommon form of the element iron. The compound was unusual because the iron in it gave up six electrons from its *valence shell* to the other atoms in the compound. (The valence shell is the outermost ring of electrons in an atom; it gives up or acquires electrons as it forms chemical bonds with other atoms.) In most of its compounds, iron gives up either two or three electrons to surrounding atoms. Occasionally, iron releases four or five electrons, but only one previous compound was known in which iron loses six electrons. Called *ferrate,* this oxygen-containing compound is used in soil and wastewater treatment, batteries, and disinfectants. The new compound is very different in chemical composition from ferrate, however, and should have some unique properties, according to its discoverers, researchers from the Max Planck Institute for Bioinorganic Chemistry in Mulheim, Germany, and from Stanford University in Palo Alto, California.

The scientists made the new molecule by exposing simpler iron compounds to intense light beams at the very low temperature of -196 °C (-321 °F). Instead of containing oxygen, like ferrate does, the new compound of Fe VI (iron that has lost six electrons) possesses a nitrogen atom attached to an iron atom. The lead Max Planck investigator, chemist John F. Berry, now at the University of Wisconsin in Madison, noted that such a molecule is likely to be very reactive and might be used to transfer nitrogen atoms to very specific sites in molecules in order to create new drugs and enzymes. ■ Gordon Graff

COMPUTERS AND ELECTRONICS

Anticipation and hype surrounding major product launches from Microsoft Corporation, Apple Inc., and consumer electronics companies dominated the computer and electronics industry in 2006 and 2007.

Microsoft launches Vista. After years of delays, Microsoft Corporation of Redmond, Washington, launched the consumer version of the Windows Vista operating system in January 2007. It costs up to $399 as a stand-alone program. It is the company's first new operating system since Windows XP was released in 2001. It is also Microsoft's first operating system that can be downloaded from the Internet.

One of the features included with Vista is its three-dimensional user interface, which allows the user to make better use of desktop space. The desktop also features a faster search function. Vista offers a greater level of security than previous versions of Windows by providing more protection against *spyware* (software that tracks a user's internet activities) and other malicious software. Vista's increased power requirements (for example, it needs one gigabyte of RAM in order to run) means that many consumers will need to upgrade their existing computers or purchase new ones in order to use the operating system.

Microsoft reported the sale of 20 million consumer copies of Vista worldwide during the software's first month on the market. That figure included copies ordered by personal computer (PC) makers to install on new machines, stand-alone copies sold in retail stores, and

SEE ALSO CONSUMER SCIENCE, **VOICE OVER INTERNET PROTOCOL,** PAGE 140.

downloads from the Windows Marketplace Web. These numbers are expected to rise as consumers purchase new computers.

Apple launches iPhone. Chief Executive Officer Steve Jobs of Apple, Inc. in Cupertino, California, unveiled the long-awaited iPhone in January 2007. The sleek phone, available to consumers in June 2007, is controlled by touch, plays music, surfs the Web, and runs the Macintosh computer operating system. A four-gigabyte model was expected to cost $499, while an eight-gigabyte iPhone was $599. The phones operate exclusively on the network offered by AT&T Incorporated of San Antonio.

The iPhone is less than 1.27 centimeters (0.5 inch) thick—thinner than almost any other phone on the market. It comes with a two-megapixel digital camera built into the back, as well as a slot for headphones and a *SIM* card (Subscriber Identity Module card, an electronic chip that holds subscriber information). The phone automatically synchronizes the user's media, including movies, music, and photos. The device can also connect to e-mail, Web bookmarks, and nearly any type of digital content stored on a computer.

When Jobs unveiled the iPhone, he was changing the company's 30-year-old name,

PRINT YOUR OWN TOYS

Technology developer Desktop Factory, Inc., of Pasadena, California, announced plans in May 2007 to produce its first three-dimensional printer. The 3-D printer, which will be about the size of a desktop laser printer, will build models out of specks of liquid or powdered plastic that can be hardened by heat, light, or chemicals. Consumers could use such a printer to make a variety of products, including toys or replacement parts for devices such as cell phones.

COMPUTERS AND ELECTRONICS continued

Apple Computer Inc., to Apple Inc., reflecting an increased focus on consumer electronics and e-commerce offerings (iPod, AppleTV, and iTunes).

NINTENDO STRIKES AGAIN

A retiree lands a blow as he plays a boxing video game on the new Nintendo Wii, which was released in the United States in November 2006. Wii includes a wireless, motion-sensitive remote control, which allows for more interactive play than any other video game system. Players can swing the controller like a racket to play a tennis game, brandish it like a sword in an adventure game, or manipulate it like a steering wheel in a driving game. Wii is part of an effort by Nintendo to expand the video game market beyond its traditional audience of children and young males.

Blu-ray vs. HD-DVD. At the annual Consumer Electronics Show in Las Vegas in January 2006, Sony Corporation of Tokyo debuted its new high-definition format for video called Blu-ray. Toshiba Corporation of Tokyo introduced a competing product called HD-DVD. Industry observers projected that one of these DVD formats would quickly dominate the other, mirroring the fight for market share between Betamax and VHS in the 1980's. By 2007, the winner for DVD format had yet to emerge.

Blu-ray players have greater storage capacity than HD-DVD players, but the latter cost less. Although sales of both types of players were lackluster in 2006, Toshiba's HD-DVD outsold the Blu-ray players made by Sony Corporation and Samsung of the United States. Sony anticipated a boost for Blu-ray with its release of the PlayStation 3 game console, which debuted in November 2006 and includes a Blu-ray player.

According to Nielsen VideoScan, Sony's projection came through in early 2007, with Blu-ray discs outselling HD-DVD's three to one.

Hollywood studios have been caught in the protracted battle. Metro-Goldwyn-Mayer, the Walt Disney Company, 20th Century Fox, and Sony Pictures release DVD's only in Blu-ray. Universal Studios releases exclusively in HD-DVD format. Warner and Paramount Pictures release in both Blu-ray and HD-DVD's. Makers of video game consoles are also divided, with Blu-ray used in Sony's PlayStation 3 and HD-DVD capability in Microsoft's Xbox 360.

Wii vs. PS3. When archrivals Sony Corporation and Nintendo Company Limited of Kyoto, Japan, launched new game consoles in November 2006, thousands of eager fans camped out on sidewalks in front of stores for as much as a week in advance. Both PlayStation 3 and Wii rely on advances in sophisticated motion-sensing technology that brought down the price and the size of the consoles.

Sony's PlayStation 3 cost $499 for a 20-gigabyte drive and $599 for a 60-gigabyte hard drive and built-in wireless capability. Both versions contain the new Cell computer chip, and the more expensive model supports the Blu-ray video disc format for high-definition video. The PS3's video game graphics rival those of a big-budget Hollywood movie. Unfortunately for Sony, consumers have complained about the console's small catalog of PS3 games and the machine's inability to properly play all games made for previous editions of the PlayStation (PS1 and PS2). After slow sales during the first part of 2007, Sony announced in April that it would stop making the 20-gigabyte hard drive PS3.

The Nintendo Wii (pronounced *we*) is a very different system than the PS3. Nintendo's game console is more accessible to consumers, beginning with its price tag of $250. The Wii features a tiny Wiimote—a wireless, handheld remote control that can track the user's movements, such as mimicking the swing of a golf club or the swagger of a sword. The Wii's relatively skimpy storage and processing power were big risks in an industry where consoles routinely become more powerful. Throughout 2006 and 2007, Wall Street pressured video game companies to expand beyond their traditional 20-something, male customer base, and the Wii was the first major system to achieve this. With its unique configuration and game offerings, the Wii quickly caught on with girls, women, and older adults.

Virtual worlds go mainstream. Another big trend among video gamers was the growth of virtual worlds—real-time, Web-based fantasy, where users interact through their *avatars* (characters) by sending instant messages or voice over the Internet.

Originally founded by entrepreneurs and run by programmers at small technology companies, virtual worlds are increasingly attracting the interest of big corporations. In March 2007, Sony announced it would launch Home, a virtual world for the PS3. Due to the popularity of Second Life, a Web-based phenomenon with nearly 7 million "residents" created by Linden Labs of San Francisco in 2006, Toyota Motor Corporation, Adidas AG of Herzogenaurach, Germany, and American Apparel Incorporated of Los Angeles built virtual outposts within the game. Within these outposts, these companies advertise, interact with customers, and sell virtual products.

Google buys YouTube. One of the biggest deals of 2006 was the October acquisition of the video-sharing site YouTube, Incorporated, of San Bruno, California, by Internet search powerhouse Google Incorporated of Mountain View, California. The $1.65-billion

stock purchase by Google meant the end of financial worries for the popular but financially struggling YouTube, which had never turned a profit. YouTube cofounders Chad Hurley, age 29, and Steve Chen, age 28, received nearly $700 million worth of Google stock in the deal.

The acquisition by Google gave it access to YouTube's worldwide audience of 72.1 million. Most YouTube videos are posted by amateurs with digital cameras, but the site also includes copyrighted material—particularly recordings of TV shows, movies, and music videos.

Botnet invasion. For more than a decade, one of the technology industry's thorniest problems has been the increasing amount of junk e-mails, known as *spam,* which reached epic proportions in 2006. Security experts blamed the phenomenon on millions of computers worldwide that had been hijacked by disreputable hackers—networks of zombie machines collectively called *botnets*. A March 2007 report by Symantec Corporation of Cupertino, California, blamed botnets for a massive increase in spam worldwide. Spam made up 59 percent of all e-mail traffic monitored by Symantec researchers.

In December 2006, thousands of machines using a single Internet service provider generated more than 1 billion spam e-mail messages in a 24-hour period. It was the most prolific botnet campaign ever, according to computer security firm Trend Micro. By the beginning of 2007, about 80 percent of spam e-mail came from botnets, according to computer security company MessageLabs of New York City.

Silicon Valley goes green. Entrepreneurs who have made California's Silicon Valley the epicenter of the global technology industry are shifting focus—from the computers and electronics that have dominated the region for more than 50 years to environmental and alternative energy research for the 2000's. "Clean tech" has emerged as one of the biggest technology trends of 2006.

In 2006, entrepreneurs in Silicon Valley raised $1.6 billion for clean tech startups, according to the Silicon Valley Leadership Group. The most promising alternative energy project within the $1-trillion domestic energy market appears to be solar power. The first *photovoltaic* cells (which convert light, such as sunlight, into electrical energy) came out more than 50 years ago. But rising gasoline prices, global warming, and worries about the stability of the nation's electric-power grids are renewing interest in solar energy. In September 2006, chip-making equipment manufacturer Applied Materials Inc.

COMPUTERS AND ELECTRONICS continued

QUANTUM COMPUTING BECOMES REAL

An RF (radio frequency) Filter Bank inside Orion, the first quantum computer intended for commercial use, is cooled to a temperature near absolute zero (−273.15 °C [−459.67 °F]). Such filters remove electronic interference from the internal signals of the computer. Orion was unveiled by D-Wave Systems, Inc., of Burnaby, British Columbia, Canada, in February 2007.

Quantum computers manipulate 1's and 0's to make calculations, just as ordinary computers do. However, instead of numbers, a quantum computer uses electrons that alternate between a grounded energy state (to represent 0) and an excited energy state (to represent 1). Quantum computers are potentially many times faster than conventional computers and may be used in a variety of applications from solving complex scientific problems to searching extensive databases.

of Santa Clara, California, announced it would sell tools for producing solar cells. The company projected that the market for such gear would triple to $3 billion by 2010.

Net stays neutral—for now. Regardless of whether a Web site is operated by a multinational conglomerate or an individual blogger, it shows up the same way when a computer user types in the address that begins with "http://www" on a Web browser. The concept is called net neutrality, and it has been a fundamental principle of the Internet as it evolved from an academic research tool to a communication medium for hundreds of millions of people worldwide.

Advocates say that without net neutrality, only wealthy corporations would have faster, more reliable Web sites, and eventually fewer people would visit smaller, less-funded sites, blogs, and personal Web pages. Grassroots organizations and Internet giants alike favor net neutrality, insisting that it allows entrepreneurs and startups to compete effectively against established companies. They worry that without such a model, Internet providers would charge customers billions of dollars to download e-mail, videos, music, and games.

But cable and telephone companies that provide Internet access to homes throughout the United States want to switch to a two-tiered model. Verizon Communications, Incorporated, and AT&T Corp., both of New York City, Comcast Corporation of Philadelphia, and other Internet providers say that wealthy companies and individuals could pay extra monthly fees to guarantee fast service, while small business owners, bloggers, and others who do not have large amounts of money to spend would be relegated to a cheaper, but slower, Web. Internet providers acknowledge that, in the long run, they would make more money under such a plan, but they would have to invest billions of dollars to upgrade the networks.

Following the November 2006 elections, Congress began advocating for a net-neutrality law that would require cable and telephone companies to continue to provide Web sites to Internet users on an equal basis. The first significant net-neutrality legislation was introduced in January 2007. ■ Rachel Konrad

See also **CLOSE-UP: RECONSTRUCTING THE ANTIKYTHERA MECHANISM.**

CONSERVATION

In 2006 and 2007, public awareness of global warming in the United States and elsewhere increased significantly. People became more concerned about its potential impact on ecosystems and the species that live in them.

During 2006 and 2007, the Intergovernmental Panel on Climate Change (IPCC), an international group of scientists, developed a report containing global warming research and recommendations for government action. The last such report was prepared in 2001. The press extensively covered the reports of the IPCC. Parts of the current report stated that the evidence of global warming occurring because of human activity was stronger than ever before. The IPCC also predicted that 20 to 30 percent of all known species will be at increased risk of extinction with a rise in average temperature of 1.8 °C to 4 °C (3.2 °F to 7.2 °F). Most current models predict that this temperature change will happen before the end of the century.

June 2006 saw the release of former U.S. Vice President Al Gore's documentary movie, *An Inconvenient Truth*. The film informed thousands of people about the evidence for global warming and its possible effects, including damage to ecosystems.

Also in 2006, biologist Camille Parmesan, of the University of Texas in Austin, published a review of studies demonstrating the impacts of global warming on species. These studies showed a range of effects caused by global warming, including movement of species poleward to escape warmer temperatures, movement of species up mountains for the same reason, changes in species migration patterns, and changes in the growth of plankton—the base of the food web for ocean life. The first reported extinctions caused by global warming were mountain amphibians. Other species, such as Adélie and emperor penguins, as well as dragonflies in the United Kingdom, are being pushed into smaller areas due to global warming. In addition, the warming of the oceans is affecting coral reefs. Warming oceans are one of the causes of reef bleaching—the death of corals due to the death of the algae upon which they feed.

In February 2007, Australia announced that it would outlaw the sale of incandescent light bulbs, which use about four times as much electric energy as fluorescent bulbs, in an attempt to

SEE ALSO THE SPECIAL REPORT, PARADISE FOUND, PAGE 56.

reduce that country's output of carbon dioxide from electric power generation. The changes will take effect in about three years. Similar proposals have been made in the United Kingdom, as well as in California and New Jersey (where the Edison incandescent light was invented) in the United States.

In addition to these efforts, the 100th U.S. Congress considered six bills in 2007 that would begin to place limits on carbon dioxide production using the kind of cap and trade programs that were successful in reducing acid rain pollution. These programs propose that companies would be given government permits that represent how much pollution they can emit—a pollution cap. A company that exceeds the cap will be fined. However, companies that exceed the cap will be able to purchase permits from companies that are well below the cap.

DNA bar coding. Studies using DNA bar coding, a method that uses variation at a single gene to identify species, demonstrated its value in 2007. Although some scientists still criticize bar coding as simplistic, others see huge possibilities, particularly for recognizing species quickly before they become threatened or extinct. Biologists Paul Hebert of the University of Guelph in Ontario, Canada, Daniel Janzen of the University of Pennsylvania in Philadelphia, and others envision the future development of a handheld device that could quickly identify the species of an organism found in the field. The device would allow all people, not just scientists, to increase their knowledge of the species around them and even discover new species. The biologists argue that knowing local species will encourage people to foster conservation.

Studies published in 2006 and 2007 reported the discovery of 10 previously unrecognized species of parasitic flies in Costa Rica and 13 or more new species of Costa Rican butterflies and moths. The Barcode of Life Data Systems online database contained bar codes for 27,160 species as of April 2007. These species included animals, plants, fungi, and *protists* (simple, mostly microscopic organisms). This growing database would provide the basic information

CONSERVATION continued

needed to make a desktop device, and then handheld bar code devices, work. The online database continued to grow through the work of scientists who sequenced the bar codes using the complicated technology available in 2007.

Endangered species. The summer of 2006 saw an increase in the number of nests of the Kemp's ridley sea turtle (*Lepidochelys kempii*) on the Texas coast (76 nests, up from 51 in 2005). The slow recovery of this species in Texas is credited to a cooperative effort between government agencies, universities, and citizen groups. The critically endangered sea turtle, with less than 2,000 nesting individuals, comes ashore annually to nest, primarily at Rancho Nuevo, Mexico. Some turtles also nest on Padre Island in Texas, thanks to a joint effort by the governments of Mexico and the United States in the 1980's to start a second nesting population. There is a no-fishing zone offshore of Rancho Nuevo. Shrimp fishing has been identified as the leading cause of death of turtles in Texas waters, despite the use of turtle exclusion devices on nets. In 1998, scientists and concerned citizens began an effort to create a marine preserve off Padre Island to protect the population of turtles there.

The U.S. Fish and Wildlife Service has removed the grizzly bear (*Ursus arctos horribilis*) population in Yellowstone Park from the Endangered Species Act list. The delisting may allow people to hunt the bears outside of the park (where one-third of the affected bears live) and may allow commercial development inside their habitat. The controversial delisting is opposed by some environmental organizations and a group of 250 scientists. Other groups representing wildlife biologists, the National Wildlife Federation, and the Wildlife Society support the delisting. When this population of bears was listed as endangered in 1975, there were about 325 individuals—now there are 500 to 600 individuals.

The American crocodile (*Crocodylus acutus*) population in the United States was reclassified on the Endangered Species Act listing from "endangered" to "threatened" in April 2007. The U.S. crocodiles, which live only in southern Florida, were listed in 1975 when the population numbered only 200 to 300 individuals. Current estimates for the number of crocodiles in south Florida are 1,400 to 2,000 individuals. Outside the United States, in the Caribbean and South America, crocodiles continued to be listed as endangered.

In December 2006, the Fish and Wildlife Service proposed adding the polar bear (*Ursus maritimus*) to the endangered species list as "threatened." The service will consult with researchers over the next year. The listing would recognize the results of studies indicating that reductions in polar sea ice due to global warming have hurt populations of polar bears. For example, the western Hudson Bay population of bears declined in number by about 17 percent from 1995 to 2005. Research showed that the cause of this decline was a loss of sea ice. The bears are also showing lower body weights as a result of loss of feeding time on the ice.

Threatened grouper species. In March 2007, a workshop held by the Global Marine Species Assessment in Hong Kong added 12 species of groupers to the 8 already present on the World Conservation Union (also know as IUCN—International Union for Conservation of Nature and Natural Resources) Red List of threatened species. These reef fish are a food and income source in Southeast Asia and elsewhere. Of the 162 species of groupers worldwide, most are large, long-lived, and slow-growing. Most species reach reproductive maturity only after several years. These characteristics make groupers especially vulnerable to extinction from overfishing. The workshop highlighted the need to limit catches, to create protected areas on deepwater reefs where the fish are often found, and to stop the common practice of fishing where groupers gather to reproduce.

Two species of grouper in North American waters were already on the IUCN list. The Warsaw grouper (*Epinephelus nigritus*), which inhabits the western and southern Atlantic and Gulf of Mexico, is listed as critically endangered. It is threatened by overfishing. This remarkable fish can live 41 years and becomes reproductive at age nine. More remarkably, these fish mature first as females and then change into males as they get older, a common trait in groupers and wrasses. These large fish grow to about 2.3 meters (7.5 feet) in length and can weigh 200 kilograms (440 pounds). The Nassau grouper (*Epinephelus striatus*), found in the western and southern Atlantic and Caribbean Sea, is threatened by overfishing in the Caribbean. U.S. populations are protected, but there may be illegal fishing affecting these populations. The Nassau grouper grows to about 1 meter (3.3 feet) in length and 25 kilograms (55 pounds) in weight, can live for 29 years, and matures after 4 to 7 years. This species has separate males and females. The Nassau grouper is now listed as endangered under the U.S. Endangered Species Act. The workshop added five new species from U.S. waters to the IUCN list.

Forest ecosystems. In a bid to slow greenhouse gas emissions resulting from tropical deforestation, Australia, in March 2007, dedicated 200 million Australian dollars (U.S. $161 million) to reduce deforestation in tropical forests of Southeast Asia. Indonesia, located in Southeast Asia, has been the site of rapid deforestation, making it the third-largest emitter of greenhouse gases, after the United States and China, according to the World Bank. Indonesia's deforestation rate is second only to Brazil's. The fund set up by Australia will be administered by the World Bank and used in replanting programs and to develop economic alternatives to logging. Other countries are expected to join Australia in contributing to the fund. A very important effect of this reforestation initiative will be the protection of tropical-forest ecosystems.

The forests of Indonesia, specifically the islands of Borneo (part of which is in Malaysia and includes the Kingdom of Brunei) and Sumatra, are the home of orangutans *(Pongo pygmaeus* and *Pongo abelii),* great apes and close genetic relatives of human beings. Orangutans are under extreme threat of extinction because of habitat loss from illegal logging of their forests. Orangutans lost 80 percent of their habitat in the 1980's and 1990's. As a result, the population declined by about one-third by 2007. The decline from 1998 to 2007 was estimated at

"CUTE KNUT"

Knut, a polar bear cub, cuddles in a blanket at the Berlin Zoo in Germany in March 2007. Cute Knut, as he came to be called, was rejected by his mother after his birth in December 2006. His twin, who was also rejected, died. Zookeepers intervened and bottle-fed Knut until he became old enough to eat on his own. Some animal rights activists argued that hand rearing a polar bear whose mother had abandoned it was a violation of animal rights. Others supported the zoo officials' decision.

CONSERVATION continued

1,000 individuals a year, with expected extinction in the wild by about 2017 if nothing changes. Other threats to orangutan populations come from hunting and the pet trade (both illegal), as well as loss of habitat from palm plantations that produce palm oil.

Although orangutans are of special importance to human beings because they are close

TRAGEDY IN TASMANIA

A Tasmanian devil is afflicted with devil facial tumor disease (DFTD), a cancerous growth that appears to be transmissible. Researchers at the Mt. Pleasant Laboratories in Launceston, Tasmania, reported such findings in February 2007. Tasmanian devils, which are found only on the island of Tasmania, have powerful jaws and tend to bite each other on the face during territorial battles and courtship. The researchers found that cancer cells in the facial tumors of all of the animals they studied shared the same genetic abnormalities. They believe that as the animals bite each other, bits of tumor tissue break off one animal and stick to the open wounds of another, spreading the disease.

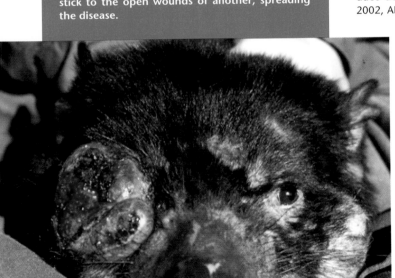

relatives, the loss of forest habitat in Indonesia and elsewhere in Southeast Asia is expected to lead to dramatic losses in other species as well, many of which have never been seen or described by biologists. WWF (formerly the World Wildlife Fund) reports that during 2006, 52 new species were identified in the forests of Borneo alone.

Similar loss of forest habitat, combined with hunting for their meat, threatens the African populations of some great apes—the gorilla (*Troglodytes gorilla*), chimpanzee (*Pan troglodytes*), and bonobo (*Pan paniscus*). The conservation of these species is complicated by extreme poverty and ongoing warfare in many of the countries in which these species live. The population of mountain gorillas has fallen to about 700. After the discovery in January 2007 of two mountain gorillas shot dead in Virunga National Park in the Democratic Republic of Congo, the Congolese government and United Nations troops attempted to open discussions with the dissidents responsible for killing the gorillas in order to stop such activity.

The Amazon Region Protected Areas (ARPA) program is a 10-year project that seeks to reduce deforestation in the Amazon. Begun in 2002, ARPA is a joint effort of the Brazilian government, the World Bank, WWF, and other agencies. The project has helped to create about 20 million hectares (49 million acres) of protected forest, and as a result, a Brazilian government study reported a decline in the rate of deforestation in the Amazon Basin during the year prior to August 2006.

In February 2006, the United States Agency for International Development announced the beginning of a five-year program to promote conservation in the Amazon Basin. The project, called the Amazon Basin Conservation Initiative, seeks to fund long-term conservation projects in the Amazon that take into account the economic needs of human populations.

■ David Barker,

See also **CLOSE-UP: FINDINGS OF THE INTERGOVERNMENTAL PANEL ON CLIMATE CHANGE.**

DEATHS OF SCIENTISTS

Notable people of science who died between June 1, 2006, and May 31, 2007, are listed below. Those listed were Americans unless otherwise indicated.

Robert Adler

Adler, Robert (1913–Feb. 15, 2007), Austria-Hungary-born physicist and inventor who coinvented the television remote control device. Adler spent most of his career at Zenith Radio Company (now Zenith Electronics Corporation, a subsidiary of South Korean LG Group) of Lincolnshire, Illinois. Adler's Space Command ultrasonic remote control, which was introduced in 1956, used high-frequency sound to operate a television set. The device made a clicking sound when a viewer pressed the button and remained an industry standard for 25 years.

Austrian, Robert (1916–March 25, 2007), medical researcher and physician who developed a modern vaccine against bacteria that cause pneumonia. The introduction of penicillin and other antibiotics in the 1940's led to the withdrawal of the first pneumococcal vaccines from the market. Austrian determined that pneumococcal infections remained a serious health threat—particularly to the elderly and chronically ill. He identified the types of bacteria that most frequently cause the disease, supervised the development of a vaccine, and conducted trials that proved the vaccine's effectiveness.

Backus, John W. (1924–March 17, 2007), computer scientist who led the team that in 1953 developed Fortran, revolutionary software that became one of the most widely used early computer programming languages. Fortran was an intuitive computer language based on English shorthand and algebra—rather than 1's and 0's—that engineers and scientists could use to write programs themselves.

Bacon, Roger (1926–Jan. 26, 2007), materials scientist whose studies of carbon and graphite fibers in the 1950's led to their use as protective materials for spacecraft and satellites.

Froehlich, Harold E. (1922–May 19, 2007), aeronautical engineer whose most famous project was the piloted submersible *Alvin*. Scientists exploring the seafloor in *Alvin* made many significant discoveries, including the surprising existence of large populations of bottom-dwelling organisms around volcanic hot springs in the ocean crust, about 2,000 meters (6,000 feet) below the sea's surface. In 1985, oceanographer Robert Ballard used *Alvin* to locate the wreck of the luxury liner *Titanic*.

Gennes, Pierre-Gilles de (1932–May 18, 2007), French theoretical physicist who won the 1991 Nobel Prize in physics for his work investigating how molecules become more orderly or disorderly under the influence of such things as temperature and electric and magnetic fields. De Gennes won special recognition for his work with liquid crystals, substances that can flow like a liquid yet have properties that are characteristic of a solid crystal. The most common use of liquid crystals is in liquid crystal displays (LCD's).

Hillier, James (1915–Jan. 15, 2007), Canadian-born physicist who codeveloped the first practical, commercially successful electron microscope. Hillier's prototype, which had a magnification of 7,000 times, led to the development of modern electron microscopes, some of which have magnifications of 2 million times.

Hoffleit, E. Dorrit (1907–April 9, 2007), astronomer who studied bright stars (those visible without a telescope) and catalogued more than 11,000 of these celestial objects. Hoffleit began her career in 1929, when few women held professional positions in astronomy. She specialized in locating variable stars, stars whose brightness changes over time. She also served as director of the Maria Mitchell Observatory, a private center in Nantucket, Massachusetts, that encourages women to study science.

DEATHS OF SCIENTISTS continued

Ingram, Vernon M. (1924–Aug. 17, 2006), German-born biologist who discovered that a *mutation* (change) in a single *gene* (part of a cell that determines inherited characteristics) causes sickle cell anemia. Sickle cell anemia is a hereditary blood disease that causes periodic attacks of pain and fever and may cause sudden death. Ingram's finding paved the way for prenatal (before birth) diagnosis of the disease and the discovery that other diseases—including hemophilia and cystic fibrosis—result from mutations in a single gene.

Paul C. Lauterbur

Lauterbur, Paul C. (1929–March 27, 2007), physical chemist who, together with Sir Peter Mansfield, won the 2003 Nobel Prize in physiology or medicine for the development of magnetic resonance imaging (MRI). MRI produces three-dimensional images of living organs and tissues in the body, allowing physicians to identify abnormalities without opening the body using surgery.

Lederberg, Esther (1922–Nov. 11, 2006), microbiologist whose discovery in 1951 of a virus—known as lambda phage—that can live inside bacteria without killing them formed the basis of laboratory studies of viruses and genetics. Scientists use the lambda phage as a laboratory model for studying more complicated viruses, including some that produce tumors. Lederberg also contributed to research that earned her husband, Joshua Lederberg, a Nobel Prize in physiology or medicine in 1958.

Alan MacDiarmid

MacDiarmid, Alan (1927–Feb. 7, 2007), New Zealand-born chemist who, together with U.S. physicist Alan J. Heeger and Japanese chemist Hideki Shirakawa, won the 2000 Nobel Prize in chemistry for discovering and developing plastic materials that conduct electricity. Such materials are used to make a number of products, including solar cells and displays in mobile telephones and television sets.

Maiman, Theodore (1927–May 5, 2007), physicist who in 1960 built the first laser. A laser is a device that produces a powerful, narrow beam of light that travels in only one direction. Lasers are used in a wide variety of tasks, including guiding missiles, repairing eye damage, reading bar codes, and printing documents.

Miller, Stanley L. (1930–May 20, 2007), biochemist who became known as the father of "origin of life" chemistry. In a classic experiment in 1953 at the University of Chicago, Miller, then a graduate student, provided the first experimental evidence that amino acids—the building blocks of proteins found in all living things—could have developed early in Earth's history from elements present at that time.

Morris, Craig (1939–June 14, 2006), archaeologist whose work revolutionized scientific understanding of Inca culture before the Spanish conquest in the early 1500's. He excavated the largest known settlement of preconquest Inca, called Huánuco Pampa, in Peru. He also served as dean of science at the American Museum of Natural History in New York City.

Murra, John V. (1916–Oct. 16, 2006), Ukrainian-born anthropologist who proposed the widely accepted theory that the ancient Inca empire of South America was held together by a unique economic system he called "the vertical archipelago." Under this system, Inca who lived in the lowlands traded corn and other agricultural goods for such items as llama and alpaca wool, which were harvested by Inca who lived in the mountains.

Myers, Ransom A. (1952–March 27, 2007), marine ecologist who determined that overfishing was responsible for the current collapse of fish stocks around the world. In the early 1990's, Myers reported that the Canadian government's failure to effectively manage the Atlantic cod fishery had led to the collapse of Atlantic cod stocks. In 2003, he completed an analysis of Japanese fishing records that showed that 90 percent of the world's sharks, tuna, swordfish, and other ocean predators had been destroyed by commercial fishing practices.

Paczynski, Bohdan (1940–April 19, 2007), Polish-born astrophysicist who pioneered a technique called gravitational microlensing that led to the discovery of the first planet outside our solar system. In this technique, a distant star or other celestial body temporarily brightens if another object moves directly into the line of sight between Earth and that object. Paczynski also correctly theorized that mysterious bursts of gamma rays, first detected in the 1960's, originated in distant galaxies rather than in the Milky Way.

Rimland, Bernard (1928–Nov. 21, 2006), psychologist who, in the 1960's, demonstrated a biological origin for *autism*, disproving the commonly held theory that cold, distant mothering caused the disorder. (Autism is characterized by a limited ability to communicate and interact with other people.) Rimland also developed guidelines for diagnosing and treating autism.

Schirra, Walter M., Jr. (1923–May 3, 2007), one of the seven original United States astronauts and the first to fly in three different types of spacecraft. Following his first spaceflight in 1962, Schirra participated in the first (nondocking) space rendezvous. In 1968, he piloted Apollo 7, the first U.S. spacecraft to carry three astronauts.

Schwartz, Melvin (1932–Aug. 27, 2006), physicist who, with U.S. physicists Leon Lederman and Jack Steinberger, won the 1988 Nobel Prize in physics for work on subatomic particles called *neutrinos*. Made in great numbers by the sun, neutrinos are difficult to detect when they reach Earth. Schwartz and his colleagues created their own neutrinos. While studying the interactions of the neutrinos with other matter, they discovered a new kind of neutrino called a muon.

Skovmand, Bent (1945–Feb. 6, 2007), Danish plant scientist who helped plan the "doomsday vault," a seed bank under construction on a Norwegian Arctic island. The Svalbard International Seed Vault, which is being carved into a mountainside, is designed to preserve some 3 million strains of crop plants from nuclear war and natural disasters and to make them available for breeding.

Tharp, Marie (1920–Aug. 23, 2006), oceanographic cartographer who created the first detailed maps of the ocean floor, paving the way for acceptance of the theories of continental drift and plate tectonics. In the 1950's, Tharp noticed what appeared to be a depression running from north to south in the Atlantic Ocean. She suggested that the depression indicated that the seafloor was spreading and offered proof of the then-controversial theory that continents move about on the surface of Earth.

James A. Van Allen (right)

Van Allen, James A. (1914–Aug. 9, 2006), physicist who, in 1958, discovered what came to be called the Van Allen belts, two zones of electrically charged particles that surround Earth. The outer belt traps particles that erupt or stream from the sun. The inner belt catches particles released by Earth's atmosphere by cosmic rays, high-energy particles from outer space.

■ Kristina Vaicikonis

DRUGS

The United States Food and Drug Administration (FDA) approved 18 new drugs in 2006 and 7 more as of April 2007. In 2006, the FDA also allowed the manufacture of 71 new versions of existing drugs, including different doses, different forms, and different combinations of drugs already on the market. In addition, the agency approved 371 *generic medications* (less expensive copies of brand-name drugs).

Vaccine to prevent cervical cancer. In June 2006, the FDA approved a vaccine that prevents infection by four types of the sexually transmitted human papillomavirus (HPV), a known cause of certain types of cervical cancer. According to data from clinical trials, the vaccine, called Gardasil, is effective at preventing cervical cancer in nearly 75 percent of women. Gardasil is known to be effective for at least three and a half years but may require a booster after that.

The FDA approval was the result of a 20-year, multibillion-dollar research drive spearheaded by the National Cancer Institute, an agency of the National Institutes of Health in Bethesda, Maryland; Merck & Co., Inc., of

A VACCINE FOR ALL GIRLS?

A nurse administers the new human papillomavirus (HPV) vaccine to a 14-year-old girl. The vaccine—the world's first to prevent certain types of cervical cancer—was approved by the U.S. Food and Drug Administration in June 2006. The U.S. Centers for Disease Control and Prevention in Atlanta, Georgia, recommended that all girls ages 11 to 12 and any female aged 13 to 26 who had not been previously vaccinated receive the injection. However, calls for mandatory vaccination of all young women attending public junior high schools, middle schools, and high schools stirred controversy throughout the United States.

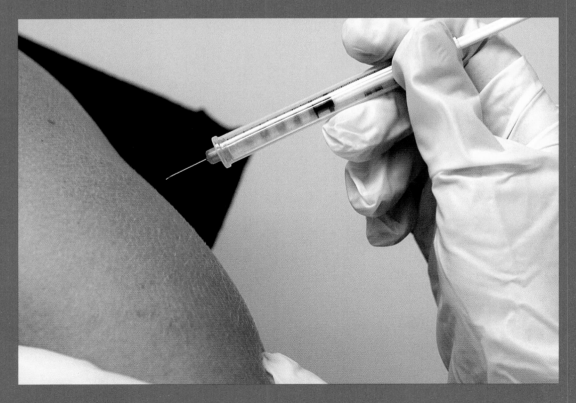

Whitehouse Station, New Jersey; and London-based GlaxoSmithKline PLC. At the molecular level, the vaccine consists of a ball-shaped assemblage of 360 proteins that mimics the exterior of the HPV and triggers the body's immune response. In March 2007, GlaxoSmithKline submitted an application to the FDA for approval of its proprietary version of the HPV vaccine, to be branded as Cervarix.

Anticancer medications. In June 2006, the FDA approved the drug dasatinib (sold under the brand name Sprycel) to treat patients suffering from chronic myeloid leukemia who have developed resistance or intolerance to other anticancer drugs. Chronic myeloid leukemia is a disease primarily of the elderly, and survival rates are relatively low, due in part to the tendency of older patients to develop resistance to cancer-suppressing drugs.

In October 2006, the FDA approved vorinostat (sold under the brand name Zolinza), the first in a new class of anticancer drugs called histone deacetylase inhibitors (HDI's). Researchers believe that HDI's turn off genes that promote rampant cell growth. Vorinostat specifically targets a rare skin cancer called cutaneous T-cell lymphoma and is designed to be used when the cancer returns after other treatments have become ineffective. Many researchers believe that HDI's offer the promise of therapies that could treat a wide variety of cancers while minimizing side effects.

In March 2007, FDA approval of the chemotherapy drug lapatinib (sold under the brand name Tykerb) added another weapon to the arsenal against advanced breast cancers, which are typically aggressive cancers. The drug specifically targets a protein called HER-2, which is overproduced by about one-fourth of all breast cancer tumors. In clinical tests, lapatinib in combination with another anticancer drug, capecitabine (sold under the brand name Xeloda), delayed tumor growth for approximately twice as long as capecitabine used alone. Trials also indicated that lapatinib was an effective replacement for another HER-2-specific anticancer drug, trastuzumab (sold under the brand name Herceptin), when patients develop resistance to that medication. Data from clinical trials also suggested that lapatinib may be effective in treating other types of cancer and in preventing recurrence of breast cancer after initial surgery, but further research would be required to develop those applications.

New HIV medications. In June 2006, the FDA approved darunavir (sold under the brand name Prezista) to treat people infected with the human immunodeficiency virus (HIV), which causes AIDS. Darunavir is a *protease inhibitor.* It blocks production of *protease,* an enzyme that the HIV virus needs to replicate itself within human cells. A variety of protease inhibitors have been available for some time to treat people infected with HIV, but the virus tends to become resistant to a particular drug over time. Medical experts said that darunavir would give a new option to HIV patients whose drug therapies were failing.

In July 2006, the FDA approved a three-in-one pill to treat HIV-infected people in the United States. The pill, called Atripla, combined the existing HIV medications Emtriva, Sustiva, and Viread. Medical experts predicted that the streamlining of medication schedules made possible by the combined, three-in-one pill would result in positive outcomes in a higher percentage of HIV patients.

In September 2006, the FDA approved posaconazole (sold under the brand name Noxafil) to treat oropharyngeal candidiasis (OPC), a fungal infection of the mouth and throat. OPC occurs in people with compromised immune systems, such as cancer patients who have received extensive chemotherapy, transplant patients taking immunosuppressive drugs, and HIV-infected patients. In such persons, invasive fungal infections such as OPC can be life-threatening. Other drugs are available to treat invasive fungal infections, but these are ineffective in some people or become ineffective over time.

Macular degeneration treatment. The first drug shown to improve vision in patients with macular degeneration received approval from the FDA in June 2006. The drug, ranibizumab (sold under the brand name Lucentis) is injected directly into the eye in a series of monthly treatments. Age-related macular degeneration (AMD) is a leading cause of blindness in people over 55 years of age. In a form of the disease called wet macular degeneration, vision is impeded by abnormal growth of blood vessels in the eye and their subsequent leakage of blood. Injectable ranibizumab interferes with the activity of a particular protein that is essential for new blood vessels to form. In clinical trials, 95 percent of subjects maintained their level of vision, and 40 percent experienced improvement of vision.

Contraceptive implant. The FDA in July 2006 approved Implanon, an implantable

DRUGS continued

contraceptive device. Implanon is a slender rod 4 centimeters (1.6 inches) long that is surgically implanted just below the skin in a woman's upper arm to provide protection against becoming pregnant for up to three years. The implant steadily releases tiny amounts of progesterone, the female sex hormone. The release of the hormone tricks the woman's ovaries into retaining eggs rather than releasing them into the womb for conception. When marketed in mid-2007, Implanon was the only implantable contraceptive available in the United States.

Other new drugs. The FDA approved the hypertension drug aliskiren (sold under the brand name Tekturna) in March 2007. Hypertension, or high blood pressure, affects one-third of all adults in the United States and can lead to life-threatening conditions such as heart attack or stroke. Aliskiren can be used either alone or in combination with other hypertension medications. According to data from clinical trials, aliskiren controls blood pressure twice as long as most other medications—up to 24 hours on one dose.

Also in March 2007, the FDA approved eculizumab (sold under the brand name Soliris), the first-ever prescription drug for treatment of paroxysmal nocturnal hemoglobinuria (PNH), a rare blood disorder. In persons with PNH, red blood cells develop abnormally, then are broken down by body systems designed to maintain a normal, healthy population of red blood cells. This process leads to harmful concentrations of hemoglobin and other materials in the blood. The new treatment does not cure PNH but blocks the breakdown of red blood cells and prevents the secondary effects caused by extensive destruction of red blood cells.

Soliris, marketed by Alexion Pharmaceuticals Corporation of East Hanover, New Jersey, won FDA approval as an *orphan drug,* a product designed to treat a small percentage of the population. (PNH affects about one person in 1 million.) Under the orphan drug program, the FDA provides incentives, including special patent protections, to companies to develop and market treatments for small populations.

■ Robert Knight

See also **CHEMISTRY.**

ECOLOGY

What role does *predation* (predatory behavior) play in the way that organisms interact with each other and their environments? Organisms are classified according to their places in food webs. Their roles include primary producers (plants), herbivores (the eaters of plants), decomposers (organisms that feed on dead organic material), and predators (organisms that eat other organisms). Because most ecosystems contain many, many organisms, their interactions are complex and often difficult to study. However, in the Nov. 10, 2006, issue of *Science,* zoologists Jacqueline T. Ngai and Diane S. Srivastava of the University of British Columbia in Vancouver, Canada, illuminated the role of predators in *nutrient recycling,* the movement of nutrients through the ecological web. The scientists did this by studying a very simple ecological system—that which includes bromeliads.

Bromeliads are a large family of tropical and subtropical plants, the best-known members of

which are Spanish moss and pineapples. Members of one group of bromeliads, the tank-formers, create an aquatic environment by tightly interlocking their leaves to form chambers that fill with rainwater and become small ecosystems. These aquatic ecosystems can include living insects as well as *detritus* (debris) made up of dead insects, leaves, and anything else that might fall in. In the system studied by these scientists, the major predator was the damselfly (*Mecistogaster modesta*). Damselfly larvae feed on other insects in a bromeliad chamber; the other insects feed on detritus. The productivity of such bromeliads is limited by the amount of nitrogen that is available. Nitrogen becomes available with the digestion or decay of detritus.

Before the work of Ngai and Srivastava began, it was generally believed that predators decreased nitrogen recycling by consuming and lowering the number of decomposers. However, in this system, the predators actually increased nitrogen recycling, making more nitrogen available to the bromeliads. The scientists say that, normally, when the insect decomposers emerge from their *pupal* (referring to the stage in the life of an insect between the larval and the winged adult stage, when the insect is usually enclosed within a tough casing) cases as adults and fly away from the bromeliad, they take a lot of nitrogen with them in their bodies. Predators, by killing the decomposers, keep them within the bromeliad for recycling. The nitrogen gets back to the bromeliad with the decay of either the decomposers themselves or the fecal droppings of the predators. The scientists think that this process in bromeliad ecosystems can be

BIODIVERSITY BUILDS STRONG ECOSYSTEMS

An experimental plot containing 4 species of flowering prairie plants (foreground) is less productive than adjacent plots (middle, left; middle, right) containing 8 and 16 species of plants, respectively. Researchers at the University of Minnesota and the University of Nebraska reported conclusively in June 2006 that ecosystems containing many plant species are more productive and survive adverse conditions better than plots with less biodiversity.

ECOLOGY continued

generalized for other, larger ecosystems—for example, a wetland in which migratory birds leave seasonally, much like the insects emerging from pupae.

Plant productivity. Many plants produce seeds in very large quantities, but not every year; however, trees in the same area tend to be coordinated in their seed production. The result is a boom and bust cycle of seed production that is called *seed masting.* Ecologists believe that masting is a way in which plants control the numbers of seed eaters around them. The theory is that seed eaters' populations cannot grow too large because they do not have a steady, dependable source of food (seeds). Rather, seed production is unpredictable. Seed eaters can produce many young when the mast crop comes in, but they must start from low numbers and cannot keep up with the large seed production, thus allowing many seeds to escape being eaten so they can grow into new trees. By the time the plants mast again, seed eaters will have again declined. A research study published in the Dec. 22, 2006, issue of *Science* calls this theory into question.

The research was carried out by biologist Stan Boutin at the University of Alberta in Edmonton, Canada, and colleagues of his at several other Canadian, American, and European universities. The scientists studied American and European red squirrels (*Tamiasciurus hudsonicus* and *Sciurus vulgaris,* respectively), two similar species. Rather than finding that the squirrels increased breeding after the trees masted, the researchers found that the squirrels increased breeding in anticipation of the masting by the trees. In other words, the squirrels had more litters and produced more young before masting so that population numbers were high when the seed crop appeared, not afterward. For example, before masting took place, female squirrels mated and were pregnant with their second litters before they had weaned their current litters—an unusual sequence of events.

The scientists ruled out other explanations for the squirrels' breeding behavior by very careful analysis of large data sets from both the squirrels and the masting trees in Europe and North America. Although the researchers do not know how the squirrels can anticipate upcoming masting by the trees, they point out

this amazing coevolutionary process: Trees mast to protect their seeds from large populations of seed eaters; the seed eaters then learn to predict when masting will occur in order to circumvent the strategy of the trees. This process of one species evolving, which forces another species to evolve in order to keep up, is what ecologists call *coevolution.*

Three-way mutualism. Interactions within ecosystems can take the form of *mutualism* (close dependence on each other) rather than predation. With predation, the predator benefits but the prey loses; with mutualism, both organisms benefit. In the Jan. 26, 2007, issue of *Science,* Luis M. Márquez of the Plant Biology Division of the Samuel Roberts Noble Foundation in Ardmore, Oklahoma, and his colleagues, as well as researchers at the University of Washington in Seattle, described a three-way mutualism that confers heat tolerance on a plant.

The scientists studied the grass *Dichanthelium lanuginosum* growing in high soil temperatures in Yellowstone National Park (primarily in northwestern Wyoming). The plants can grow in soils as hot as 65 °C (149 °F). The grasses that can tolerate high temperatures grow with a *symbiotic* fungus; in this case, the fungus *Curvularia protuberata* grows within the grass plant itself in a mutualistic interaction. (Symbiosis describes an association of two different organisms for the benefit of one or both of the organisms.)

The scientists found that when the fungus was absent, the grasses died at the high temperatures in which they normally can thrive. Then the researchers discovered a virus living symbiotically with the *Curvularia* fungus. They named the virus *Curvularia* thermal tolerance virus. Subsequently, they did experiments on plants that had fungi with and without virus present. In all experiments, it was the virus that conferred the heat tolerance on the plants, not the fungus. When the virus was present in the fungus, the plants were heat tolerant; when the virus had been killed off, the plants could no longer tolerate the heat. When the virus was reintroduced into the fungus within the plants, heat tolerance was restored. Although the exact mechanism of interaction is unknown, it is clear that the virus provides heat tolerance to the plant.

■ Robert Tamarin
See also **BIOLOGY; CONSERVATION.**

ENERGY

Research related to fossil fuel exploitation in 2006 and 2007 focused on extracting fossil fuels, such as oil, from more challenging locations and developing technology that will allow fossil fuels to burn more cleanly, releasing fewer pollutants and other gas emissions into the atmosphere.

In September 2006, engineers drilled through more than 6,096 meters (20,000 feet) of rock below the seafloor of the Gulf of Mexico to successfully extract oil from a test well. Located 282 kilometers (175 miles) offshore, the Jack 2 reservoir lies 8 kilometers (5 miles) below the surface of the gulf. Despite its promising flow rate of more than 6,000 barrels of crude oil per day, the Chevron Corporation of San Ramon, California, notes that the oil from the new reservoir could cost three to four times as much to extract as oil from land-based and shallow-water locations. The discovery does, however, lend credibility to the theory that wells in such deep-water locations could produce crude oil in large volumes, an idea experts have been skeptical about.

Germany took steps in May 2006 to curb greenhouse gases produced by burning traditional fossil fuels. In partnership with Vattenfall AB of Stockholm, Sweden, construction began on the world's first coal-fired power plant that does not produce carbon dioxide emissions. Located in Spremberg in eastern Germany, the plant will utilize oxyfuel combustion, a process in which the coal is burned in nearly pure oxygen rather than in air. The resulting nitrogen-free emissions can be concentrated to an almost pure stream of carbon dioxide. The carbon dioxide gas is then compressed so that it is transformed into liquid. This liquid is then transported through pipelines to a storage facility underground. The only emissions emerging from the stacks of the power plant consist of harmless water vapor.

Approximately 35 percent of the energy in the coal used in the oxyfuel process is turned into electric power. If the pilot plant proves viable, Vattenfall plans to build a larger, 300-megawatt facility by 2015. The pilot plant, which is scheduled to begin operation in 2008, is

 SEE ALSO SCIENCE STUDIES, RENEWABLE ENERGY, PAGE 100.

expected to produce only 30 megawatts of electric energy.

Wind energy. Researchers at Sandia National Laboratories in Albuquerque, New Mexico, and Knight & Carver (K&C) of San Diego have designed a new wind-turbine (large windmill that resembles an electric fan) blade specifically for use at low-wind sites. The first Sweep Twist Adaptive Rotor (STAR) was tested in San Diego in January 2007. The researchers planned to produce more blades by April 2007 so they could be tested on a turbine in Iowa.

NUCLEAR FUSION MARCHES ON

A scientist kneels inside the Tokamak Fusion Test Reactor vacuum vessel at the Princeton Plasma Physics Laboratory in Plainsboro, New Jersey, before the reactor was successfully disassembled. The test reactor was one of a series of international projects designed to test the viability of producing electric power from nuclear fusion. In March 2007, construction began on the International Thermonuclear Experimental Reactor in southern France—the most advanced and powerful fusion reactor ever built—with a design similar to that of the Princeton experimental reactor's.

ENERGY continued

The gentle sweep of the curved tip of the STAR turbine blade allows it to twist more than traditional designs during turbulent weather conditions. This flexibility reduces the number of repairs and replacements needed for the wind turbine. It also enables longer blades, which improves the efficiency rate at which wind is turned into energy— capturing from 5 to 10 percent more energy than shorter turbines.

Solar energy. Research on *photovoltaic power* (electric energy generated when acted upon by radiant energy such as from the sun) broke new records in December 2006 when a multifunction concentrator solar cell produced by Spectrolab Incorporated, a Boeing Company, located in Sylmar, California, achieved a conversion efficiency of 40.7 percent. Most solar cells have an efficiency of only 12 to 18 percent.

The record-breaking Spectrolab cell is a multijunction solar cell, made up of layers within individual cells. Each layer captures part of the sunlight passing through the cell. This allows the cell to get more energy from the sun's light. Additionally, an optical concentrator allows cells to capture more intense sunlight, thus increasing the whole cell's energy efficiency. The multijunction solar cell holds great promise for commercial application of solar energy. It allows for the collection of large amounts of energy in hopes of reducing consumers' reliance on fossil fuels or their need to supplement solar power with fossil fuels.

Nuclear energy. In March 2007, engineers in southern France began building the advanced Jules Horowitz Reactor (JHR), which will be used to test and evaluate advanced nuclear technologies. Beginning in 2014, the plant is expected to operate for 50 years, within a complex of research facilities that will also house the International Thermonuclear Experimental Reactor (ITER), the most advanced and powerful *fusion* (the action or process of combining two atomic nuclei to produce a nucleus of greater mass) reactor ever built. Fusion is the source from which the sun and stars derive their energy. While scientists have long known how to produce fusion on Earth, they have yet to find a way to harness that power to produce electricity. Currently, the favored approach involves creating an ultrahot *plasma* (atomic nuclei lacking their electron shells) and containing it within a

magnetic field (the space around a magnet in which its power of attraction is effective). The ITER project, which is designed to demonstrate such a concept, is scheduled to be completed in about 10 years.

Biofuels. A 55-megawatt power plant in Benson, Minnesota, fueled by tons of turkey droppings, along with wood chips and sawdust, was set to begin operations in July 2007. Officials with Fibrominn LLC, established by Fibrowatt LLC of Newton, Pennsylvania, which built the facility, say the plant will burn about 635 million kilograms (700 thousand tons) of waste from turkey processing per year and is expected to produce enough electric power to supply 50,000 homes. The plant is the first large-scale facility of its kind in the United States. During the process, dried manure is burned to heat a water boiler. The boiler creates steam that runs the turbine, creating electric power. Detractors of the project remind consumers that the process is labor-intensive, due to the difficulty of preparing the manure for burning, and that containing the foul odors associated with it will be costly. The plant, however, is just one of five projects the company is currently planning in the field of litter-fired plants.

Wave and tide energy. Marine power joined the list of alternative and renewable energy sources as interest in wave energy grew in the first years of the 2000's. The world's first commercial wave farm was scheduled to begin producing electric power in the summer of 2007 off the coast of Portugal. In the United States, the first utility-scale wave project, off the coast of Oregon, won preliminary federal approval in 2007. America's first tidal energy project became operational in December 2006 when two underwater turbines were installed in New York City's East River. The three-bladed turbines, which resemble wind turbines, are made by Verdant Power LLC of Arlington, Virginia. In April 2007, Verdant added four more 35-kilowatt turbines. Company scientists began working on a next-generation design that was to be cheaper to mass-produce. They hoped to eventually install a farm of at least 100 turbines at the East River site.

■ Tom Clynes

See also **CLOSE-UP: FINDINGS OF THE INTERGOVERNMENTAL PANEL ON CLIMATE CHANGE.**

ENGINEERING

Scientists at Cornell University in Ithaca, New York, have created a nano-sized lamp. The lamp is in the form of a fiber 200 nanometers in diameter. Imagine splitting a hair of your head into 400 pieces lengthwise; each would be the size of the nanolamp, because human hair is approximately 80,000 nanometers wide. In the February 2007 issue of *Nano Letters,* researchers reported that the nanolamp emits orange light when 3 to 4 volts are applied across two micro-sized electrodes. Not only does the nanolamp emit light, it is also flexible. These characteristics hold great promise for many applications, such as sensors, microscopy, and flat-panel displays.

As cell phones, laptop computers, flat-panel displays, and MP3 players shrink in size, there is an increasing need to innovate technology to reduce electronic parts to nanometer size. Such technology is also useful for medical procedures. The nanolamp is one example of the current thrust in nanotechnology, as well as a demonstration of close collaboration between experts in different areas of sciences and engineering. The Cornell team, led by Harold Craighead, director of the Nanobiotechnology Center, consisted of nine researchers from applied physics, chemistry, materials science, and engineering.

The fibrous nanolamp is made by a process called electrospinning. The technique is similar to pouring syrup on a rotating pancake with a high-voltage current being applied across the syrup and the pancake, explained José Moran-Mirabal, one of the researchers on the nanolamp team. In this case, the pancake is a surface with micron-sized patterns of gold electrodes, and the syrup is a metal complex–polymer mixture in a solvent. When the syrup is poured, the solution forms fibers as the solvent dries. The fibers then travel down onto the flat pancake. The fibers emit orange light when a voltage is applied across the gold electrodes, producing the nanolamp.

Robotic surgery. In 2007, researchers reported advances in the use of robotic tools for surgical procedures, including new applications, a greater sense of touch during surgery, and systems that allow doctors to operate remotely. The introduction of robotics in medicine gives surgeons greater control and precision during surgeries. Patients experience less pain because robotic surgery is less invasive, replacing large surgical cuts with small incisions for miniature robotic arms.

In July 2006, researchers at the University of Minnesota in Minneapolis reported robotic surgery for cardiac cell therapy. Doctors and scientists used robotic tools to deliver stem cell treatment to repair a damaged heart in pigs. "In people with heart failure, open surgery can be risky; finding a minimally invasive technique to deliver cell therapy to the damaged cardiac tissue would reduce the risk to patients," said Doris A. Taylor, professor of physiology. Robotic tools can inject stem cells into a precise location without stopping the heartbeat. This procedure would have tremendous benefit for patients with heart failure.

Successful robotic surgery was also performed in patients needing multiple bypasses. In

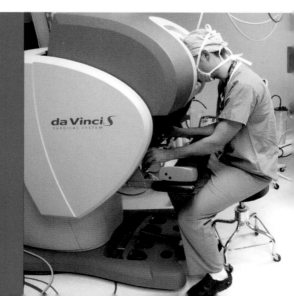

ROBOTS IN THE OPERATING ROOM

A nurse adjusts a robotic surgical system prior to heart surgery in November 2006. The machine, equipped with surgical arms with operating instruments attached, is part of a trend toward using robots to perform various surgical procedures. Robots allow surgeons to perform very precise maneuvers with greater control through smaller incisions than those required in traditional surgery performed through direct contact with a surgeon's own hands.

ENGINEERING continued

October 2006, at the University of Maryland Medical Center in Baltimore, surgeons made three small incisions to perform multiple-vessel coronary artery bypass surgery. Small instruments and a three-dimensional, high-resolution camera were placed inside the patients, allowing surgeons to maneuver robotic arms to perform the bypass. The robotic arms enabled the surgeons to carry out complex motions and reach areas that are normally accessible only with open-heart surgery. But open-heart surgery has greater risk for infection. Using the robots reduces this risk, and the patients who undergo robotic-assisted bypass surgery have shorter recovery time—four days hospital stay versus six days for tradition bypass surgery.

Despite the obvious benefits of robotic surgery, doctors have reported the absence of a sense of touch as they are operating through a set of mechanical arms, which hinders their dexterity and their ability to feel different substances within a patient's body. In November 2006 at Johns Hopkins University in Baltimore, engineers reported new ways to give doctors more "feel" during robotic surgery. The research team, led by Kim Okamura, designed a prototype for a mechanical device that gives touchlike sensations. For example, the device used different light signals to indicate the proper amount of force surgeons need to tie a suture. Developments in the materials sector are also improving this aspect of robotic surgery.

In May 2007, surgeons Mika Sinanan and Andrew Wright of the University of Washington's Medical Center and Thomas Lendvay of Children's Hospital and Regional Medical Center in Seattle remotely operated a robot that performed surgery in an underwater capsule off the coast of Florida. The capsule, part of NASA's Extreme Environment Mission Operations Project (NEEMO) simulates a spaceship. The surgeons in Seattle maneuvered the robot

A TRAIN TO THE TOP OF THE WORLD

The Sky Train rumbles through the 1,686-meter (5,532-foot) tunnel in Kunlun Mountain—the longest tunnel through frozen soil in the world—on its journey from Golmud, Qinghai Province, China, to Lhasa, the capital of Tibet. Also know as the "Rocket to the rooftop of the world," the train travels on the world's highest passenger railroad, which reaches an elevation of 4,905 meters (16,093 feet). Oxygen must be pumped into the train's compartments to ensure that passengers do not become ill from altitude sickness at the heights at which the train travels.

to test the feasibility of sending remote-controlled surgical robotic systems into space. The mission included four crew members inside the underwater capsule to assemble the robot and the three surgeons working in front of a computer in Seattle.

In Seattle, the doctors used rubber to simulate skin during the experiment. The keystrokes and images of the suturing motion were transmitted along an Internet connection to and from the robot in the underwater capsule and the computer on land. This robotic technology allows surgeons to operate from a distance. The technology could be applied to perform surgery on wounded soldiers on battlefields or on patients in remote areas and developing countries that lack hospitals and health care.

New materials. The global search for renewable energy requires the development of new materials to produce efficient plastic solar cells that are inexpensive and lightweight. In April 2007, researchers at Wake Forest University in North Carolina announced the development of plastic solar cells that can convert sunlight to electricity at about 6 percent *efficiency* (surplus of output energy when accounting for the amount of input energy). Plastic solar cells formerly had an efficiency of about 3 percent. Although traditional silicon solar panels have an efficiency rate of 12 percent, they are large, heavy, and difficult to

SUPER-THIN SOLAR POWER

Rick Hess, president of Konarka Technologies, Inc., in Lowell, Massachusetts, holds a strip of Power Plastic, a flexible plastic solar cell strip. The strip can be wrapped around portable electronic devices—and even woven into power-producing clothing—to generate electrical power directly from sunlight or indoor light. Power Plastic consists of plastic film that looks much like photographic film. Nanoscale particles of the semiconducting chemical titanium dioxide are applied to the film and then coated with a light-sensitive dye. When light strikes the dye, the particles generate electricity. The product, which was demonstrated in July 2006, weighs less and is less expensive to produce than silicon-based solar cells.

conform to different shapes. The new plastic solar cells were made by embedding nano-sized fibers within another plastic that absorbs light. This design allows more light to be collected by the device. The team hopes to increase the plastic solar cells' efficiency closer to 8 percent in order to make them marketable for roofing tiles, building facades, or the roofs of trains and other vehicles.

In June 2006, scientists created a material called a nanosheet that has the sensitivity of human skin. Hundreds of times thinner than a strand of human hair, the sheet could be used to cover the surface of a surgical instrument or a robotic hand, for example, to mimic the sensitivity of touch. The nanosheet was developed by Vivek Maheshwari at the University of Nebraska in Lincoln and Ravi Saraf at the Virginia College of Osteopathic Medicine in Blacksburg. They made the skinlike sheet by dipping a sensor into a solution of microscopic particles that then adhered to its surface. The researchers tested their idea by dropping an object onto the nanosheet; the force of the impact resulted in an electrical current that caused the affected areas of the sheet to light up. Because this sensitive sheet can detect different forces, it has the potential to identify different types of tumors, gallstones or kidney stones, and other masses within the body—an added value for robotic surgery.

■ Irene Y. Tsai

ENVIRONMENTAL POLLUTION

Reproduction in wild mussels, a shellfish growing in United States waters, may be at risk as a result of exposure to commonly used antidepressants, such as fluoxetine hydrochloride (sold under the brand name Prozac), according to a study presented at the Society of Environmental Toxicology and Chemistry in Montreal, Canada, in November 2006. Released in the urine of patients being treated for depression, antidepressants are only partially removed from wastes in sewage treatment plants. The study showed that as a result, these drugs, along with dozens of other medicines, end up in lakes, rivers, streams, and oceans into which sewage treatment plants discharge their treated wastes. Here, the drugs can alter reproduction and other biological functions in a potentially wide range of aquatic species, the researchers said.

To test the effects of fluoxetine on reproduction in freshwater mussels, researchers from North Carolina State University in Raleigh and the National Institute of Standards and Technology in Charleston, South Carolina, exposed pregnant female zebra mussels to various concentrations of the drug in a controlled laboratory experiment. They found that pregnant females exposed to levels similar to those found in surface waters released mostly viable offspring. Those exposed to the highest levels of fluoxetine, however, released very few viable young.

Although the mussels in this study responded adversely only to concentrations of fluoxetine much higher than those encountered in surface waters, researchers pointed out that, in nature, mussels are typically exposed to numerous antidepressant drugs for long periods. Multiple, prolonged exposure, researchers speculate, could negatively affect female mussels, they contend.

Less estrogen in treated water. Two research teams report findings that could help cities and towns improve operations at sewage treatment plants to remove the myriad drugs, such as antidepressants, and natural substances, such as estrogen, that are present in human wastes. These compounds often escape removal in sewage treatment plants and are subsequently released into waterways, where they can have a multitude of negative effects on aquatic organisms.

One team, led by Kung-Hui Chu, an environmental engineer at Texas A&M University in College Station, isolated a bacterium in sewage treatment plants that completely breaks down estrogen derived from human urine. The study was reported in the Jan. 15, 2007, issue of *Environmental Science and Technology*.

Although the bacterium is present in sewage treatment plants, natural estrogen is only partially broken down in these facilities. Low levels of estrogen commonly found in waters downstream from sewage treatment plants have been shown to dramatically alter reproduction in several species of fish. The researchers hope to find ways to increase the population of the estrogen-destroying bacteria in sewage treatment plants to reduce the release of this biologically active chemical into surface waters.

Another team, led by Nancy W. Shappell and colleagues at the U.S. Department of Agriculture's Agricultural Research Center in Fargo, North Dakota, is exploring the possibility of estrogen removal using artificial wetlands. Placed at the discharge point of sewage treatment plants, artificial wetlands could allow additional microbial degradation that could greatly reduce estrogen levels in the discharge. This research team also published its study in the January 15 issue of *Environmental Science and Technology*.

The researchers studied a small pig farm at North Carolina's Agricultural and Technical State University in Greensboro, where waste was treated in artificial wetlands. The researchers found that artificial wetlands reduced estrogen concentrations by 83 to 93 percent after a 20- to 50-day retention period.

Some sewage treatment plants currently use artificial wetlands to remove wastes containing nitrogen from human sewage. Some scientists contend that this technology could reduce natural and perhaps even synthetic estrogens from birth control pills and a host of other medicines that are currently released into surface waters.

Flame retardants in fish. Flame retardants and other similar, persistent chemicals are rapidly accumulating in marine fish and mammals. This accumulation could have a negative effect on these animals' reproduction, according to a study presented at the November 2006 meeting of the Society of Environmental Toxicology and Chemistry.

Researchers at the State University of New York at Albany and the Florida Fish and Wildlife Conservation Commission measured levels of flame retardants in the marine food chain. These chemicals, known as polybrominated diphenyl ethers (PBDE's), are used to treat fabrics items, such as pajamas and curtains, to reduce their flammability. They are becoming widely dispersed in the environment.

The researchers found low levels (43 parts per billion) in prey species, such as ocean perch. In predatory fish and mammals that feed on these and other prey species, however, the researchers found disturbingly high levels of PBDE's. Concentrations averaged 750 parts per billion in sharks and nearly 1,200 parts per billion in dolphins. The researchers also found that concentrations of another persistent synthetic group of chemicals, polychlorinated biphenyls (PCB's)—once used in electrical insulators—were even higher. Concentrations were 25,800 parts per billion in sharks and 162,000 parts per billion in dolphins. Researchers are concerned about the potential effects of these chemicals on reproduction and fetal development of predatory fish and mammals, especially since the concentrations are doubling every two to four years in bull sharks and bottlenose dolphins.

Lead in swans. Trumpeter swans in the Pacific Northwest may be dying from lead poisoning, according to another study reported at the Society of Environmental Toxicology and Chemistry in November 2006. Since 1999, 2,100 trumpeter swans—about 15 percent of the population in northwest Washington and southwest British Columbia—have perished. The vast majority of these birds, researchers report, died as a result of ingesting lead shotgun pellets.

Like many other birds, swans require grit to grind their food in the *gizzard,* a special compartment located in the digestive tract before the stomach. Grit breaks down food much as teeth do in mammals. Swans typically ingest small pebbles along with their food. In their winter grounds, swans forage in hunting areas where lead shotgun pellets may occur in high concentrations. The swans ingest the pellets along with pebbles and, researchers found, eventually succumb to lead poisoning.

More than 1,700 birds were autopsied, said team member Laurie Wilson of Environment Canada in Gatineau, Quebec, and contained an average of 22 lead pellets. About 4 percent of the birds had at least 100 pellets.

CHINA FACES POLLUTION WOES

Children at a school in Lanzhou in China's Gansu province wear masks to protect themselves from pollution generated by nearby factories. In April 2007, the chief economist of the Paris-based International Energy Agency forecast that before the end of the year, China would outpace the United States as the world's largest emitter of greenhouse gasses.

ENVIRONMENTAL POLLUTION continued

Although banned nationwide from use in Canada in 1999, lead pellets persist in the soil. Researchers hope to identify lead hot spots within the foraging grounds of the birds' winter habitat and bury or remove the lead.

Polar bears and PCB's. Danish and Canadian researchers reported in August 2006 that exposure of polar bears to several persistent chemical pollutants caused the *gonads,* the male and female organs that produce sperm or eggs, to shrink. These pollutants are acquired through the food chain and could have long-term negative effects on reproduction in polar bears, a species also threatened by global warming as Arctic ice melts. The bears inhabit the ice during the winter as it provides access to food sources, such as seals.

Researchers collected the gonads from 55 male and 44 female polar bears killed legally by subsistence hunters in eastern Greenland. They then correlated gonad size to the concentration of three persistent chemicals: PBDE's and the insecticides DDT and chlordane. The researchers found that the length of the testes decreased with increasing concentrations of these chemicals. This relationship was especially prominent in young males. The researchers found that the size of the ovaries also declined with increasing concentrations of these chemicals.

DDT and chlordane have been banned in many countries, including the United States and many European nations, because of their toxic effects on human beings and other species. Some PBDE's are banned in Europe but legal in most of the United States. Although banned or restricted, these synthetic organic chemicals persist in the environment because there are no naturally occurring microorganisms capable of breaking them down. In addition, these chemicals are stored in the fat of organisms that ingest them and are passed up the food chain. Their concentrations are highest in organisms at the top of the food chain.

Researchers believe that polar bears could suffer further decline as a result of exposure to these chemicals. Some scientists speculate that these same chemicals may also account for the well-documented decline in human sperm counts in many countries.

Mercury hot spots. Mercury, a pollutant released by coal-fired power plants, tends to accumulate in certain regions, creating toxic hot spots. To identify mercury hot spots, David C. Evers and his colleagues from the BioDiversity Research Institute in Gorham, Maine, measured mercury levels in yellow perch and common loons in the northern United States and southern Canada.

In their study, published in the January 2007 issue of *BioScience,* the researchers identified five mercury hot spots: the Androscoggin and Kennebec rivers in Maine, the Merrimack River that courses through Massachusetts and New Hampshire, the Adirondack Mountains in New York State, and central Nova Scotia in Canada.

The researchers attributed the high levels of mercury to the proximity of these areas to coal-fired power plants used to generate electric energy, but also to wind currents and rainfall patterns that deliver the pollutants to these regions and landscape features that influence rainfall patterns. High concentrations of mercury from extensive use of coal could be detrimental to the wildlife that inhabits these regions and also to any human population that receives its drinking water from them.

Chemical disrupts egg development. Exposure to a chemical found in some plastics, called bisphenol A, alters the genetic makeup of eggs in female offspring of mice while they are developing in their mother's uterus, according to a study published in *PLoS Genetics* in January 2007. Bisphenol A is added to polycarbonate plastic, a hard plastic used to make baby bottles and water bottles. It is also used to line steel and aluminum cans.

Bisphenol A has been shown to adversely affect reproduction in adult male and female mice. In the new study, by Patricia Hunt and her colleagues at Washington State University in Pullman, the researchers implanted tiny pellets containing bisphenol A in pregnant mice and then studied the effects on the eggs of their female offspring. Up to 40 percent of the eggs in exposed mice contained abnormal numbers of chromosomes, compared to 3 percent in the control group.

Abnormal chromosome numbers may result in spontaneous abortion and genetic defects in surviving offspring. Bisphenol A is commonly found in human adults in concentrations of several parts per billion.

■ Daniel Chiras

See also **CLOSE-UP: FINDINGS OF THE INTERGOVERNMENTAL PANEL ON CLIMATE CHANGE.**

FOSSIL STUDIES

Beautifully preserved fossilized *embryos* (animals in the early stage of development before birth or hatching) are found in late Proterozoic-Era (about 580 million years old) phosphate-rich mineral deposits in Doushantuo, China. In June 2006 paleontologists Jun-Yuan Chen of the Nanjing Institute of Geology and Paleontology at the Chinese Academy of Science in Nanjing, China, and David J. Bottjer of University of Southern California in Los Angeles, reported important new information on these fossils that links them to the world's earliest animals.

On the embryos, the paleontologists recognized distinct *lobes* (rounded projecting parts). These features are associated with early development in which cells later form specialized structures in the animal when it reaches adulthood. This type of developmental pattern is seen in *mollusks* (snails, clams, and squids) and *annelids* (segmented worms). Mollusks and annelids are considered *complex animals* (multicellular), and this makes the fossilized embryos an extraordinary find. They indicate the presence of complex organisms at least 40 million years before they were previously thought to have evolved during the so-called *Cambrian explosion,* a period of very rapid appearance of many major groups of animals in the fossil record about 543 million to 530 million years ago (the Cambrian Period).

Further investigation of the embryo fossils was reported in October 2006 by paleontologist James W. Hagadorn of Amherst College in Amherst, Massachusetts. Hagadorn and several colleagues were able to see internal structures and count up to 1,000 individual cells using

X-ray photography. They also found evidence of *asymmetrical* cell division (resulting in cells of unequal size) in some embryos—a feature typical of multicelled animals.

Because small, soft-body forms do not usually leave fossil records, paleontologists have debated whether animal groups, such as mollusks and annelids, really originated during the Cambrian Period or whether they occurred earlier. With the identification of lobes and X-ray imaging of the embryo fossils, evidence supports the argument that complex animals like mollusks and annelids appeared before the Cambrian Period.

The world's oldest tree. In April 2007, a group of paleontologists headed by Linda VanAller Hernick and Frank Mannolini of the New York State Museum of Albany, New York, reported on their reconstruction of a nearly complete fossil tree. The tree, a species from the genus *Wattieza,* was created from fossilized bits of the

PREHISTORIC JAWS

The bite of a great white shark would have been no match for a fish that swam in the oceans more than 400 million years ago and probably grew to 10 meters (30 feet) in length. Scientists have determined that the heavily armored *Dunkleosteus terrelli* could clamp its jaws with a force of 5,000 newtons (1,100 pounds per square inch). By comparison, *Tyrannosaurus rex* had a biting force of about 13,000 newtons (3,000 pounds per square inch). Scientists were able to make these determinations by creating a biomechanical model of the ancient fish after studying its fossil remains.

FOSSIL STUDIES continued

tree found in rock from the Middle Devonian Period (about 385 million years ago), near Gilboa, in the Catskill region of eastern New York.

The first time the ancient tree became newsworthy was in 1870, with the discovery of fossilized stumps during the construction of a reservoir along Schoharie Creek in Gilboa—about 16 kilometers (10 miles) from the location of the recently reconstructed tree. Although the tree stumps had been known for nearly 140 years, the size of the trees and their foliage remained unknown.

Scientists had estimated that the tree must have been at least 8 meters (25 feet) tall and had palmlike branches with fernlike foliage, rather than rounded leaves typical of most modern trees. The ancient tree developed before *conifers* (trees that reproduce with cones, such as pine). During the Devonian Period, the ancient tree grew in the floodplains of rivers that flowed from the Acadian Mountains in what is today eastern New York State and New England. The trees probably reproduced with *spores* (material that bursts from within a capsule in a primitive form of plant reproduction) and lived rooted in ancient soils. In 2004, these assumptions were proved to be on target with the finding of fossilized remains of branches and a tree trunk. For three years, VanAller Hernick, Mannolini, and their team painstakingly excavated fossilized bits of the tree and pieced them together.

Wattieza is believed to have been part of a great evolutionary change in which forests were beginning to dominate. Paleontologists have suggested that the rise of forests during the Middle Devonian Period may have impacted land animals by providing a greater source of food in the form of leaf litter. In addition, because trees extract carbon dioxide, they remove this *greenhouse gas* (a gas that warms the atmosphere by trapping heat of solar radiation reflected from Earth's surface) from the atmosphere. This action may have helped to cause an interval of global cooling in the Carboniferous Period (from 354 million to 290 million years ago), which occurred after the Devonian Period.

Carboniferous coal swamp of Illinois. In April 2007, *paleobotanist* (a scientist who studies ancient plants) William DiMichele of the Smithsonian Institution in Washington, D.C., and several colleagues described the remains of an ancient tropical swamp forest preserved in mudstones above a coal seam. The swamp was revealed

within the roof of a large, underground coal mine near Georgetown, Illinois, during mining activities. The swamp fossils, remains of plants, were from the Late Carboniferous or Pennsylvanian Period (about 300 million years ago) and were preserved in fine-grained mudstones. The variety of fossilized plants included ferns, shrubby horsetails, and giant trees that once grew to heights of more than 30 meters (100 feet).

DiMichele believes that the plants were preserved as a result of ancient flooding of the low coastal swamp by a shallow sea. The salty seawater killed the plants, which then fell to the seafloor and were buried by the deposits of muddy sediments from nearby rivers. Over time, the layers of peat below the mudstones formed coal through extreme heat and pressure; the plants above remained buried in mudstone. These conditions provided an ideal environment for the preservation of the swamp vegetation.

Because of the rapid preservation, the fossils are believed to be in about the same location as they were when they were living plants. This has allowed paleontologists to reconstruct the ecology of the ancient coal swamp. By studying the fossils, the scientists are finding that the organization of the ancient coal swamp is similar in some ways to that of modern, living rain forests.

Amber discoveries. The year 2006 proved to be a significant period for discoveries in *amber* (a hardened yellowish-brown gum, the resin of fossil trees). In June 2006, entomologists Enrique Peñalver and David Grimaldi of the American Museum of Natural History in New York City and paleontologist Xavier Delclòs of the University of Barcelona in Spain reported the rare discovery of amber containing remnants of spider silk with attached prey. Spider silk is almost unknown in the fossil record. The amber represents a blob of resin from a conifer tree that fell on and engulfed a spider web before hardening. The amber specimen was collected from sediments from the Early Cretaceous Period (about 110 million years ago) in the Aragon region of northeastern Spain. The strands of silk are so well preserved that they still show small droplets of glue that the spider secreted to help trap its prey. Although the spider itself was not present, a few of its victims were stuck to the silk, including a mite, a fly, a beetle, and the leg of a wasp. This unusual fossil proves that more than 100 million years ago, some spiders made vertical webs to trap prey, just as their living relatives do today.

In September 2006, John J. Flynn, a paleontologist with the American Museum of Natural History, reported an amber find exposed in the banks of the Amazon River in Brazil. This petrified resin, only the third known occurrence in South America, is from the Miocene Epoch (from 24 million to 19 million years ago). It preserved a variety of animals, including some species of insects and other *arthropods* (joint-legged animals), and 30 species of plants, as well as fungus and bacteria fossils. These fossils indicate conditions similar to those of the present Amazon rain forest, suggesting that the tropical forest ecosystem seen today may already have existed in the Miocene.

In October 2006, paleontologist and amber specialist George O. Poinar of Oregon State University in Corvallis and entomologist Bryan N. Danforth of Cornell University in Ithaca, New York, reported the discovery of the most ancient, well-preserved fossil bee found in amber. The amber, discovered in Myanmar (formerly Burma), was dated from the Early Cretaceous Period. This fossilized bee provides indirect evidence of bee-pollination of flowers. The structure of the bee's legs shows that it was capable of transporting plant pollens in the same manner that is used by modern-day bees.

One of the oldest amber samples found to date was revealed in December 2006 by paleontologist Alexander Schmidt of Humboldt University in Berlin, Germany. The amber, which was found in the Dolomite Mountains of northern Italy, is about 220 million years old (the Triassic Period).

A microscopic view of the amber revealed that it held the fossils of a number of microorganisms, including bacteria, simple green algae, a *ciliate protozoan* (a single-celled organism that moves via hairlike structures), and an *ameba* (a single-celled organism that moves via fingerlike structures called pseudopods). These findings, in numbers and proportions, are very similar to what would be found in a sample taken from a moist forest environment, such as wet bark. This led the scientists to conclude that very little has changed within microbe ecosystems of moist forest environments over the past 200 million years.

Two-headed champsosaur. Throughout nature there is evidence that *genetic mutations* cause abnormalities, such as an extra finger on a person's hand. (Genetic mutations are changes within a gene or chromosome of animals or plants resulting in the sudden appearance of a new or duplicated feature.) These types of mutations are not limited to modern organisms, as was seen in December 2006 in the fossilized remains of a juvenile champsosaur (also called choristoderan). Paleontologist Eric Buffetaut of the Centre National de la Recherche Scientifique in Paris reported finding a two-headed champsosaur within volcanic sediments from the Early Cretaceous in northeastern China. This unusual specimen represents a rare preservation of a mutation. The 7-centimeter (2.8-inch) juvenile champsosaur possesses two fully formed heads and two necks that split at the trunk of the dinosaur's body. This small fossil was preserved in the remains of a fossilized nest, surrounded by several other reptile fossils. Similar mutations are widely observed in modern reptiles, including snakes, but they are rare and have never been previously seen in fossils.

Pygmy and giant dinosaurs. Animals that are isolated on small islands may undergo rapid evolutionary change that results in new, small species. This phenomenon, referred to as the Lilliput effect (from the tiny inhabitants of the island of Lilliput in Jonathan Swift's 1726 novel, *Gulliver's Travels*), has been observed in elephants, possibly people, and now in dinosaurs. In June 2006, paleontologist P. Martin Sander of the University of Bonn in Germany reported dwarfism in a Jurassic sauropod.

Sauropod dinosaurs included the largest animals to ever walk on land, among them *Apatosaurus*, *Brachiosaurus*, and *Diplodocus*. Most of these dinosaurs were from 20 to 30 meters (65 to 98 feet) long and some weighed over 90,000 kilograms (100 tons). Sander and his colleagues describe a new small sauropod, *Europosaurus holgeri*, based on 11 well-preserved skeletons from Late Jurassic marine sediments found in northern Germany. *Europosaurus* adults were only about 6 meters (20 feet) in length. By studying the structure of the bones, the paleontologists determined that these animals were dwarfs because of a slowing down of the normal growth rate. This process led to small adults. Sander and his colleagues also determined that these animals apparently lived on a small island less than 200,000 square kilometers (124,274 square miles) in an area in the Saxony Basin of present-day Germany. The island would not have provided enough plant food to support normal, gigantic sauropods. *Europosaurus* adapted to the limited food resources of the island through dwarfism.

In contrast to the pygmy dinosaurs are newly discovered sauropod bones reported in December 2006 by paleontologists Rafael Royo-Torres, Alberto Cobos, and Luis Alcalá of Foundation Conjunto Paleontologico in Teruel,

FOSSIL STUDIES continued

Spain. These dinosaur remains from the Jurassic-Cretaceous boundary (about 115 million years ago) include a humerus (upper arm bone) that is about 1.8 meters (5.9 feet) long. Based on these findings, the paleontologists estimate that the sauropod weighed from 40,000 to 48,000 kilograms (88,185 to 105,821 pounds). This is the largest known dinosaur from Europe and one of the largest in the world. It belongs to a primitive family of the sauropod group, which had not previously been known to include extremely large members. These bones show that the capacity for large size evolved more than once in sauropod history.

An ancient gliding mammal. The ability to glide from tree to tree using skin membranes can be seen in such animals as "flying squirrels" and flying lemurs. These animals stretch out a web of skin between their front and hind legs to catch air currents that allow them to glide.

In September 2006, paleontologist Jin Meng of the American Museum of Natural History described a newly identified ancient gliding mammal from the Late Jurassic or Early Cretaceous Period (about 150 million years ago) in Inner Mongolia, in northern China. This animal, about the size of a squirrel, belongs to a primitive and previously unknown group of mammals and is not closely related to any of the gliding mammals alive today. The fossil shows that the animal had a relatively large *patagium* (wing flap) on each side of its body. Its teeth were highly specialized, with high, cone-shaped cusps that seem to have been adapted for biting insects. The small, furry animal is more than 70 million years older than the next oldest gliding mammal and indicates the independent evolution of gliding ability.

■ Carlton E. Brett

See also **GEOLOGY.**

BIG AND LITTLE SAUROPODS

Sauropods like the one in this artist's re-creation lived approximately 150 million years ago. These large *herbivores* (plant eaters) typically had long necks, small heads, long tails, and thick legs. They were the largest dinosaurs and the largest land animals to ever live. Most sauropod species ranged in size from 20 to 30 meters (65 to 98 feet) and weighed as much as 90,000 kilograms (100 tons). New discoveries in 2006 revealed both the smallest known sauropod—only 6 meters (20 feet) long—and one of the largest—weighing from 40,000 to 48,000 kilograms (88,185 to 105,821 pounds).

GENETICS

Neandertals have been extinct for many thousands of years, but in November 2006, two groups of scientists provided a first look at their genetic makeup by analyzing *DNA* recovered from fossil bones. (DNA, deoxyribonucleic acid, is the molecule genes are made of.) Svante Pääbo, a geneticist at the Max Plancke Institute in Leipzig, Germany, led one group. Paabo had previously worked with Allan C. Wilson of the University of California at Berkeley, a pioneer in the use of ancient DNA to study extinct organisms. Edward M. Rubin, the head of the United States Department of Energy's Joint Genome Institute in Walnut Creek, California, led the other group.

To get the Neandertal DNA, both groups used pieces of a bone belonging to a Neandertal that lived about 38,000 years ago. They chose this particular bone specimen, designated Vi-80, after preliminary tests showed that it contained reasonably high levels of amino acids, the building blocks of proteins. This meant that it was also likely to have usable DNA. The scientists were also concerned about the possibility that the fossil material might be contaminated with DNA from modern human beings. Fortunately, compared with several others that they tested, the Vi-80 specimen showed a very low level of contamination.

With this material in hand, both groups set out to recover Neandertal DNA and study its precise makeup by determining the sequence of its individual chemical subunits. In DNA, there are four different chemical subunits (called bases), which are strung together inside each gene in a certain order, like four letters that can be rearranged to spell out different words.

Although the two groups of scientists were working with material from the same bone specimen, each group used different methods to study the DNA. The group led by Rubin began with a traditional approach—creating what is known as a library by introducing small segments of the Neandertal DNA into individual bacterial cells. Each individual segment of DNA was then analyzed in detail using a new method called *pyrosequencing.* In this method, pulses of light are used to detect which of the four possible bases are found strung together in a segment of DNA. Rubin's group was able to analyze about 65,000 bases in the Neandertal DNA.

SEE ALSO THE SPECIAL REPORT, **THE LATEST BUZZ ABOUT HONEY BEES,** PAGE 42.

Pääbo's group used a new method to prepare the DNA recovered from the bone material. Instead of bacterial cells, they used tiny beads, each of which carried one individual segment of DNA. After making copies of the DNA on each bead, Paabo's researchers also used pyrosequencing to rapidly determine the order of the bases in the DNA. In the end, they were able to identify more than 1 million bases of Neandertal DNA.

Although many scientists were excited by these successes, both groups acknowledged that this work was only the beginning, The human *genome* (the complete set of genes in a cell) is made up of more than 3 billion individual bases of DNA, so even the 1 million bases identified by Pääbo's group could provide only a limited comparison. They did, however, show that at least some of the DNA came from the Y *chromosome,* which meant the bone had to be from a male. (A chromosome is the physical structure in a cell that carries a gene. Only males have a Y chromosome.) Ultimately, the scientists hoped that when more Neandertal material was available, it would provide a better understanding of the relationship between modern human beings and this ancient group.

Autism Genome Project. The first results from the Autism Genome Project, an international effort to identify genes that contribute to autism, were announced in March 2007. Bernie J. Devlin of the University of Pittsburgh in Pennsylvania and Stephen W. Scherer of the Hospital for Sick Children and the University of Toronto in Toronto, Canada, are leading this project. Another project studying the genetic basis of autism, led by Jonathan Sebat and Michael Wigler of the Cold Spring Harbor Laboratory in New York, also announced its findings.

People affected with autism typically show impaired social and communication skills as well as other disordered behavior. Males are affected about four times more often than females. Only about 10 percent of autism cases

GENETICS continued

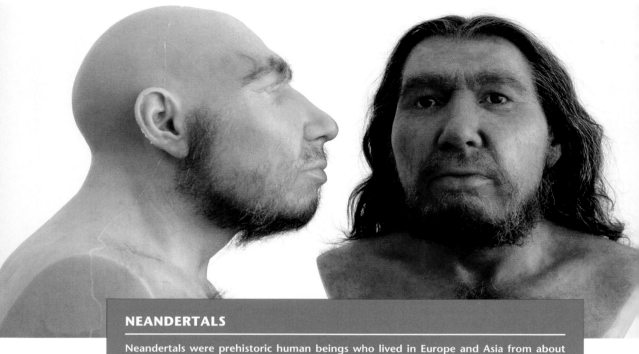

NEANDERTALS

Neandertals were prehistoric human beings who lived in Europe and Asia from about 150,000 to 35,000 years ago. Many scientists classify Neandertals as an early subspecies of *Homo sapiens,* the species of modern people. However, other scientists think they belong in a separate species, *Homo neanderthalensis.* Neandertal adults stood about 165 centimeters (5 feet 4 inches) tall. They had strongly built bones and muscular bodies. Neandertal skulls were large and differed from those of modern people by having a large, projecting face; a low, sloping forehead; and a *browridge,* a raised strip of bone across the lower forehead. The Neandertal jaw also lacked a chin. The models of a Neandertal head shown here illustrate these characteristics.

have a known cause; several agencies have organized research efforts to identify genes that may contribute to this disorder.

The scientists working on the Autism Genome Project studied individuals from more than 1,000 families that had at least two people affected with some form of autism. To identify genetic changes that might be common to affected people, the researchers used a method called *genome scanning.* In this method, genetic material from each individual is analyzed using DNA chips. Each chip contains 10,000 different possible variant forms of genes. Using this approach, the scientists found that genes in one particular region of chromosome number 11 were implicated.

They also found that genes that produce proteins known as neurexins seemed to be involved in autism. Neurexins are found at the junctions where nerve cells connect to transmit signals back and forth between the brain and other parts of the body.

The group led by Sebat and Wigler used a different approach. The researchers compared genetic material from people, both affected and unaffected, with genetic material from their parents. The scientists found changes in certain portions of the genetic material of affected people that they classified as *candidate regions* for further investigation. Their next step is to look closer at the actual genes found in these candidate regions. Most scientists view these results as a promising start but acknowledge that much more work must be done to discover genes that contribute to autism.

Other genome news. The Honeybee Genome Sequencing Consortium announced the complete deciphering of DNA making up the genome of the honey bee (*Apis mellifera*) in October 2006. The consortium is a large international group of researchers led by George M. Weinstock of the Baylor College of Medicine in Houston, Texas, and Gene Robinson of the University of Illinois at Urbana-Champaign. The honey bee is not the first insect to have its genome completely analyzed; other insect genomes analyzed previously include *Anopheles gambiae,* the malaria-carrying mosquito, and the fly *Drosophila melanogaster,* which is often used in genetic research. However, the honey bee represents the first time that an insect with such a sophisticated form of social structure has had its genome analyzed. In a honey bee hive, each individual has a defined position, ranging from the queen, the egg producer, all the way down to workers with specific jobs such as foraging for food or defending the nest. Honey bees also are known to be able to communicate critical information to other members of the hive using elaborate dances and possess a remarkable ability to recall the locations of flowers with good supplies of nectar.

Scientists hope that the complete set of genetic information from the honey bee will shed some light on the genes that either control or help to shape these behaviors. Although the analysis is not yet complete, the researchers have already learned that honey bees have a large number of genes that are designed for detecting odors and using nectar. They have fewer genes for tasting ability and some types of immune protection, compared with other insects. Finally, some of the honey bee genes that control behaviors known as circadian rhythms appear to be quite sophisticated and different from those of other insects. Circadian rhythms are like biological clocks that determine patterns of daily activities such as waking and sleeping.

Scientists hope to understand how worker bees are able to carry out sophisticated tasks for the hive despite having relatively tiny brains. The researchers also believe that it will now be easier to learn why some African honey bees are more aggressive than other bees.

Wilms tumor gene. The discovery of a gene that may be responsible for a large number of cases of Wilms tumor was announced in February 2007 by a group of researchers led by Miguel N. Rivera and Daniel A. Haber of Massachusetts General Hospital and Harvard Medical School in Boston. Wilms tumor is the most common form of pediatric kidney cancer.

To find this gene, the researchers used a method called *genome-wide scanning* to analyze large amounts of genetic material obtained from tumors of patients with this form of cancer. The researchers discovered that part of one chromosome (the X chromosome) was missing in 5 of the 26 specimens from tumors of male patients. A closer look showed that, in each case, one specific segment of the X chromosome was missing. This segment contained just one gene, which the scientists designated WTX for *Wilms tumor on the X*. The researchers suspected that the WTX gene belongs to a class of genes known as tumor suppressor genes. These genes normally play a role in preventing cancers from occurring. If the WTX gene were lost, as would be the case if that segment of the X chromosome were missing, its protective function would also be lost.

Tumor suppressor genes are also found on other chromosomes. In these cases, people normally have two copies of each gene. Cancers are thought to occur only when both copies of the gene are lost or knocked out. However, because the WTX gene is on the X chromosome, the situation is different. Human males have just one X chromosome (paired with a Y chromosome) in each cell, and so the loss of just this one copy can lead to problems. Human females have two X chromosomes, but very early in female development, one of the X chromosomes becomes nonfunctional in each cell. This means that both males and females have the same number of working copies of any gene on this chromosome. Further analysis of tumor specimens from female patients showed that, in several cases, mutations were present in the WTX gene on the functional X chromosome. This meant that the female patients, too, had lost the protective function of this gene.

Although problems with this gene do not explain all cases of Wilms tumor, the critical role that this gene plays in at least a substantial number of cases has led researchers to suspect that problems with other genes on the X chromosome may play an underappreciated role in a wide range of human cancers. As was shown for WTX, it may be that just one mutation in a gene on the X chromosome is enough to initiate events that lead to the formation of cancers in both males and females.

GENETICS continued

Premature birth gene. In September 2006, a research group led by Jerome F. Strauss III of Virginia Commonwealth University in Richmond announced the discovery of a gene that may be responsible for a large number of premature births among African American women. Premature births have long been recognized to be two to three times more common among African American women compared to women of European origin. This disparity does not appear to be due to differences in socioeconomic status or access to health care. The specific type of premature birth looked at in this study is known as preterm premature rupture of membranes (PPROM). This is a condition that occurs when the *amniotic sac* (a membrane containing fluids that surrounds the fetus) breaks prematurely. PPROM accounts for about one-third of all premature births. The study carried out by this research group suggests that many of these premature births can be explained by the fact that African American women are more likely than other groups to have a certain version of a specific gene.

The gene identified by this research group as potentially responsible is known as SERPINH1. Genes represent a set of instructions for how to make proteins, and this particular gene makes a protein known as heat shock protein 47. In cells, heat shock proteins often work as chaperones for other proteins to ensure that they are properly folded or protected from being damaged. This particular heat shock protein (designated hsp47) chaperones collagen. Collagen is a fibrous protein that, among other things, gives strength to structures in the body, including the amniotic sac.

The role of the SERPINH1 gene in creating collagen had been described previously, but in this new study, the researchers considered how one particular version of this gene might contribute to the high incidence of premature birth in African American women. This version has a mutation that affects the amount of the heat shock protein it can produce. The researchers showed that this specific version of this gene, designated SERPINH1-656 T, is less active than normal. They also showed that certain African American women—specifically, women with ancestors from the west African country of Sierra Leone—were much more likely to have this

THE MARSUPIAL THAT ROARED

The gray, short-tailed opossum may be small in stature, but it is a big player among laboratory animals used to study the causes of human diseases. It is the first *marsupial* (a mammal whose young are born in an extremely immature state) to have the entire structure of its *DNA* (its hereditary material) decoded and analyzed. The detailed study of the biochemistry of this small animal is part of a larger study to compare the genomes of a variety of animals to that of humans. This information will help scientists better understand human evolution by comparing regions in the DNA structure of humans versus opossums and determining which have changed little over time and which have changed rapidly. Also, detailed analysis of the opossum genome will allow medical researchers to improve experiments in which the animal is used as an experimental model of human systems.

particular version of the gene than other women. The researchers speculated that women carrying the less-active version of the gene are also more likely to have amniotic sacs that are weaker because they have less collagen. During pregnancy, their amniotic sacs are thus more susceptible to breakage earlier than normal.

Many scientists were intrigued with this study because it appeared to represent a case where a genetic variant associated with ethnic background, called an *ancestry informative marker,* seemed to be helpful in pinpointing the mutation. Others cautioned that focusing on racial differences is fraught with potential social problems. They also believe that better prenatal care for members of all ethnic groups might be more effective than genetic research in resolving these issues.

Dog size gene. The discovery of a gene that appears to play a major role in determining the size of dogs was announced in April 2007 by a research group led by Elaine Ostrander of the National Institutes of Health in Bethesda, Maryland. The researchers began their study by looking at Portuguese water dogs. They chose these dogs because a wide range of different-sized animals has been produced within this breed.

To identify a specific gene (or genes) that might be responsible for these size differences, the researchers focused on the genes from a section of chromosome number 15. They had previously shown that genetic differences somewhere on this part of the chromosome were strongly associated with size differences among a large collection of Portuguese water dogs from a single, well-characterized *pedigree.* (A pedigree is a record of the ancestors of an animal or plant and their traits.) By analyzing the genetic material from 463 dogs within this pedigree, the researchers found one particular gene that showed consistent differences in small dogs compared with large dogs. The gene they identified is known as insulinlike growth factor 1 or IGF1.

Although it is not clear how this gene may ultimately determine body size in dogs, the researchers note that this same gene has previously been shown to be associated with body size in both people and mice. Since dog varieties show the greatest range of size variation of any living species, the researchers are optimistic that this work will provide a greater understanding of the role that genes play in determining body size.　■ David Haymer

See also **MEDICAL RESEARCH.**

GEOLOGY

Until the 2000's very little was known about climatic conditions in the Arctic Ocean in the distant past. During the summer of 2004, the Arctic Coring Expedition (ACEX) used a fleet of icebreakers and an icebreaker drill ship to recover cylindrical cores of sediments from Lomonosov Ridge. The ridge is a long, narrow, submarine feature crossing the Arctic Ocean from Greenland to Siberia, rising about 3,500 meters (11,500 feet) above the deep seafloor to depths as shallow as 954 meters (3,130 feet) beneath the sea surface. The drilling took place near the North Pole.

Scientific results from the study of samples taken by the expedition began to be reported in 2006. *Paleobotanist* (a biologist who studies ancient plant life) Henk Brinkhuis of the University of Utrecht in the Netherlands and other members of the expedition reported one of the most intriguing results in the June 1, 2006, issue of *Nature.* They found evidence that the surface waters of the Arctic Ocean were fresh during an

800,000-year period in the Middle Eocene, about 50 million years ago. The evidence came from fossils of a plant, Azolla, that today is found in standing water in ponds, swamps, and rice paddies in tropical and warm temperate regions.

Azolla is a tiny fern that floats on the surface of water with its roots hanging below. In some layers of the sediment, both the leaves and spores of this plant occurred in enormous abundance. Brinkhuis believes that there were large mats of these tiny ferns floating on the surface of the Arctic Ocean. The water temperatures must have been at least 10 °C (50 °F) for these plants to have grown in such profusion.

During the Middle Eocene Period, the area of the Arctic Ocean with fresh surface waters was about 14 million square kilometers (5.4 million square miles). This is 170 times as large as today's Lake Superior, which has an area of about 82,400 square kilometers (31,820 square miles). This was probably the largest area of fresh water that has ever existed on the surface of Earth.

GEOLOGY continued

Ancient El Niño. Did Earth experience permanent El Niño conditions from 5 million to 3 million years ago? The term *El Niño* refers to an unusual condition that develops periodically in the Pacific Ocean. The name, which originated in South America, refers to the Christ child, since Christmas is when this oceanographic change often starts. Most of the time, the waters of the tropical Pacific are cold in the east, along the coasts of South and Central America, and warm in the west, off the coast of China. This normal situation is referred to as La Niña. The cooler waters of the eastern Pacific rise from the deep ocean interior, *up-welled* (brought to the surface) by the trade winds that blow from east to west on either side of the equator.

REVERSING THE FLOW

A new study of sedimentary rock (rock formed when mineral matter or remains of plants and animals settle out of water) indicates that the world's second-largest river, the Amazon, once flowed from east to west—opposite its present-day direction. Two scientists from the University of North Carolina, Russell Mapes and Drew Coleman, crisscrossed about 80 percent of the Amazon basin collecting the mineral zircon from the river's sediment. This mineral can be dated to determine its age. They found zircons in the central part of South America along the Amazon that they determined came from the east because of their age. Rocks in eastern South America are much older than those on the western side of the continent. This is the result of geological activity that created the Andes Mountains that run along South America's western spine. The Andes are much younger than the east coast mountains and hills. The scientists concluded that between 65 million and 145 million years ago, the Amazon must have flowed east to west carrying the minerals from the older Atlantic coast to the center of the continent.

The three diagrams (right) show three stages of development of the Amazon River. In the top diagram, the river flows westward from an ancient ridge of highlands on South America's east coast—65 million to 145 million years ago.

The middle diagram—about 5 million to 23 million years ago—shows a new ridge of mountains (Purus Arch) that formed in the center of the continent. The river then flowed from this ridge eastward to the Atlantic. At the same time, other rivers flowed east and west between the Early Andes and the Purus Arch.

The bottom diagram shows the present day state of the Amazon Basin. The river flows east from the Andes across most of South America and empties into the Atlantic Ocean.

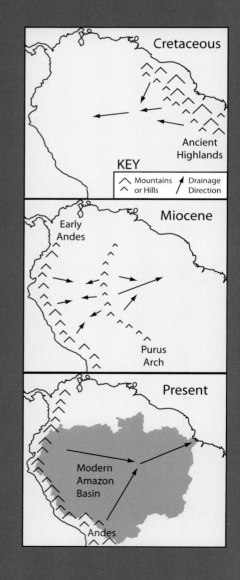

Cretaceous

KEY

Mountains or Hills — Drainage Direction

Ancient Highlands

Miocene

Early Andes

Purus Arch

Present

Modern Amazon Basin

Andes

From time to time, the trade winds lose their strength and, without the supply of cold water from below, the surface waters warm. This results in an El Niño, when the waters are warm on both sides of the Pacific. The rise in the temperature of the eastern Pacific affects the weather not only in western South America but also in North America and other parts of the world. During an El Niño, areas that are otherwise dry may experience a lot of rainfall, and areas that are usually wet may experience drought conditions.

In the June 9, 2006, issue of *Science*, geologist Alexey Federov of Yale University in New Haven, Connecticut, and a group of coworkers from other institutions in the United States compared records of sea surface temperatures for the eastern and western tropical Pacific back to 5 million years ago. The temperatures of the ancient ocean waters were determined from *alkenones,* chemical compounds made by marine organisms that lived in the surface waters. Certain alkenones are produced only when the temperature is within a narrow range. The researchers also examined the ratio of magnesium to calcium in the limestone shells of other organisms that lived near the surface. This ratio is also strongly dependent on temperature. They discovered that the east-to-west temperature difference across the Pacific did not come into existence until about 3 million years ago. They call the conditions that existed from 5 million to 3 million years ago a "permanent El Niño." When the temperatures of the eastern Pacific were warm, the average temperature of Earth was about 3 °C (5.4 °F) warmer than it is today.

No one is quite sure what caused the permanent El Niño, but some researchers have suggested that the *global thermohaline conveyor* was not working at this time. The global thermohaline conveyor is a deep-water current system that carries cold water from the polar regions to the tropics. The term *thermohaline* refers to the temperature and saltiness of the water. Cold, salty waters are denser than ordinary seawater. Today, cold, salty waters sink in the North Atlantic and flow in the depths through the South Atlantic down to the Southern Ocean that rings Antarctica. There, the deep flow turns left into the Indian Ocean and finally into the Pacific. Some of this water returns to the surface to cool the eastern Pacific. Fedorov's group argued that at the time of the permanent El Niño, the North Atlantic was warmer and fresher, and if the global

conveyor existed, it was very weak. Their paper has attracted a lot of attention, and some scientists speculate that the current period of global warming may result in a shift of the climate to conditions like those described by Fedorov's group.

Volcanic action in Ethiopia. Geologists believe that Earth's crust consists of a series of large, stiff rock plates. The plates grow along one side with the addition of volcanic material and are destroyed on the other side by sinking below an adjoining plate. This theory of plate tectonics explains many of the large features of Earth's surface. Most of the plate boundaries lie beneath the sea. The places where the plates are growing and material is being added are usually mid-ocean ridges, which typically lie at a depth of about 2,500 meters (8,200 feet) beneath the sea surface. However, there are two places where plates grow above sea level—in Iceland and in an area of northeastern Africa called the Afar.

The Afar, in Ethiopia, is one of the hottest and driest places on Earth. There, the plates are pulling Arabia apart from Africa. The largest on-land plate separation event ever observed occurred in the Afar in the fall of 2005. In the Aug. 15, 2006, edition of *Eos, Transactions, American Geophysical Union,* geologists Gezahegn Yirgu and Dereje Ayalew of the Department of Earth Sciences and geophysicist Atalay Ayele of the Geophysical Observatory of Addis Ababa University in Ethiopia described what had happened.

A series of 162 earthquakes, many of them around magnitude 5 (large enough to be easily felt and even cause some damage to buildings), began on Sept. 14, 2005, and continued until October 4. The quakes were centered along a 60-kilometer (37-mile) stretch of the plate boundary. On September 26, a volcanic vent 400 meters (1,300 feet) long, 80 meters (260 feet) wide, and 50 meters (165 feet) deep opened at a place called Da'Ure, and a column of black ash rose from it. Most of the ash fell close to the vent, but some was found 40 kilometers (25 miles) away. The later phase of the eruption was accompanied by a "boiling noise" that the geologists described as sounding like a helicopter. They believe this noise was from bubbling lava deep within the vent. The volcanic activity died away by October 15, but a survey of the region found that many fissures had opened in the ground and there had been movement of many of the faults.

GEOLOGY continued

Lakes under Antarctic ice. Lakes beneath the ice of Antarctica were first discovered about 20 years ago. Using radar, scientists have found more than 150 lakes beneath the glaciers since then. The largest, Lake Vostok, has an area of roughly 14,000 square kilometers (5,400 square miles), about the size of the state of Connecticut. Now scientists have discovered that these subglacial lakes play an important role in determining how the Antarctic ice moves.

In the Feb. 22, 2007, issue of *Nature,* geologist Robin E. Bell of Columbia University's Lamont-Doherty Earth Observatory in Palisades, New York, and several coworkers reported the discovery of a series of subglacial lakes in East Antarctica, having a total area similar to that of Lake Vostok. These lakes lie beneath the region where the Recovery Glacier ice stream starts its rapid descent toward the coast. The Recovery ice stream has its source in a very flat region about 2,500 meters (8,200 feet) high. It narrows as it descends toward the sea and attains flow velocities

of 100 meters (3,050 feet) per year while still 500 kilometers (300 miles) from the coast. The subglacial lakes act to lubricate the ice stream. When the bottom of the glacier meets the lake waters, it is able to move much more freely than when it is moving over rock, and it speeds up.

Because of the changes in the surface appearance of the ice, the existence of lakes had been predicted in this area. The water from subglacial lakes occasionally breaks out though cracks in the ice and may cause catastrophic floods. It is suspected that the lakes beneath Recovery Glacier are actively filling and draining, affecting the stability of the glacier. The Recovery glacial system is one of the most important in the Antarctic, delivering about 32 billion metric tons (35 billion tons) of ice to the ocean each year. If it became unstable, it could affect sea levels around the world.   ■ William Hay

See also **ATMOSPHERIC SCIENCE; FOSSIL STUDIES.**

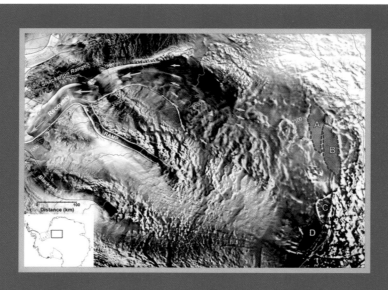

FAST FLOWING ICE

This National Aeronautics and Space Administration (NASA) satellite image of East Antarctica shows the location of the Recovery Glacier ice stream (arrows). Ice streams are fast-flowing regions within a glacier that move ice and melt water to the ocean. The image also pinpoints four lakes (A, B, C, and D) miles beneath the surface of the glacier that feed the ice stream and accelerate its movement.

MEDICAL RESEARCH

According to an analysis published in April 2007, breast cancer rates in women in the United States declined significantly between 2001 and 2004, and the drop seemed to be related to a decrease in the use of hormone replacement therapy (HRT). The analysis was performed by a research team led by Donald Berry, head of the Division of Quantitative Sciences at the University of Texas M. D. Anderson Cancer Center in Houston.

Many women use the female hormones estrogen and progesterone to manage hot flashes and other symptoms that are common during menopause. But in 2001, a major study called the Women's Health Initiative (WHI), sponsored by the National Heart, Lung, and Blood Institute in Bethesda, Maryland, showed an increased risk in such conditions as breast cancer, heart disease, stroke, and blood clots among postmenopausal women who were using HRT that included both estrogen and progestin. As a result of these findings, the WHI study ended in 2001. Subsequently, the number of prescriptions written for the two most commonly prescribed forms of HRT (which contained both estrogen and progestin) dropped from 61 million in 2001 to 21 million in 2004.

In early 2006, the National Cancer Institute (NCI) in Bethesda, released data showing that the rate of breast cancer in women declined by 6.7 percent from 2002 to 2003. This was in contrast to steadily increasing rates during the 1980's and 1990's. The research team also analyzed the period from 2001 to 2004 and found an average of 8.6 percent fewer cases of diagnosed breast cancer annually. However, this rate of change occurred mostly between the years 2001 and 2003. During the period from 2003 to 2004, there was essentially no change in the rate of breast cancer.

Based on these data, the investigators examined all the factors that could have played a role in the declining rates of breast cancer, such as mammogram screening and diet. The only factor that was significantly different was the use of HRT, which fell in 2002 and 2003. From 2003 to 2004, HRT use did not increase nor decrease. Also during this period, there was essentially no change in the number of breast cancer incidences.

Berry's team cautioned that its analysis did not prove a definitive link between HRT and the incidence of breast cancer. Proof of that link would require research involving randomized

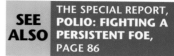

SEE ALSO THE SPECIAL REPORT, **POLIO: FIGHTING A PERSISTENT FOE,** PAGE 86

clinical trials in which one group of women used HRT and a control group did not.

Drug-eluting stents. Several studies published in 2006 and 2007 raised questions about the safety of drug-eluting stents. *Stents* are tiny, lattice-shaped metal tubes that are surgically placed in blood vessels that have become narrowed due to *atherosclerosis* (a build-up of deposits known as plaque). Stents hold the blood vessel open so that blood can flow through it.

Bare-metal stents are used to prevent arteries from becoming blocked again by plaque, a condition called restinosis. These stents, which were introduced in 1994, have reduced the rate of restinosis from 20 percent to 50 percent. *Drug-eluting stents* (stents that are coated with medications that help prevent the arteries from becoming blocked) were developed to reduce the rate of restinosis even further.

In 2003 and 2004, the United States Food and Drug Administration (FDA) in Washington, D.C., approved the use of drug-eluting stents. Drug-eluting stents quickly began to replace bare-metal stents. By 2006, an estimated 4 million people in the United States had a drug-eluting stent implanted in one or more arteries.

But in September 2006, the safety of drug-eluting stents was called into question during the World Congress of Cardiology/European Society of Cardiology annual meeting in Barcelona, Spain. Studies suggested that people who had received drug-eluting stents were slightly more likely to have a severe heart attack or die than those who had received bare-metal stents, because *thrombosis* (blood clots) occurred more frequently in blood vessels with drug-eluting stents.

In response, the FDA called a meeting of its Circulatory System Devices Advisory Panel in December 2006. The panel observed that about 60 percent of drug-eluting stents had been used in situations that were not included in the original safety trials and it was in these situations that complications most often occurred. The panel said that the benefits of drug-eluting stents appeared to be greater than the risks when the devices were used in situations that had been safety tested.

MEDICAL RESEARCH continued

The panel's recommendation that drug-eluting stents continue to be used judiciously was reinforced by the results of another study published in March 2007. Investigators led by Gregg W. Stone, assistant professor of medicine and cardiology at Columbia University Medical Center in New York City, reviewed data from four studies and found that stent thrombosis was more common after one year with drug-eluting stents than with bare-metal stents. However, the drug-eluting stents were more effective in preventing restinosis. Death and heart attack rates were essentially the same after four years of placement for both types of stents. Because drug-eluting stents are not without risk, the FDA and other researchers called for further study to ensure their safety and effectiveness.

DRUG-ELUTING STENTS

A stent releases medication into an artery to help prevent the artery from becoming reclogged with deposits called plaque. (Stents are tiny mesh tubes that are implanted into narrowed arteries to help expand the artery and allow greater blood flow.) Bare-metal stents, which were introduced in 1994, sometimes became overgrown with normal cells as the artery healed. Drug-eluting stents, which were approved by the FDA in 2003 and 2004, were thought to help prevent some of the overgrowth and subsequent renarrowing of the artery. However, in 2007, researchers reported that death and heart attack rates have remained essentially the same for people receiving either type of stent.

Drug-resistant tuberculosis. Tuberculosis (TB) is an infectious disease caused by the organisms *Mycobacterium tuberculosis* and *Mycobacterium bovis*. TB starts in the lungs but may spread to other parts of the body. Symptoms of TB include coughing, weight loss, fatigue, and loss of appetite. Without treatment, TB often leads to disability and death. Generally, TB can be cured by powerful antibiotics, if they are taken properly. But in the 1990's, new strains of TB that were resistant to these drugs appeared. These strains, called multi-drug resistant tuberculosis (MDR TB), could not be cured using standard treatments but required an intensive regimen of even more potent drugs, called second-line drugs. These second-line drugs are more toxic and expensive and may cause serious side effects.

Some cases of TB do not even respond to second-line drugs. TB that shows resistance to one or more second-line drugs is called extensively drug-resistant tuberculosis (XDR TB). In March 2006, researchers from the United States Centers for Disease Control (CDC) in Atlanta, Georgia, released data showing that the number

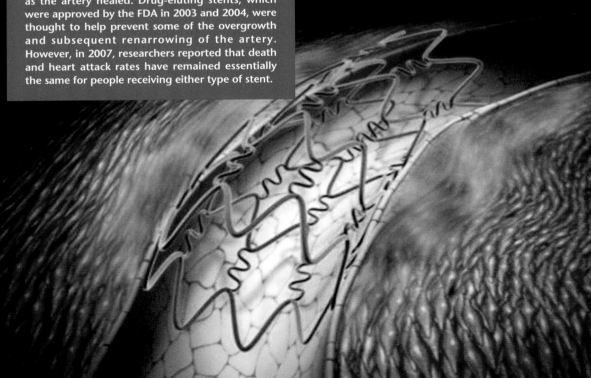

of XDR TB cases worldwide was growing rapidly. XDR had been found in South Africa, Europe, Asia, and North and South America. In an outbreak in a rural hospital in South Africa in early 2006, 536 cases of tuberculosis were confirmed. Nearly half (41 percent) were MDR TB, and of those, 24 percent were XDR TB.

The World Health Organization (WHO), based in Geneva, stated that drug-resistant TB develops when drugs are improperly prescribed, when patients take poor-quality drugs or not enough, or when a regular regimen of medication is not followed. Poverty, which severely impedes people's ability to get the drugs they need to fight TB, may also contribute to improper use of drugs and, thus, resistance.

The CDC's annual analysis of TB in the United States was published in April 2007. Data showed that the overall TB rate in the United States declined in 2006, while MDR and XDR TB continued to pose challenges. Between 1993 and 2006, 49 XDR TB cases were reported to the CDC. These XDR TB cases were spread across the country. These data suggest that the risk of XDR TB is low in the United States. However, researchers observed, because TB spreads easily from person to person, XDR TB would continue to pose a serious risk to the United States as long as it existed anywhere else in the world.

Effective detection and treatment of MDR and XDR TB are needed, said researchers from the CDC and WHO. In February 2007, WHO's XDR TB Global Task Force called for the development of new anti-TB drugs, better diagnostic tests, and international standards for testing TB strains for susceptibility to second-line drugs.

More secondhand smoke. According to the Office of the Surgeon General in Rockville, Maryland, there is no risk-free level of exposure to secondhand tobacco smoke. Nonsmokers exposed to secondhand smoke at home or work increase their risk of developing heart disease by 25 to 30 percent and lung cancer by 20 to 30 percent. The only way to protect nonsmokers from exposure to secondhand smoke is to eliminate smoking in indoor spaces.

These were some of the key findings of a comprehensive report on the effects of

RISKY BEHAVIOR

A mother holding a cigarette exposes her infant to the dangers of secondhand smoke. According to a report released by U.S. Surgeon General Richard H. Carmona in June 2006, infants and children exposed to secondhand smoke are at increased risk for sudden infant death syndrome, respiratory infections, ear problems, and asthma.

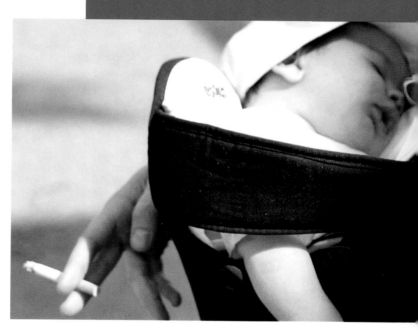

involuntary exposure to tobacco smoke issued in June 2006 by U.S. Surgeon General Richard H. Carmona. While regular reports had been issued by the Office of the Surgeon General addressing the health consequences of tobacco smoking since 1964, this was the first report since 1986 to focus solely on the effects of involuntary exposure to secondhand tobacco smoke.

As the adverse health effects of smoking became widely known starting in the mid-1980's, smoking decreased in popularity. In 2006, about 80 percent of adults in the United States were nonsmokers. But many millions of Americans were still exposed to secondhand smoke in their homes and workplaces. The risk appeared greatest for infants and children, whose bodies are still developing. Children exposed to secondhand smoke are at an increased risk for sudden infant death syndrome; respiratory infections, such as bronchitis and pneumonia; ear problems; and severe asthma.

MEDICAL RESEARCH continued

The surgeon general's report also reviewed the effects of brief exposure to secondhand smoke. Even brief exposure increased the risk of blood clots, raised blood pressure, allowed the build-up of plaque in arteries, and increased the risk of lung cancer. In 2005, exposure to secondhand smoke led to the deaths of 3,400 nonsmokers due to lung cancer.

The report also analyzed methods to create smoke-free environments. Several of the studies reviewed for the report showed that nonsmokers can be protected from exposure to secondhand smoke only by the elimination of smoking in indoor spaces. Nonsmokers are still exposed to secondhand smoke in buildings where smokers are separated from nonsmokers or where air cleaning or ventilation systems are installed. Operating a heating, ventilating, or air-conditioning system can distribute secondhand smoke throughout a building.

In 2006, approximately 30 percent of indoor workers in the United States were not covered by smoke-free workplace policies. People working in blue-collar or service industry jobs were less likely to work in a smoke-free environment, with restaurant workers being the least likely of all to be protected. Of the 6.6 million restaurant workers in the United States, only 43 percent were covered by smoke-free policies. Based on these findings, the surgeon general urged the creation of comprehensive policies, regulations, and laws to protect people against involuntary exposure to secondhand smoke.

Gene therapy for skin cancer. For the first time, researchers in 2006 used gene therapy to successfully treat cancer. A team of 16 investigators led by Steven Rosenberg, chief of surgery at the NCI, reported the details of the procedure in August.

Genes are the biological markers of heredity that determine traits such as eye color and height. Genes also contain the instructions for making specific proteins, including the proteins that affect the ability of immune system cells to fight disease. Gene therapy is an experimental treatment in which genes are inserted into cells to prevent or fight disease.

Rosenberg's study involved 17 people who had advanced *metastatic melanoma*, severe skin cancer that had spread throughout their bodies. Melanoma, the most serious and aggressive type of skin cancer, accounts for about 4 percent of all skin cancers. The American Cancer Society estimates that more than 60,000 cases of melanoma are diagnosed and almost 8,000 people die of the disease each year in the United States.

Earlier researchers had observed that some people produce *lymphocytes* (blood cells that fight infection) that attack and destroy cancer cells. Investigators had developed a method to use these naturally occurring lymphocytes to treat metastatic melanoma. In this method, the cancer-fighting lymphocytes are removed from the patient and grown in a laboratory. Meanwhile, the person undergoes radiation treatment to deplete their remaining normal lymphocytes. Then the cancer-fighting lymphocytes are reintroduced. Scientists have successfully treated some people using this method. However, it can be used only for melanoma and only in people who already have the cancer-fighting lymphocytes.

Rosenberg's team set out to create the cancer-fighting lymphocytes in cancer patients who did not naturally produce them. First, the scientists drew a small amount of blood from each person in the study. Then they infected the blood cells with a virus. When the virus entered the cells, it inserted genes that contained the information needed to express (build) specific proteins called T cell receptors (TCR's) into the cells' DNA. (DNA, deoxyribonucleic acid, is the molecule that is chiefly responsible for the transmission of inherited characteristics.) TCRs increase the ability of lymphocytes to attack cancerous tumors. Finally, the researchers injected the altered lymphocytes into the blood of patients in the study.

There were three groups of participants in the study. The first group of three people did not benefit from the treatment. Before trying the treatment in the second and third groups, the researchers were able to improve the treatment of lymphocytes in the lab so the lymphocytes were growing rapidly when they were introduced into the participants.

One month after receiving the infusion of TCR-expressing lymphocytes, participants in the second and third groups still had 9 to 56 percent of the altered lymphocytes in their blood. None of the participants experienced toxic side effects from the genetically modified cells. Two of the participants appeared to be cured by the treatment. In these patients, tumors that had spread to other parts of the body either disappeared or grew small enough to be removed. A year and a half later, both people were still alive and showed no signs of cancer.

The study suggested that gene therapy may become an important tool in treating advanced cancers of all kinds. However, the NCI investigators cautioned that their work was preliminary, partly because the study was limited to 17 people.

Pain killers and heart health. Combining a daily dose of aspirin with the popular painkilling medication ibuprofen may increase the risk of heart attack and death in people who have both heart disease and *osteoarthritis* (arthritis caused by the breakdown of the cartilage of the joints). A team led by Michael E. Farkouh, associate professor of medicine and cardiology at Mount Sinai School of Medicine in New York City, reported these results in February 2007.

Earlier studies had suggested that two types of drugs often prescribed for people with arthritis may increase the risk of cardiovascular events such as heart attacks, strokes, and sudden cardiac death. Drugs known as cyclooxygenase-2 (COX-2) inhibitors—medications that relieve pain and inflammation—came under scrutiny in 2004. Two drugs in that class, Vioxx and Bextra, were withdrawn from the market because they had caused cardiovascular problems in some patients. Other studies have suggested that nonsteroidal anti-inflammatory drugs (NSAID'S), including naproxen (sold as Aleve) and ibuprofen (sold as Advil or Motrin), may also cause cardiovascular problems.

However, little research had been done on the interaction between NSAID'S and aspirin in people with heart disease. Aspirin is often prescribed for people with heart disease to decrease the blood's clotting abilities and thus reduce the risk of blood clots, heart attacks, and strokes.

During the 12 months of the study, investigators tracked the cardiovascular health of 18,523 people older than 50 years of age. All the study participants suffered from osteoarthritis. Of the participants in the study, 16.6 percent had heart disease that placed them at high cardiovascular risk, and 83.4 percent were considered at low cardiovascular risk. Investigators compared

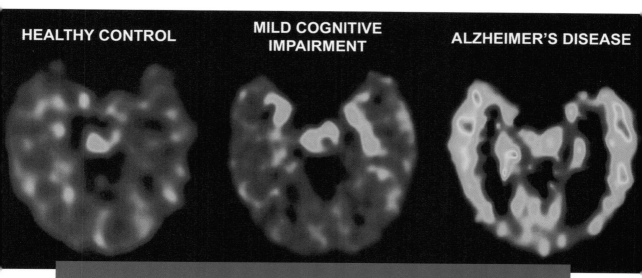

HEALTHY CONTROL   MILD COGNITIVE IMPAIRMENT   ALZHEIMER'S DISEASE

NEW WINDOW ON ALZHEIMER'S

Brain scans captured with a special form of positron emission tomography (PET) show the progression from a healthy brain to one affected by mild cognitive impairment to a brain with Alzheimer's disease (AD). (Mild cognitive impairment is a condition that increases the risk for developing AD.) Researchers at the University of California in Los Angeles reported in December 2006 that they had developed a molecule that binds with the plaques and tangles of AD and allows the condition to be detected in a PET scan at an early stage. Previously, only an autopsy, conducted after death, could definitively confirm the presence of AD. The researchers hoped that such scans could be used to make earlier diagnoses and thus begin treatment that may delay the development of AD.

MEDICAL RESEARCH continued

the effects of combining low-dose aspirin with the different pain medications on the likelihood of cardiovascular events. The scientists divided the participants into groups. One set of groups took aspirin along with ibuprofen, naproxen, or the COX-2 inhibitor lumiracoxib (sold as Prexige). The other groups took only one type of pain medication (ibuprofen, naproxen, or the COX-2 inhibitor.) Also, this latter group did not take any aspirin during the trial.

The drugs did not change the risk of heart attack in people at low cardiovascular risk. But people at high cardiovascular risk who were taking lumiracoxib had more heart attacks than those who took only naproxen. Heart attack rates did not change for those who took only ibuprofen. However, ibuprofen remained a risk factor because study participants at high cardiovascular risk who took both aspirin and ibuprofen were nine times more likely to suffer a heart attack than those taking a combination of aspirin and lumiracoxib or aspirin and naproxen.

According to the study's authors, these results indicated that ibuprofen may interfere with aspirin's anticlotting mechanism. The researchers suggested that people with cardiovascular conditions who are taking aspirin for their heart should not also take ibuprofen. The researchers also advised that doctors use caution in prescribing COX-2 inhibitors for people who are at a high risk of heart attack or other cardiovascular problems.

Vitamin D. Vitamin D is a hormone made in the body. Vitamin D levels are affected by sunlight; consumption of foods rich in vitamin D, such as fatty fish; and vitamin supplements. Evidence gathered throughout 2006 and 2007 showed that vitamin D plays a key role in lowering the risk of developing multiple sclerosis (MS), in healing wounds, and in preventing cancer.

A team led by Alberto Ascherio, associate professor of nutrition and epidemiology at the Harvard School of Public Health in Boston, published these findings in December 2006. MS is a chronic degenerative disease of the central nervous system. Ascherio's team analyzed vitamin D levels in samples of *blood serum* (clear fluid left behind when substances that cause clotting are removed from blood) of 257 U.S. Army and Navy personnel who had been diagnosed with MS between 1992 and 2004. The researchers then compared those levels to vitamin D levels in a group of people who had not developed MS.

The study showed that MS risk declined dramatically with increased vitamin D levels. The risk of developing MS was 62 percent lower among people in the top fifth of vitamin D concentration than among those in the bottom fifth. These findings supported a growing body of research suggesting that vitamin D plays an important role in immune function. According to most experts, *autoimmune* reactions play a key role in the development of MS. In autoimmune disorders, the immune system attacks the body's own healthy tissue and organs.

Further evidence of vitamin D's role in regulating the immune system appeared in March 2007. Researchers at the University of California—San Diego (UCSD) found that vitamin D plays a key role in healing skin wounds. The study was led by Richard L. Gallo, professor of medicine and chief of UCSD's Division of Dermatology and the dermatology section of the Veterans Affairs San Diego Healthcare System. Examining how the immune system is controlled in the skin, Gallo's team found that genes controlled by vitamin D3 help wounds to heal. Skin wounds need vitamin D3 to protect against infection and begin the normal repair process.

Vitamin D was also linked to cancer prevention. In August 2006 a team of investigators from Imperial College, Hammersmith Hospital, in London published research showing that Vitamin D levels were lower in women who had primary breast cancer than those who did not. Research showed that vitamin D levels decreased as the disease progressed, suggesting that breast cancer interferes with the body's ability to process vitamin D.

Another study associating Vitamin D with cancer prevention was published in February 2007. Researchers led by Edward Gorham, a research epidemiologist with the Naval Health Research Center in San Diego, reported that a large daily dose of vitamin D could reduce the incidence of colorectal cancer with minimal risk. Gorham's team reviewed five studies that measured vitamin D levels in a total of 1,448 people and tracked them for the occurrence of colorectal cancer for periods from 2 to 25 years. The amount of dietary vitamin D that appeared to protect against colorectal cancer was 1,000 to 2,000 international units a day.

■ Renée Despres

See also **DRUGS; NUTRITION; PSYCHOLOGY; PUBLIC HEALTH.**

NOBEL PRIZES

The 2006 Nobel Prizes in science were awarded in October for imaging the process by which cells communicate genetic information; findings about energy left over from the early universe; and the discovery of an important method of controlling the activity of genes in living cells. Each prize was worth about $1.4 million.

The Nobel Prize in chemistry was awarded to biochemist Roger D. Kornberg of Stanford University in California for creating highly detailed images of the process cells use to copy and transport the genetic information needed to maintain life. During this process, called transcription, cells use ribonucleic acid (RNA) to copy the blueprints for creating proteins that are encoded in DNA (deoxyribonucleic acid, the molecule that directs the formation, growth, and reproduction of cells and organisms). RNA then carries the instructions for these essential substances to the cells' protein factories.

Kornberg produced images of this process on the molecular level using *crystallography,* a technique for visualizing the arrangement of atoms. According to the Academy, "the pictures are so detailed that separate atoms can be distinguished and this makes it possible to understand the mechanism of transcription and how it is regulated."

The Academy also noted that alterations in the transcription process contribute to the development of cancer, heart disease, and various kinds of inflammation. Understanding the transcription process is also important for scientists attempting to use *stem cells* to replace cells in diseased or damaged organs. (A stem cell has the ability to develop into any of the different cell types that make up the tissues and organs of the body.) In 1959, Kornberg's father, biochemist Arthur Kornberg, shared the Nobel Prize in physiology or medicine for producing DNA by artificial means.

The Nobel Prize in physics was shared by Americans John C. Mather of the Goddard Space Flight Center in Greenbelt, Maryland, and George F. Smoot of the Lawrence Berkeley National Laboratory in Berkeley, California, for their findings about *cosmic microwave background* (CMB) *radiation.* (The CMB is energy that formed in the heat of the early universe and cooled as the universe expanded.) The Royal

Swedish Academy of Sciences honored the two scientists for research that "marked the inception of cosmology [the study of the universe and its origins] as a precise science."

The nearly uniform temperature of the CMB radiation in all directions indicated that matter must have been spread evenly throughout the early universe after the *big bang.* (The big bang is the widely accepted theory that a cosmic explosion 14 billion years ago led to the expansion of the universe.) The CMB radiation formed about 400,000 years later. However, the apparent smoothness of the CMB radiation puzzled scientists because the universe now has a clumpy structure, with concentrations of galaxies separated by vast regions of empty space. For modern galaxies to form, certain regions of the early universe had to contain slightly more matter than others.

For their studies, Mather and Smoot used temperature measurements of CMB radiation by the Cosmic Background Explorer satellite launched in 1989. In data from the satellite, Mather found a particular pattern predicted by the *big bang theory.* Smoot found slight temperature variations in the measurements that also provided strong support for the theory.

The Nobel prize in physiology or medicine was shared by Andrew Z. Fire of Stanford University and Craig C. Mello of the University of Massachusetts Medical School in Worcester for their discovery of a fundamental biological process used by cells to "silence" genes. The process, called RNA interference (RNAi), destroys the ability of RNA to help produce the proteins essential to the structure and functioning of cells. RNAi plays a crucial role in living organisms by controlling the actions of certain unstable genes and defending the body against viruses. Fire and Mello were honored for revealing "a natural mechanism for controlling the flow of genetic information," which "heralded the start of a new research field." Shortly after Fire and Mello discovered RNAi in 1989, the process became an important tool for studying how genes function.

Within cells, RNA, which usually consists of a single strand, plays a role in *gene expression,* the process by which genes direct the formation, growth, and reproduction of cells and

NOBEL PRIZES continued

organisms. Biologists had observed that injecting certain types of RNA into the cells of plants interfered with the production of proteins. In experiments with roundworms, Fire and Mello discovered that injecting double-stranded RNA into the animals halted the expression of a specific gene by destroying the mRNA carrying instructions from that gene. Scientists are investigating the use of RNA interference to treat diseases caused by viruses, such as hepatitis and AIDS. They are also studying ways to use RNA interference to treat cancer and other diseases that involve the abnormal function of genes. ■ Barbara A. Mayes

See also **CHEMISTRY; MEDICAL RESEARCH; PHYSICS.**

LIKE FATHER, LIKE SON

The 2006 Nobel Prize in chemistry was awarded to biochemist Roger D. Kornberg of Stanford University in California. Korrnberg was honored for creating detailed images of the process cells use to copy and transport the genetic information needed to maintain life. Kornberg's father, biochemist Arthur Kornberg, shared the 1959 Nobel Prize in physiology or medicine for producing DNA (deoxyribonucleic acid, the molecule that genes are made of) by artificial means.

A computer model illustrates the process described by Kornberg. In the model, a large, white RNA-polymerase molecule holds a DNA strand (depicted in blue) in place while the appropriate RNA building block (red) inserts itself to form a copy. A small structure in the polymerase (green) advances the DNA as each segment of the strand is replicated.

NUTRITION

Thinking about when, where, and what to eat is an important part of a healthy weight-management program. The term *dieting* refers to restricting certain types of food and the amount eaten, thereby reducing calorie intake in an attempt to lose weight. However, when such activity becomes obsessive, it can lead to unhealthy eating behaviors and impermanent weight loss. In fact, more often than not, dieting alone is not the answer to a weight problem. In the April 2007 issue of *American Psychologist*, psychologist Traci Mann of the University of California in Los Angeles and her coauthors report the results of their analysis of 31 diet studies that followed dieters for two years or longer. "You can initially lose 5 to 10 percent of your weight on any number of diets, but then the weight comes back," said Mann. In fact, the researchers found that up to two-thirds of people on diets regained more weight than they lost within four or five years.

If dieting does not work, what does? "Eating in moderation is a good idea for everybody, and so is regular exercise," Mann said. "Exercise may well be the key factor leading to sustained weight loss. Studies consistently find that people who reported the most exercise also had the most weight loss." Mann is interested in studying whether a combination of diet and exercise is more effective than exercise alone.

Healthier obese children. Physical exercise, nutrition education, and behavior therapy lead to better weight and improved health in obese children. Thomas Reinehr and colleagues at the Vestische Hospital for Children and Adolescents in Germany enrolled 203 obese children aged 6 to 14 in a one-year intervention program and then reevaluated the children one year after the program ended. Obesity was defined as having a *body mass index* (BMI) above the 97th percentile, meaning that the child had a greater BMI than 97 percent of children of the same age and sex. (BMI represents the proportion between a person's height and weight.) Only those overweight children who attended exercise classes for at least eight weeks were studied. The control group consisted of 37 obese children whose families lived too far away to travel to the obesity clinic. In addition, the researchers examined 12 normal-weight children matched for sex and age for comparison. The Obeldicks intervention program (named for a popular European comic character) included physical exercise, nutrition education, and behavioral therapy. The goal was to improve health by reducing weight. Measures of cardiovascular health included blood pressure, blood glucose (sugar), blood lipids (triglyceride, cholesterol), and blood insulin. At the beginning of the study, the obese children were at greater risk for heart disease than the normal-weight children because, in addition to being overweight, they had higher blood pressure and higher blood levels of insulin, triglyceride, and LDL-cholesterol (bad cholesterol) and lower levels of HDL-cholesterol (good cholesterol).

A team of pediatricians, dietitians, psychologists, and exercise physiologists trained the children and their parents. The children were divided into groups according to their sex and age. The one-year training program was divided into three phases. During the first three months, the children attended classes in nutrition and eating-behavior twice each month and participated in exercise therapy weekly. Education classes were also held for the parents. In the next six months, individual psychological family therapy was provided for 30 minutes each month and the exercise classes continued weekly. In the final three months, further psychological care was available if necessary. The exercise therapy continued weekly throughout the one-year program. Children played ball games, jogged, and jumped on a trampoline. They were instructed to regard physical exercise as part of everyday life and to reduce the amount of time spent watching television.

At the beginning and end of the program, the children kept three-day food records by weighing and recording the types and amounts of food they ate. These records showed that over the course of the program, the children reduced their intake by an average of 200 calories per day. Most children (72 percent) participating in the program achieved a reduction in BMI and cardiovascular risk factors in the intervention period, whereas there were no changes for the obese children who did not participate.

Importantly, Reinehr's study also showed that the positive health effects achieved by the intervention continued for at least one year

NUTRITION continued

after the classes ended (two years from the beginning of the study). Unfortunately, those children who did not reduce their BMI during the intervention gained weight in the followup period. This study demonstrated that a program of physical exercise, behavior therapy, and nutrition education can have beneficial health effects on most obese children who are motivated to participate (a requirement of both the study and control groups).

Calcium intake in boys. Recommendations for calcium intake for boys in the United States are based primarily on data from girls. Michelle Braun of Purdue University in West Lafayette, Indiana, and her colleagues thought there might be differences in how much calcium boys could absorb and retain because boys tend to develop larger skeletons than girls.

Boys aged 12 to 15 participated in three-week calcium balance studies. The subjects lived on the Purdue University campus in a camp environment and were studied twice: once while they consumed meals containing low amounts of calcium and again while they ate high amounts of calcium. Thirty-one boys completed one, three-week study period and 26 boys completed two, three-week study periods.

Dietary intake was controlled, with subjects ingesting only foods prepared by the researchers. The subjects were randomly assigned to receive one of five dietary calcium intakes ranging from 693 to 1,986 milligrams per day. These levels of intake were achieved by using a beverage fortified with calcium citrate malate, which was served at each meal. Duplicate meals, the same as those eaten, were prepared and saved for an analysis of calcium content.

Subjects collected all their urine and feces for the duration of the study so that researchers could measure the amount of calcium excreted. The amount of calcium retained was calculated by subtracting the amount excreted from the amount ingested.

The results in boys were compared with those obtained from 35 adolescent girls who participated in a similar study. Calcium retention was higher in the boys than in the girls by an average of 171 milligrams per day, and the difference was consistent across the different intake levels. This higher calcium retention was achieved because boys absorbed more calcium and lost less calcium in urine. Despite this difference for boys, Braun and her colleagues concluded that their new data support the current recommendation of the Institute of Medicine, in Washington D.C.—an advisory organization chartered by the National Academy of Sciences— that all adolescents aged 9 to 18 years should ingest 1,300 milligrams of calcium per day, even though that amount was originally based primarily on data from girls. Because boys utilize calcium more efficiently than girls do, boys do not require higher calcium intakes to achieve their larger skeletons.

■ Catherine J. Klein

See also **MEDICAL RESEARCH.**

DIET OR EXERCISE?

A mother and her 15-year-old daughter jog around a track as part of their fitness routine. Researchers in 2007 increasingly found that though changes in diet lead to successful weight loss, dieting alone is not enough to sustain the weight loss over time.

OCEANOGRAPHY

It is well documented that chronic overfishing has depleted fish populations worldwide. Less understood are the consequences of removing these fish, particularly the largest top predators, from the marine ecosystem. The principles of ecology predict that the loss of top predators, such as large sharks, may have a cascading effect on species lower on the food chain; in this model, large sharks act as stewards of the marine food chain by keeping it in balance.

A study released in March 2007 and led by biologists Ransom A. Myers (who died just days before the study's release), Julia K. Baum, and Travis D. Shepherd of Dalhousie University in Nova Scotia, Canada; Sean P. Powers of the University of Southern Alabama in Mobile; and Charles H. Peterson of the University of North Carolina in Chapel Hill documented a link between overfishing of large sharks off the East Coast of the United States and the collapse of the scallop fishery in North Carolina. The study was based on analyzing fishing and research survey data for 11 species of large sharks— greater than 2 meters (6.6 feet) long—that feed primarily on rays; *skates* (fish similar to rays but lacking a tail and stinging barb); and smaller

SEE ALSO THE SPECIAL REPORT, **PARADISE FOUND,** PAGE 56.

sharks. This analysis showed a dramatic drop in the numbers of these sharks from 1970 to 2005.

The study also showed that the disappearance of the sharks was accompanied by a rise in the abundance of most of the prey species on which these sharks feed. For example, the loss of predators had led to a tenfold increase in the population of cow nose rays since the 1970s, based on surveys of coastal waters between Florida, New Jersey, and New York. Cow nose rays live on the bottom of the seafloor and regularly migrate in fall from coastal waters off the Mid-Atlantic states to warmer waters off Florida. On their way, they enter the *sounds* (water passages that connect larger bodies of water) of North Carolina.

North Carolina's sounds were once home to the state's century-old scallop fishery. Due to low scallop populations, the fishery was closed at the end of the 2004 season. Observations of ocean bottoms show migrating rays feeding extensively on adult scallops, a feeding pattern that probably contributed to the scallop fishery's collapse in 2004.

Biodiversity benefits. *Biological diversity* (variety of organisms and genetic diversity) seems to make marine ecosystems as a whole more resilient to human-caused environmental problems, such as overfishing, water pollution, and habitat destruction. This trend, an international team of 12 scientists reported in November 2006, seems to be true regionally as well as globally.

An international team of scientists headed by Boris Worm of Dalhousie University in Nova Scotia, Edward Barbier of the University of Wyoming in Laramie, and Nicola Beaumont of Plymouth Marine Laboratory in the United Kingdom showed that species-rich marine ecosystems provide a

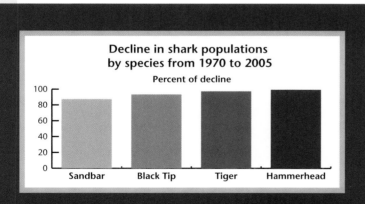

Decline in shark populations by species from 1970 to 2005

Percent of decline

(Bar chart showing percent of decline for Sandbar, Black Tip, Tiger, and Hammerhead sharks, with y-axis from 0 to 100.)

SHARKS IN DECLINE

A study released by Canadian and American biologists in March 2007 revealed an alarming decline in the number of large sharks off the East Coast of North America. The decline has led to the collapse of the scallop fishery in North Carolina. As the numbers of large sharks declined, migrating rays and skates (raylike fish that lack a tail and stinging barb)—whose populations are usually kept in check by the sharks—began feeding extensively on the scallops.

OCEANOGRAPHY continued

variety of "services" that translate into benefits for people. For example, fish provide food and jobs for fishers, and coastal wetlands filter and detoxify waste and provide natural protection against flooding.

A review of 12 coastal and estuarine ecosystems showed that species-rich ecosystems also produce more fish and provide better nursery habitats for young animals, including commercially important fish and shellfish, than species-poor areas. Biodiversity was also associated with enhanced filtering and detoxification of pollution, due to the presence of wetlands and underwater plants such as sea grass, as well as filter-feeding invertebrates such as oysters.

Biological diversity, however, does not render an ecosystem immune to destructive human activities. To examine the patterns of biodiversity on a larger scale, the group analyzed fish-catch data collected by the United Nations Food and Agriculture Organization from 1950 to 2003 in the world's 64 largest marine ecosystems, each of which has an area greater than 150,000 square kilometers (93,206 square miles).

About 83 percent of the global fisheries' yields were caught in these 64 ecosystems during the study period. The analysis of fish-catch data showed that about 29 percent of the currently fished species have been so exploited or affected by pollution and habitat loss that they were categorized as having "collapsed." The scientists defined *collapsed* as meaning that catches in 2003 were down to $\frac{1}{10}$ or less of maximum catches in recent years.

The scientists reported that at the current accelerating rate of depletion of fish species, all the fisheries that were active in 2003 in the 64 study areas could collapse by 2050. To address whether this dire trend could be reversed by closing some areas to fishing, the scientists analyzed data from 48 *marine reserves*—regions of the ocean in which fishing and other human activities are prohibited or restricted. They found that marine reserves and fishery closures were associated with a 23 percent increase in biodiversity as compared to nearby unprotected areas.

Consistent with their studies of coastal and estuarine ecosystems, the scientists found a statistical link between species variety and certain beneficial services because of biodiversity within large marine ecosystems. For example, the proportion of collapsed fisheries was significantly lower in large species-rich ecosystems; the number of fish brought onshore was also higher. Finally, biodiversity was connected to faster rates of recovery of overexploited species and greater stability of catches.

Microscopic ocean life. Microbes (organisms too small to see with the unaided eye), represent about 90 percent of the living *biomass* (the total amount of material) in the ocean. They are vital to marine ecosystems because some microbes, such as phytoplankton, are able to convert sunlight into food and are themselves eaten by other organisms, such as zooplankton and fish, within the food web.

Microbes may be as much as 100 times more diverse than previous studies have suggested. In July 2006, a team of microbiologists at the Marine Biological Laboratory in Woods Hole, Massachusetts, led by Mitchell T. Sogin and Hilary G. Morrison, reported that they found more than 20,000 kinds of microorganisms in one liter of seawater. They had only expected to find between 1,000 and 3,000 species.

They saw the same pattern—startling underestimates of the diversity of microbial life—in seawater samples taken from eight sites in the

THREAT TO CORAL

Coral in the Caribbean Sea near Caye Caulker, Belize, shows the effects of bleaching, a condition in which it dies and turns white. Several reports by the Intergovernmental Panel on Climate Change (IPCC) in 2007 noted that warming seas are threatening the health of the world's coral reefs by increasing their exposure to bleaching.

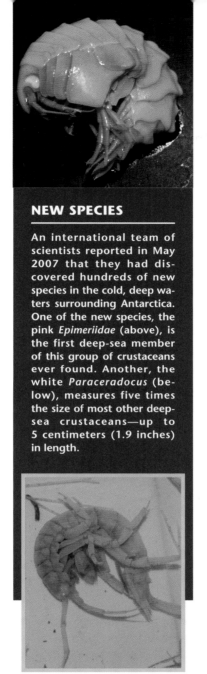

North Atlantic and North Pacific oceans. This pattern led the team to estimate that there could be from 5 million to 10 million different kinds of bacteria in the oceans—only 5,000 species of which have been formally described by scientists.

Sogin and Morrison said that previous underestimates of the diversity of microbes in these waters could be explained partly by the relative scarcity of some of the newly discovered species. In addition, only recently have scientists developed the necessary genetic techniques to distinguish genetic differences among organisms and thus identify a greater diversity.

Climate change. Earth is getting warmer, a trend evident in rising average global air and ocean temperatures, in widespread melting of snow and ice, and in rising average global sea level. People are contributing to this trend.

These were among the central ideas of a highly publicized report on the physical basis of climate change published in February 2007 by the Intergovernmental Panel on Climate Change (IPCC). A second report published in April discussed the implications of climate change on ecosystems and people. The third, released in May, addressed the issue of how to *mitigate* (limit) factors that are causing climate change.

The ocean was a focus of the reports because of its importance to the planet's *heat budget* (the differences between the amount of solar energy absorbed and redistributed by the ocean) and *freshwater cycles* (where it rains, when, and how much). The IPCC reported that the upper 700 meters (766 yards) of the global ocean has warmed about 0.1 °C (.18 °F) from

NEW SPECIES

An international team of scientists reported in May 2007 that they had discovered hundreds of new species in the cold, deep waters surrounding Antarctica. One of the new species, the pink *Epimeriidae* (above), is the first deep-sea member of this group of crustaceans ever found. Another, the white *Paraceradocus* (below), measures five times the size of most other deep-sea crustaceans—up to 5 centimeters (1.9 inches) in length.

1961 to 2003.

Warming seas are probably altering the distribution of algae, zooplankton, and fishes, particularly at high latitudes, and changing the timing of fish migrations, according to the report. Continued warming is projected to threaten the health of the world's coral reefs by increasing their exposure to coral bleaching.

Another ocean observation relevant to discussions of climate is that global average sea level has risen about 20 centimeters (7.9 inches) since the mid-1800's, primarily because of the *thermal expansion* of water (the expansion of water as it heats). Melting of glaciers, ice caps, and ice sheets on land have also contributed to the rise in sea level. Scientists predict the rise will continue, making millions of people more vulnerable to flooding and potentially destroying coastal wetlands.

The ocean is also becoming more acidic as it absorbs higher levels of carbon dioxide from the air—yet another change that is consistent with warming caused by human activity. Highly acidic waters can dissolve calcium carbonate, a main component of marine shells and coral reefs.

Climate change so far, however, is most pronounced in the Arctic, where, for example, summer sea ice is vanishing. The loss of sea ice increases the amount of heat absorbed by the ocean (because ice reflects sunlight and water absorbs it). Loss of sea ice also represents a loss of habitat for top predators such as polar bears

■ Christina Johnson

See also **CLOSE-UP: FINDINGS OF THE INTERGOVERNMENTAL PANEL ON CLIMATE CHANGE.**

PHYSICS

In April 2007, an overflowing crowd at the spring meeting of the American Physical Society in Jacksonville, Florida, was treated to a first glimpse of long-awaited results from the Gravity Probe B (GP-B) space mission, a joint effort of Stanford University in Stanford, California, the National Aeronautics and Space Administration (NASA), and the Lockheed Martin Corporation based in Bethesda, Maryland. The experiment had been conceived in 1959 by Stanford professors Leonard Schiff, William Fairbank, and Robert Cannon, none of whom lived to see it completed. Today, the project is headed by Stanford's Francis Everitt. It was designed to test aspects of the theory of general relativity, announced in 1915 by the German-born American theorist Albert Einstein.

At the heart of the GP-B spacecraft are four gyroscopes, each consisting of a quartz sphere 3.8 centimeters (1.5 inches) in diameter, spinning at 4,000 revolutions per minute. They are spherical to within 15 *nanometers*—one billionth of a meter (1/25,400,000 inch)—making them possibly the most perfect spheres ever manufactured. Each sphere is coated with a thin layer of *niobium* (a white or steel-gray chemical element) and chilled to within about one degree Celsius of absolute zero (the theoretical temperature at which atoms and molecules of a substance have the least possible energy—that is, −273.15 °C [−459.67 °F]). At this temperature, the niobium becomes a *superconductor*—it conducts an electric current with zero resistance. A spinning superconductor generates a magnetic field that can be tracked by highly precise sensors to determine the direction in which the spin axis of the gyroscope is pointing. This direction is recorded and compared to that of a reference star, IM Pegasi, observed by an on board telescope.

If gravity as described in 1686 by English physicist Isaac Newton were the only force acting on the gyroscopes, the spin axes would remain pointing in whatever direction they were set. General relativity, however, predicts that the axes will drift very slightly from their original positions.

GP-B was launched into a *polar orbit* (passing over both the North and South poles of Earth while in orbit) at an altitude of 640 kilometers (400 miles) in April 2004. After four months of testing and adjustment, it began taking data in August. This phase of the experiment lasted 50

SEE ALSO   THE SPECIAL REPORT, A COSMIC ASSIGNMENT, PAGE 26.

weeks. Since then, scientists have been analyzing the four trillion *bytes* (units of computer memory) of data that GP-B generated.

This experiment was by no means the first test of general relativity. In 1919, observations taken by Einstein during a total eclipse of the sun confirmed that beams of starlight passing near the sun were deflected by its gravity, which distorts the space near it, the so-called *geodetic effect*. The deflection was twice that predicted by Newton's theory. These observations made Einstein an international celebrity. Since then, very few tests have occurred; however, all, including the first analysis of the data from GP-B, have confirmed aspects of the geodetic effect. GP-B was built not to reconfirm the geodetic effect, but mainly to observe a more subtle effect, known as *frame dragging*.

According to the theory of general relativity, space is not emptiness. Space contains energy and mass and plays an active role in physical processes, such as the rotation of planets. The theory of general relativity predicts that a massive spinning object, such as Earth, will drag space along with it, like a spoon stirring a liquid. This effect is called frame dragging. This effect would also cause a drift in a gyroscope's spin axis. Because Earth's gravity is small when compared with that of other objects in space, such as the sun, the dragging effect is tiny—about 170 times smaller than the geodetic drift. The GP-B data analysis has not yet reached the level of refinement required to measure Earth's dragging effect accurately. However, the scientists analyzing the data are confident that they can reach this goal before the end of 2007.

Though difficult to observe near Earth, frame dragging can become a huge effect in the vicinity of a massive, rapidly spinning *black hole* (a region of space whose gravitational force is so strong that nothing can escape from it). A black hole is believed to be the source of the vast amounts of energy released from so-called *active galaxies* (galaxies in which a significant portion of their energy output comes from sources other than stars, dust, and interstellar gas).

642 kilometers (401 miles)

Frame-dragging Effect
0.041 arcseconds/year
(0.000011 degrees/year)

Guide Star
IM Pegasi
(HR 8703)

Geodetic Effect
6.6 arcseconds/year
(0.0018 degrees/year)

TESTING EINSTEIN'S THEORY

Gravity Probe B, launched by the National Aeronautics and Space Administration (NASA) in 2004, orbits Earth as it collects data to test the general theory of relativity, published by German-born physicist Albert Einstein in 1916. The theory predicts two effects of gravity: that a large body such as Earth warps the space and time in its vicinity; and that a rotating mass such as Earth drags its local space and time with it by a certain measure. In April 2007, physicists who conducted a preliminary analysis of the Gravity Probe B data reported that the probe had confirmed that Einstein's predictions were correct within an accuracy of 1 percent.

PHYSICS continued

Wireless power. In the early 2000's, many people owned a number of electronic devices such as cell phones, MP3 players, and portable computers. Almost all these devices run on rechargeable batteries. Each device comes with its own charger, and it is rare that the chargers can be used interchangeably with different devices.

In November 2006, a team of physicists headed by Marin Soljacic, along with Aristeidis Karalis and John Joannopoulos, at the Massachusetts Institute of Technology (MIT) in Cambridge announced a development that may soon provide a better way to keep electronic devices powered. This development, known as nonradiative wireless energy transfer, has shown that electrical energy can be transferred over modest distances without the use of wires.

The MIT system uses a *transformer* (a device for changing an electric current into one of higher or lower voltage) that produces a magnetic field that *oscillates* (moves to and fro between two points) at a frequency of 6.4 megahertz. To tap the energy within the magnetic field, a device such as a cell phone is tuned to the field's frequency, just as a radio receiver is tuned to the frequency of a radio station.

Obtaining power wirelessly is not a new concept. In the late 1800's, American inventor Nikola Tesla, who was born in what is now Croatia, proposed, and later demonstrated, power transmission over distances of many miles using radio waves. However, Tesla's system had a fatal flaw. The energy from radio waves *radiated* (flowed) all the time and in all directions, with only a tiny fraction of it reaching any desired device. This result was an unacceptable waste of energy, so the system was abandoned.

In the system demonstrated at MIT, energy flows only when a specified device comes within about 5 meters (16 feet) of the power source. Using a limited-range setup prevents a large amount of energy from being wasted and irradiated into the environment. However, only about 30 to 60 percent of the energy actually reaches the device. Soljacic and his team believe they can improve upon the system's efficiency and range of this system. The system could then serve a large building or perhaps even a neighborhood.

An elliptical universe? The Wilkinson Microwave Anisotropy Probe (WMAP), a joint effort by Princeton University in Princeton, New Jersey, and the NASA Goddard Space Flight Center in Greenbelt, Maryland, has proven to be a very productive space probe. Since its launch in June 2001, it has given an estimate of the age of the universe—13.7 billion years—that is believed to be extremely accurate. It has also provided reliable estimates of the total amounts of matter and energy in the universe and offered interesting glimpses of the earliest moments of its history.

In September 2006, WMAP provided yet another unexpected insight. It appears that our universe is not perfectly spherical, but is instead an *ellipsoid* (a three-dimensional object whose cross sections are ellipses). This result comes from an analysis of WMAP data by three Italian physicists: Leonardo Campanelli of the University of Ferrara and Paolo Cea and Luigi Tedesco, both of the University of Bari.

WMAP was designed to study the *cosmic microwave background* (CMB) radiation, energy left over from the early universe. CMB radiation fills the universe nearly uniformly in all directions. It is believed to have been produced when the universe was about 400,000 years old. Before this time, the universe was filled with *plasma* (electrically charged atomic particles). Light cannot travel very far in plasma because it gets absorbed by *free electrons* (negatively charged atomic particles that are not bound to atoms) within the plasma.

CMB radiation developed after the universe had cooled enough to allow nuclei to capture electrons to form atoms, a process called *recombination*. Because the electrons were no longer free to soak up light, the universe became transparent. Nearly all the light produced during recombination is still visible today.

The CMB radiation started out mainly as light in the visible or ultraviolet range, with wavelengths of a micrometer—a millionth of a meter (.000039 inch) or less. Over billions of years, the expansion of the universe transformed the light into microwaves with wavelengths of millimeters. However, CMB radiation still displays a pattern from the time it was formed. Careful measurements reveal that the pattern is not exactly uniform but shows tiny variations that correspond to the distribution of matter at that time, creating a slightly elliptical shape.

The universe is far from being egg-shaped. In fact, it misses being a perfect sphere by very little—the difference is only about 1 percent. One likely theory for the source of the difference is a somewhat strong magnetic field that fills the entire universe and thus causes the CMB radiation pattern to be slightly elliptical.

Mapping the invisible. Of all the matter in the universe, only 15 percent is visible. The rest is thought to be mysterious *dark matter*. This type of matter does not interact with light or any other form of radiation or even with solid or liquid matter. Dark matter reveals itself solely through its gravity. The effects of dark-matter gravity show in the motions of stars and galaxies. Many scientists are sure that dark matter, although not visible, is present in the universe. However, they can only guess what it might consist of.

In January 2007, the Cosmological Evolution Survey (COSMOS) project, an international team of 90 scientists headed by Nick Scoville of the California Institute of Technology (Caltech) in Pasadena, released the first detailed map of dark matter in the universe, out

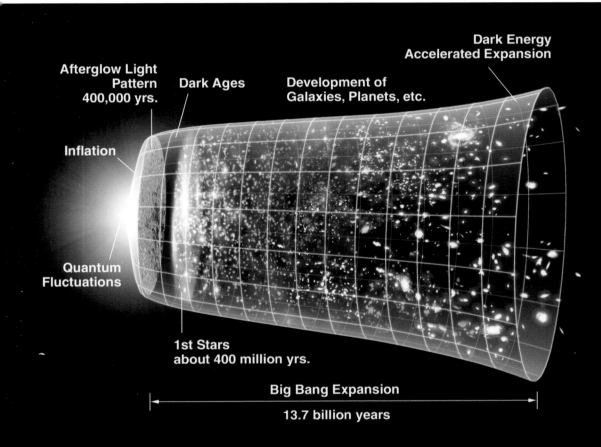

TIMELINE OF THE UNIVERSE

The Wilkinson Microwave Anisotropy Probe (WMAP), a joint effort by NASA and Princeton University in New Jersey, collects data on the cosmic microwave background (CMB) radiation in a diagram created from WMAP data. Since its launch in June 2001, WMAP has estimated the age of the universe as 13.7 billion years with unprecedented accuracy and dramatically increased the known number of galaxies in the early universe. In September 2006, researchers revealed that WMAP data indicates that the universe is elliptical rather than spherical. (An ellipsoid is a three-dimensional object whose cross-sections are ellipses.)

PHYSICS continued

COLD WAR LEGACY

Forest fires that burn in Alaska; Siberia, Russia (below); and northern Canada release small amounts of radioactive cesium, according to scientists with the Comprehensive Nuclear-Test-Ban Treaty Organization in Vienna, Austria. The researchers, who had been monitoring a "sniffer" device in the Canadian Arctic, reported their findings in June 2006. The particular form of cesium detected is produced inside nuclear reactors or nuclear bombs. According to the scientists, cesium was released during tests of nuclear bombs during the Cold War (the intense rivalry between Communist and non-Communist nations from 1945 to about 1991). It settled in soil or in the wood of trees and has become airborne in ash during the fires that regularly rage in northern forests.

to a range of 11 billion *light-years.* (A light-year is the distance light travels in one year—5.88 trillion miles [9.46 trillion kilometers].) The map was constructed from more than 1,000 hours of observations by the Hubble Space Telescope (HST) over a two-year period.

Since 85 percent of all matter in space is dark, its gravity should dominate the structure of the universe. Scientists suspect that the matter we can see has formed on a scaffolding of filaments of dark matter. Visible matter is distributed very unevenly. It clumps up in stars, which are in turn bound to galaxies that are themselves usually found in clusters. These clusters tend to form along a network of thin filaments (scaffolding), leaving most of space nearly empty. Scientists believe that, without the help of gravity from dark matter, stars might not have been able to form at all. Galactic clusters should be found in the dense regions where filaments intersect. The map from the HST does show a connection between dark and visible matter.

COSMOS used the HST's Advanced Camera for Surveys to examine images of a half million remote galaxies, looking for evidence of *gravitational lensing* (distortions in the shapes of background objects caused by large masses, such as clusters of stars, in front of them). According to the theory of general relativity, gravity warps space and time. Around a dense concentration of matter visible or invisible, the warping can focus light passing nearby, much as a crude lens would. This focusing produces distorted but recognizable images of galaxies far behind the lens.

Unfortunately, the ACS stopped working in January 2007. But it is scheduled to be replaced by an even better survey camera in an HST servicing mission in 2008.

Cosmic ray cutoff. In March 2007, a sharp cutoff in the number of high-energy cosmic rays was reported by observers using the HiRes-2 fluorescence telescope at the U.S. Air Force Dugway Proving Ground in the Great Salt Lake Desert in Utah.

Cosmic rays consist of atomic nuclei, made up mainly of positive atomic particles called protons, which are accelerated to high energies by violent processes far away in space. Most of these protons travel freely through space without encountering anything that can stop them. But if one cosmic ray proton has an energy that is above 60 million trillion electronvolts (about twice the amount of energy in a traveling baseball hit during a home run),

it can be slowed down by *photons* (particles of light from CMB radiation).

In 1966, shortly after the discovery of the CMB radiation, Kenneth Greisen of Cornell University in Ithaca, New York, pointed out that a proton with this much energy can collide with a CMB photon and transform it into a *pion* (a subatomic particle that exists for only a few billionths of a second before decaying into an electron). When this collision occurs, the proton loses energy. After many such encounters over hundreds of millions of light-years, the proton is slowed until pions are no longer produced. This effect was independently noted in 1966 by Georgii Zatsepin and Vadim Kuzman at Moscow State University in Russia, so it came to be known as the GZK cutoff or GZK limit.

Protons above the GZK cutoff are so rare that only a few would strike an area of hundreds of square kilometers each year. Huge detectors are required to obtain a reasonable sample. The HiRes-2 detector is such a detector. It began operation in 1999 under the guidance of Pierre Sokolsky and Eugene Loh of the University of Utah in Salt Lake City. The HiRes-2 relies on the fact that when high-energy cosmic rays enter Earth's atmosphere, they soon hit an atomic nucleus, producing hundreds of new particles. These in turn hit other nuclei, producing an abundance of new particles. The result is a cascade that can reach millions of particles. As they pass through the atmosphere, the particles in the cascade disturb atoms and cause them to emit light. HiRes-2 consists of 42 large mirrors that focus light on very sensitive detectors. On a sufficiently clear, dark night, HiRes-2 can see a cascade started by a proton at the GZK limit as far as 80 kilometers (50 miles) away. HiRes-2 observed eight events above the GZK limit.

Based on predictions, scientists would have expected 40 events above the GZK cutoff. Why is this discrepancy significant? In the past, at least two other detectors that study cascades by detecting particles that make it to Earth's surface (a small fraction of the total) have reported far more than eight events above the GZK limit, calling the theory into question. The experimenters, who study particles that make it to Earth, must now go back and reevaluate the way in which they estimate the cascade energy from the number of particles reaching the surface. ■ Robert March

See also **ASTRONOMY; GEOLOGY; NOBEL PRIZES.**

Invisibility Verging on Reality

The imaginations of many people ran wild with ideas about invisibility in October 2006, when a research team led by physicists David R. Smith and David Schurig of Duke University in Durham, North Carolina, and John B. Pendry of Imperial College in London, announced that they had demonstrated a working "invisibility cloak." In their demonstration, the scientists used a device consisting of a new, high-tech material to make another object invisible to the "eyes" of a special microwave detector.

Human eyes could still see the cloaked object in ordinary, visible light. Still, the demonstration marked the first time that scientists had successfully hidden an object in any of the frequencies of the *electromagnetic spectrum*. And it raised the possibility that scientists might eventually be able to make things truly invisible.

The electromagnetic spectrum consists of bands of different kinds of energy, or radiation. Each kind of electromagnetic radiation travels in waves of different lengths. Visible light, such as that given off by the sun, is one kind of electromagnetic radiation. It is in the middle of the electromagnetic spectrum, consisting of waves of medium length. Types of electromagnetic radiation with wavelengths shorter than visible light are—from longest to shortest—ultraviolet rays, X rays, and gamma rays. Kinds of electromagnetic radiation with wavelengths longer than visible light are—from shortest to longest—infrared rays, microwaves (also called short radio waves), and radio waves.

People can see objects—such as rocks, trees, birds, and buildings—because the objects reflect certain frequencies of visible light toward the eyes while absorbing other frequencies. Objects also reflect and absorb other kinds of electromagnetic radiation, which cannot be seen by human eyes but can be detected with special instruments. The Duke–Imperial College team caused an object that can normally be detected by the microwaves it reflects to be virtually invisible to an instrument that senses microwaves.

The cloaking device consisted of a disk of 10 concentric circular bands crafted from complex building blocks called metamaterials (artificial composite compounds produced through *nanotechnology,* the manipulation of individual atoms and molecules to create larger structures). By precisely adjusting the structures of metamaterials and the patterns in which metamaterials are arranged on a surface, these exotic substances can be made to interact with electromagnetic radiation in ways that do not happen in nature.

The research team produced its cloaking device out of fiberglass- and copper-based metamaterials. They positioned the device, which was about the size of a drinking-glass coaster, over a small copper cylinder. Then they focused a beam of microwaves on the cylinder. Ordinarily, an object would reflect parts of the microwave beam and block other parts of the beam. A microwave detector could then easily sense the reflected microwaves and blocked shadows. However, the microwave detector used in this experiment detected only very weak microwaves and shadows from the cylinder. This was because the metamaterials in the cloaking device *refracted* (bent) the microwaves in a way that greatly reduced the microwave reflection and shadows—rendering the cylinder virtually invisible at microwave frequencies.

The researchers noted that there would be a number of applications for a perfected microwave/radio-wave cloaking device. For example, the United States Department of Defense is interested in using the technology to affect wireless communication signals. In this type of application, the technology might be able to conceal aircraft from an enemy's radar or cloak buildings that are interfering with radar signals.

Could a cloaking device be made to work with visible light, causing objects to be invisible to the human eye? The scientists pointed out that for a metamaterial to disrupt electromagnetic waves, it has to be made of individual structures that are smaller than the wavelength of the waves. Microwaves are about 3 centimeters (1.2 inches) long, and the metamaterial nanostructures used in the 2006 experiment were each about 3 millimeters (0.12 inch) long. Thus, these structures were able to disrupt the microwaves. However, the waves that make up visible light are about 60,000 times shorter than microwaves. Designing and producing metamaterials that are tiny enough to disrupt such miniscule waves would be extremely challenging—and was not yet possible as of 2007.

If a true invisibility cloak could be invented, what might it be used for? Hiding objects of important military or industrial value from prying eyes would be one of the possible applications. Such a cloak might also be used to allow light to pass through certain obstacles, such as a building that blocks a view of a beautiful beach. People would undoubtedly develop numerous other practical and esthetic applications of such a technology.

Science fiction has often turned into science fact. Space travel, submarines, and cellular phones were all featured in novels or movies before they were invented for real. Perhaps the invisibility cloak will one day become an essential military and industrial technology—or even an exotic fashion accessory. The device demonstrated by the Duke–Imperial College team was an important first step toward achieving such remarkable goals.
■ Al Smuskiewicz

INVISIBLE MAN

Physicist David R. Smith of Duke University in Durham, North Carolina, peers out from between the circular bands of his "invisibility cloak." Smith, together with physicist John B. Pendry of the Imperial College in London, developed the device, which makes objects "invisible" in certain frequencies of the electromagnetic spectrum.

PSYCHOLOGY

Taking an antidepressant as well as a mood-stabilizing drug does not necessarily help patients with bipolar disorder during the depressive phase of the illness. However, it does not appear to cause harm, either. Such results—which contradict what many mental health professionals have long believed—were reported in March 2007 by psychiatrist Gary S. Sachs of Massachusetts General Hospital in Boston and his colleagues.

Bipolar disorder (also known as manic depression) is a serious mental illness in which a person alternates between severe depression and mania (extreme joy, overactivity, or irritability). Doctors generally prescribe mood-stabilizing drugs, including lithium or valproate, to treat mania. They often also include an antidepressant because of the serious risk for suicide during the depressive phase of the illness. However, many researchers have long worried that antidepressants could trigger the manic phase of the disease.

Sachs and his colleagues studied 366 patients with bipolar disorder at clinics throughout the United States. Half of the patients received a mood-stabilizing drug and a "placebo" (inactive substance). The other half received a mood stabilizer along with an antidepressant (either paroxetine or bupropion, sold under the brand names Paxil and Wellbutrin, respectively). After 26 weeks, 27 percent of the patients in the group taking the mood stabilizer with a placebo had experienced a stable mood for 8 consecutive weeks (a development the doctors considered stable recovery). In the group taking a mood stabilizer with an antidepressant, 24 percent had a stable recovery. The researchers considered the difference between the groups statistically insignificant.

ONLY A GAME?

A young man observes his progress during a violent video game. In July 2006, researchers led by psychologists at Iowa State University in Ames documented for the first time that exposure to violent video games—even for as short a period as 20 minutes—desensitizes players to scenes of real violence. Video game players had lower heart rates and other response measurements, compared to nonviolent game players, when they viewed such videotaped scenes as shootings and prison fights.

The researchers concluded that physicians should consider starting treatment for bipolar disorder with a mood stabilizer alone. An antidepressant may be added later, according to a patient's needs.

Antidepressants. More children and teens with such illnesses as depression, anxiety disorder, and obsessive-compulsive disorder are helped by antidepressants than are harmed by them. Yet young adults between the ages of 18 and 24 may experience an increase in suicidal thoughts when they first begin taking these medications. Researchers led by pediatric psychiatrist Jeffrey Bridge of the Columbus Children's Research Institute and Ohio State University in Columbus announced their conclusion about children and teens in April. The U.S. Food and Drug Administration (FDA) delivered its warning about young adults in May.

The researchers conducted their studies in response to a "black box" warning about the use of antidepressants in children and teens issued by the FDA in 2004. The black box warning—the FDA's most serious type of warning—was issued based on evidence that antidepressants may increase suicidal thoughts in children and teens.

Bridge and his colleagues reviewed the findings of 27 major studies conducted from 1988 to 2006—a more recent time period than that originally examined by the FDA. They found that although some children under age 18 experienced an increase in suicidal thoughts while taking antidepressants, more children taking the medications were helped than those taking a placebo. The FDA reviewed 295 studies of antidepressant use in adults before recommending that the black box warning for children and adolescents be expanded to young adults during the first month or two of treatment.

The Robin Hood impulse. People seem to have an inborn, Robin-Hood-like desire for equality in society, even when such a desire provides no direct benefit to them or their group. Researchers led by political scientist James Fowler at the University of California in San Diego reported this finding in April 2007.

Fowler and his colleagues conducted a study in which 120 college students participated in a series of video games. Each student was assigned to a team and issued a certain amount of money. Each student was also informed how much money teammates had received and was

SMOKE ON THE BRAIN

Researchers have discovered three regions of the brain that may control nicotine dependence and cravings and may help explain why only 5 percent of smokers are able to quit. Scientists at Duke University in Durham, North Carolina, reported their findings in March 2007. The three regions—the thalamus (blue in the brain scan below), the striatum (red), and the anterior cingulated cortex (green)—control the ability to calm down when stressed, to experience pleasure, and to concentrate, respectively. Each area revealed different levels of activity in brain scans, depending on whether the individual smoked to calm down, to experience pleasure, or to concentrate more effectively.

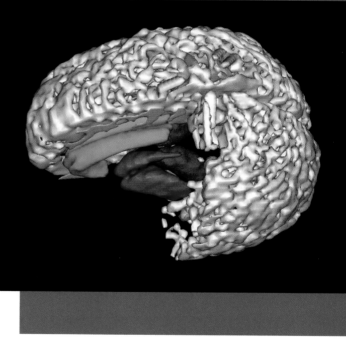

allowed to spend his or her money in order to increase or decrease the money held by other players. Repeatedly, the students were willing to spend their own money to rob their richer teammates of funds and to give money to their poorer teammates. As a result, at the end of the game, the players' income was about equal. According to the researchers, such a desire may have evolved into the patterns of cooperation and sharing that many societies exhibit today.

■ Kristina Vaicikonis

PUBLIC HEALTH

Mothers stopped telling their children to "eat your greens" after the United States Food and Drug Administration (FDA) issued an alert on Sept. 14, 2006, that bagged fresh spinach may have been the culprit in a growing outbreak of diarrheal disease caused by a harmful strain of *E. coli* bacteria. "Given the severity of this illness and the seriousness of the outbreak, FDA believes that a warning to consumers is needed. We are working closely with the U.S. Centers for Disease Control and Prevention (CDC) and state and local agencies to determine the cause and scope of the problem," said Robert Brackett, director of the FDA's Center for Food Safety and Applied Nutrition.

The first case of the disease was reported on August 23. By mid-October, 199 people had become sick. Although healthy adults recovered after a week of diarrhea, sometimes with bloody stools, others developed hemolytic uremic syndrome, a type of kidney failure that can be fatal. At least three people died, and 98 people were hospitalized because of hemolytic uremic syndrome.

The FDA, the state of California, the CDC, and the U.S. Department of Agriculture worked collaboratively to find the source of the outbreak, which occurred in 26 states and Canada. Field investigators found genetic fingerprints of the *E. coli* culprit in samples of cattle feces on one of the four ranches in California's Monterey, San Benito, and Santa Clara counties that were thought to have produced the contaminated spinach. On September 15, one company, Natural Selection, voluntarily recalled its spinach products; four more companies followed suit. In its final report, the FDA said the precise means of *E. coli* transmission remained unknown. The FDA also advised consumers to wash all produce thoroughly before eating, although "washing produce would not have prevented the recent *E. coli* outbreak involving spinach."

New cancer vaccine. On June 8, 2006, the FDA approved a vaccine, called Gardasil, to prevent cervical cancer and genital warts caused by the human papilloma virus (HPV). HPV has more than 30 strains, most of which do not cause health problems; however, some strains lead to genital warts or cancer. Gardasil protects against two strains of HPV, 16 and 18, that cause 70 percent of cervical cancers, and another two strains, 6 and 11, that cause 90 percent of genital warts. Gardasil is the first vaccine developed that can prevent cancer.

On June 30, the American Council on Immunization Practices (ACIP), a federal advisory panel, recommended that all girls aged 11 to 12 receive the vaccine routinely. It also advised that girls and women aged 13 to 26 receive a catch-up vaccination. Girls as young as 9 could begin the vaccination series.

The FDA, ACIP, and other groups, including the American Cancer Society, recommend three shots over the course of six months for girls and women who have not previously been exposed to HPV. As of 2007, clinical trials had followed women for only about five years, so it was not known how long the vaccine would provide protection or if booster vaccinations might be needed later on.

After the ACIP recommended the vaccine for girls and young women, some states introduced legislation to make the vaccinations mandatory. Such legislation would apply to school vaccine requirements, which are determined by state governments, not the federal government. On Feb. 2, 2007, Governor Rick Perry of Texas issued the first state mandate that all girls entering sixth grade, with some exceptions, be vaccinated. Some parents, advocacy groups, and public health officials opposed the mandate. This opposition caused Merck, Gardasil's manufacturer, to cease its lobbying efforts with state legislatures for fear that the strong public reaction against mandatory vaccination would undermine the strength of the recommendations drafted by the federal government and groups such as the American Cancer Society.

In a national estimate released in February 2007, federal investigators from the CDC and the National Institutes of Health reported that one in four women aged 14 to 59 was infected with HPV. The highest prevalence (44.8 percent) occurred in women aged 20 to 24. According to the American Cancer Society, as many as 11,150 women will develop cervical cancer in the United States in 2007, and about 3,670 women will die from it. For 2005, the National Disease and Therapeutic Index estimated that physicians had 357,000 first-time visits by women with HPV.

Healthier eating in the Big Apple. Diners in New York City may be more heart-healthy after the New York City Board of Health voted to require all restaurants to slash trans fats from their menu offerings and some restaurants to post the caloric content of the food. On Dec. 6, 2006, the city became the first in the nation to issue regulations in hopes of decreasing cholesterol levels and obesity among its residents.

Trans fats are liquid oils that have been *hydrogenated* (processed with hydrogen) to increase shelf life and improve the stability of flavor. Thought to be more harmful than saturated fats, trans fats increase the levels of low-density lipoprotein (LDL) in the blood, a particularly bad type of cholesterol that contributes to the risk of heart disease and stroke.

The ban against trans fats applies to all restaurants, from high-end to fast food. No more oils, margarines, or shortenings containing more than 0.5 grams (0.02 ounce) of trans fat per serving will be allowed on restaurant menus after July 1, 2008. Customers may have to say goodbye to items like chips, cakes, cookies, and some breads and salad dressings. Customers can make healthier food choices by reading the food content labeling that will be posted at all fast-food restaurants in the city.

Chefs around the city expressed concern that without trans fats, flavor would suffer. They predicted difficulty in finding a good-tasting substitute to cook deep-fried foods and other items such as doughnuts and biscuits. In response, the board of health set a later deadline for these fried foods to meet the regulatory ban. Some restaurants, including Wendy's national fast-food hamburger chain, have already switched from trans fats.

Measles goal surpassed. It is not often that the public health community can meet lofty goals for improving global health; however, UNICEF and the World Health Organization (WHO) reported that the goal to cut the incidence of measles by half had been surpassed. The United Nations (UN) General Assembly Special Session on Children had adopted the goal in 2002. In 2005, 345,000 people were estimated to have died from measles, representing a 60-percent reduction from the 873,000 who died in 1999.

Laura Wolfson and colleagues with the Measles Initiative—a partnership of the Red Cross, UNICEF, WHO, the CDC, and the UN—estimated that measles killed nearly 7.5 million people from 1999 through 2006. "The largest percentage reduction in estimated measles mortality

A clerk sorts packaged produce in a food market (above). In September 2006, the U.S. Food and Drug Administration advised consumers not to eat bagged fresh spinach because the product may be contaminated with a particularly dangerous strain of *Escherichia coli* bacteria, *E. coli* O157:H7. *E. coli* often lives harmlessly in the intestines of people, cattle, and other animals. However, *E. coli* O157:H7 caused nearly 200 people from 26 states to become seriously ill, and killed at least 3 people. The source of the infection was traced to a spinach farm in California. For a two-week period, California farmers were prohibited from selling spinach.

Farmers inspect their crop prior to sending it to market (below). On September 29, the ban on fresh spinach was lifted.

PUBLIC HEALTH continued

BIRD FLU CONTINUES

Workers on a poultry farm near Jakarta, Indonesia, sort birds suspected of being infected with avian influenza, also called bird flu. The type A influenza virus that causes bird flu is commonly carried by waterfowl, seabirds, and shore birds. However, domestic birds—such as chickens, turkeys, and ducks—are likely to develop a fatal form of the disease if they are infected. Bird flu can also be fatal to human beings, though person-to-person transmission remains limited. In June 2006, the World Health Organization (WHO) reported that eight people in a single family in Indonesia had infected one another with the disease. From 2003 to mid-2007, nearly 200 people worldwide died of bird flu.

during this period was in the western Pacific region (81 percent), followed by Africa (75 percent) and the eastern Mediterranean region (62 percent). Africa achieved the largest total reduction, contributing 72 percent of the global reduction in measles mortality," they wrote in the Jan. 20, 2007, issue of *The Lancet*.

Children die of measles in poor nations because they have not been given the vaccine, which costs 16 cents per dose. In Africa, an aggressive immunization program saved more than

1.6 million children. In contrast, more than 100,000 children continue to die each year from measles in India, which has not adopted the program promoted by UNICEF and WHO. "From 2000 to 2005, more than 362 million children aged 9 months to 14 years received measles vaccine through supplementary immunisation activities in the 47 priority countries," reported Wolfson and her colleagues. In 2005, a new goal was set: a 90 percent reduction in measles deaths by 2010.   ■ Deborah Kowal

SCIENCE AND SOCIETY

On April 2, 2007, the Supreme Court of the United States ruled that the U.S. Environmental Protection Agency (EPA) had the power to regulate greenhouse gas emissions from automobiles. The administration of U.S. President George W. Bush had argued that the EPA did not have that authority. Justice John Paul Stevens, writing for the 5–4 majority, stated that the only way the EPA could avoid taking action was "if it determines that greenhouse gases do not contribute to climate change"—a decision that seems unlikely in view of the mounting scientific evidence. Environmentalists hailed the court ruling as a landmark.

A major contribution to the scientific evidence was the 2007 report of the Intergovernmental Panel on Climate Change (IPCC), the second installment of which was released in Brussels, Belgium, on April 6. The IPCC was created in 1988 by two United Nations bodies—the World Meteorological Organization and the U.N. Environment Programme—to assess the risk of climate change caused by human activity. The panel does not perform research of its own; rather, it operates through working groups involving hundreds of scientists from all over the world who analyze thousands of peer-reviewed scientific publications. Every few years, beginning in 1990, the IPCC has issued a report reflecting the consensus of the scientists in its working groups on the state of knowledge about climate change and its implications. Most governments regard these reports as authoritative sources of information on global climate. Release of the 2007 report (the first in six years) began on February 2, when the IPCC published its summary for policymakers of the current science on climate change. On April 6, it released a summary of the expected consequences of the warming trends it has identified. The full report is scheduled for publication in November.

The February 2007 report stated that the evidence for warming, based on observations of air and ocean temperatures averaged across the entire world, was "unequivocal" and that it is "very likely" that emissions of greenhouse gases from human activities are the principal cause. The second report was equally strong in stating the severity of the problem and warning that the poorest countries will sustain the most serious impact. As global temperatures increase, these nations will face flooding of coastal areas, droughts, and increased threats of hunger and disease. The report also noted that numerous species of plants and animals face extinction if temperatures continue to rise.

As the scientific evidence grows stronger, public opinion and the views of political and business leaders have also begun to shift. Former Vice President Al Gore's film on global climate change, *An Inconvenient Truth,* received the Academy Award for best documentary film of 2007. Although President Bush described global warming as "a serious challenge" in his 2007 State of the Union address, he has opposed taking strong action to deal with the issue. The U.S. Congress, however, led by the Democrats after the 2006 elections, has taken a more aggressive approach. As of early April 2007, at least 10 bills to mitigate climate change were under consideration in the Senate and the House of Representatives.

Some U.S. states have taken aggressive measures to address the issue of climate change. On July 31, 2006, Governor Arnold Schwarzenegger of California, the nation's most populous state, announced an agreement to diversify energy sources away from those that produce greenhouse gases. Several months later, Schwarzenegger and the governors of Washington, Oregon, Arizona, and New Mexico announced a joint action initiative supporting the development of programs that reduce greenhouse gas emissions. Other states, including New York, took similar actions.

Evolution advocates score victories. A federal judge's decision in late 2005 that "intelligent design theory" is religion and not science and therefore could not be taught in public school science classes was a resounding defeat for the intelligent design (ID) movement. ID advocates see their ideas as an alternative to the theory of evolution, which was popularized by Charles Darwin in the mid-1800's and is accepted throughout the scientific community. Although opposition to the teaching of evolution by those who feel it contradicts the Bible continues to simmer in many places around the country, advocates of teaching evolution scored a number of additional victories both in the voting booth and in the courts.

SCIENCE AND SOCIETY continued

CLONING CONTROVERSY

Protesters dressed as cows demonstrate in Washington, D.C., against a report issued by the U.S. Food and Drug Administration (FDA) in December 2006. The FDA concluded that meat and milk from cloned animals is safe for human consumption. (Cloning is the process of creating an exact genetic duplicate of an organism.) According to the FDA, meat and other products from cloned cows, pigs, and goats do not differ in any way from those of naturally born animals. However, some consumer advocates expressed concern that insufficient testing had been done to allow such products to enter the human food chain, and some animal rights activists believe that cloning harms animals. The FDA planned to continue discussions of the issue throughout 2007.

In February 2006, the state school board of Ohio rejected a measure to introduce "critical analysis" of evolution (a technique used by creationists and ID advocates to challenge the concept of evolution) into the science curriculum. In September, the school board, facing a similar proposal, chose to table it indefinitely. In Kansas, where control of the state school board has flip-flopped between pro- and antievolution advocates, voters defeated several antievolution incumbents in the Aug. 1, 2006, primary election, assuring a proevolution majority on the board. In February 2007, the new board reversed the previous board's policy and approved a set of state science standards that included goals for learning about evolution.

In Cobb County, Georgia, in December 2006, the school board dropped a proposal to place warning stickers in biology textbooks. The stickers, which school officials had put in the textbooks in 2002, cautioned students that the books contained information on evolution, that "evolution is a theory, not a fact," and that it should be "critically considered." In response to a lawsuit filed by local parents, a federal judge had ruled in January 2005 that the stickers were religiously motivated and violated the First Amendment of the Constitution, which provides for the separation of church and state. The school board had appealed the decision but, faced with mounting legal costs and probable defeat, abandoned the sticker proposal.

FDA proposes policy on cloned food. On Dec. 28, 2006, six years after it began considering the issue, the U.S. Food and Drug Administration (FDA) issued a draft report concluding that milk and meat from cloned farm animals are safe for people to eat. The agency, which is responsible for regulating food safety, based its report on a detailed review of the scientific literature and studies (some of which were conducted by companies in the business of cloning) that found cloned animals "virtually indistinguishable" from noncloned livestock. Consumer advocacy organizations, such as the Center for Food Safety, immediately criticized the draft policy, saying that studies were not conclusive. They also pointed out that many people are opposed to cloning and would not buy milk or meat from cloned animals. Although the FDA decision might mean that products from cloned livestock would someday be sold to consumers, they are not likely to be widely available soon because of the high cost of cloning technology.

States take lead in stem cell research. On July 18, 2006, the U.S. Senate, by a vote of 63-37, passed H.R. 810, "The Stem Cell Research Enhancement Act." The bill had passed the House of Representatives in February 2006 by a 238-194 margin. It was intended to liberalize federal policy governing human embryonic stem cell research by allowing the government to fund research using stem cells derived from embryos that had

been donated from in vitro fertilization clinics and that would have otherwise been discarded. (Stem cells have the ability to develop into any of the different cell types that make up the tissues and organs of the body.) As expected, President Bush, who placed strict limits on embryonic stem research in 2001, quickly vetoed the bill and Congress failed to muster the votes necessary to override his veto. The bill was reintroduced in January 2007 and easily passed both the House and Senate. President Bush again vetoed the bill. While the Senate was within one vote of the two-thirds majority needed to override a veto, the House was 35 votes short, so the veto was expected to stand.

Opponents of embryonic stem cell research advocate the use of adult stem cells, suggesting that they have similar potential for medical breakthroughs without the ethical issues associated with the destruction of human embryos. In 2007, however, a key study thought to demonstrate the possibilities of adult stem cells was found to be flawed. The study, done by University of Minnesota researchers, had suggested that cells derived from the bone marrow of adult mice could grow into other kinds of tissue, including bone, brain, and blood. Since the study's publication in the journal *Nature* in 2002, other researchers had found it difficult to replicate its results. In response, the University of Minnesota convened a panel to review the study. Although the panel did not find any fabrication of research results or other misconduct, its report, completed in February 2007, indicated that the study had enough errors to call its conclusions into question.

Meanwhile, a growing number of states, unwilling to wait for the federal government, have begun their own programs to fund embryonic stem cell research. The most ambitious is California, which passed Proposition 71, a 10-year, $3-billion bond issue, in 2004. Stem cell opponents, seeking to derail the effort, launched a number of legal challenges. In February 2007, however, the California Institute for Regenerative Medicine, which had been created to develop and carry out the stem cell research program, awarded its first grants, using a $150-million state loan approved by Governor Schwarzenegger. A number of other states, including New Jersey, Maryland, Illinois, and Massachusetts, passed laws encouraging or providing funding for such research. ■ Albert H. Teich

SPACE TECHNOLOGY

Scientists made progress assembling the International Space Station (ISS) in low-Earth orbit and taking some first steps to move beyond to the moon and Mars in 2006. But a damaging hailstorm reminded would-be space travelers that even the best plans for unraveling the mysteries of space can be thrown off schedule by natural events.

Space shuttle mission. Three space shuttle missions resumed assembly of the space station after an almost three-year delay caused by the deadly Columbia accident. Then, in February 2007, a sudden hailstorm at Kennedy Space Center in Florida pummeled the soft insulating foam on the shuttle Atlantis's huge external propellant tank. The hail damaged the tank extensively as it stood on the pad with Atlantis, about three weeks before its scheduled launch date. The incident raised fears that, even after repairs, a chunk of the foam might fall off and crack part of the delicate thermal protection system that shields the orbiter and its crew from the blazing heat of reentry, repeating what happened on Columbia's final flight.

NASA's shuttle engineers analyzed repair techniques and tested them in wind tunnels to ensure that the repairs could withstand the high speed, heat, and vibration of the launch. Atlantis was rolled back to the huge Vehicle Assembly Building at the Kennedy Center, where crews sanded and plugged hundreds of dents and divots in the upper reaches of the damaged tank. The original March 15 launch date came and went.

Once underway, STS-117 repeated on the *starboard* (right) side of the space station what the crew of STS-115 accomplished on the *port* (left) side after the earlier shuttle's launch on Sept. 9, 2006. The members of STS-115 used the robot arms on the station and on Atlantis to pull a 13.8-meter (45-foot) section of the station's backbone truss out of the cargo bay and bolt it to the station. Folded against it was a 73-meter (240-foot) solar array and the machinery needed to keep it rotating as the ISS orbits Earth so that sunlight can fall directly on its electricity-producing surfaces.

The STS-115 mission went well. The shuttle and station crews easily lifted the truss section from Atlantis with the shuttle's robot arm and handed it to the station's arm. That arm, in turn, moved it to the short section of truss already

installed on the port side of the station and held it in place while mechanical bolts fastened it there permanently. After that, NASA astronauts Heidemarie Stefanyshyn-Piper, Joe Tanner, and Dan Burbank and Canadian astronaut Steve MacLean made three spacewalks. During the walks, they attached all the wires and cooling pipes connecting the new truss section and its big solar arrays to the station's electric power grid and the network of plumbing that keeps it cool enough to operate properly in the unrelenting sunlight.

Under the watchful eye of Atlantis's crew, which also included Commander Brent Jett and Pilot Chris Ferguson, and the crew of the ISS—Expedition 13 Commander Pavel Vinogradov of Russia, Flight Engineer Jeff Williams of the United States, and Thomas Reiter of Germany—ground controllers in Houston unfurled the arrays to their full length, winding them out carefully from their canisters. The maneuver was successful, and the crew landed safely at Kennedy on September 21.

In December 2006, another astronaut crew took up the shuttle Discovery to continue the work. STS-116 Mission Commander Mark Polansky, Pilot William Oefelein, and Mission Specialists Robert Curbeam, Joan Higginbotham, Nicholas Patrick, and Christer Fuglesang of Sweden worked with the ISS crew to install a short section of truss called a spacer on the port end of the truss. Then they struggled unsuccessfully to furl up an old solar array that was blocking the new array delivered by Atlantis in September. Curbeam, Fuglesang, and NASA's Sunita Williams, who had hitched a ride on Discovery to replace Reiter as ISS flight engineer, donned spacesuits for three spacewalks to connect more cables and cooling pipes and to shake, prod, and poke the balky array. When it still refused to cooperate, Curbeam and Fuglesang conducted an unplanned fourth spacewalk to work with the array until it folded up properly.

While the combined shuttle and station crews worked in space—NASA's Michael Lopez-Alegria and Russia's Mikhail Tyurin had replaced Vinogradov and Jeff Williams on the ISS—ground controllers in Houston worked on a tightly choreographed series of commands to activate the station's permanent power and cooling systems. The work had to be done carefully to avoid exposing the spacewalkers to electric shock or damaging the new equipment. In a process

WORK ON THE SPACE STATION RESUMES

NASA astronaut Heidemarie M. Stefanyshyn-Piper adjusts a mechanism that keeps solar array panels pointed toward the sun as the International Space Station (ISS) orbits Earth in September 2006. Stefanyshyn-Piper, who flew to the ISS aboard the space shuttle Atlantis, was part of the first crew to resume space station assembly since the deadly Columbia accident of 2003.

officials said was like rewiring a house while living in it, controllers eventually sent about 17,900 commands to the space station during the mission—about 5,000 more than had ever been sent during a single mission—to complete the job.

Ultimately the big array was set in motion, and Discovery was able to return to Kennedy Space Center on December 22 after some weather delays. On the ISS, the crew settled in for a festive Christmas in space, followed by a lot of hard work getting the station ready for the mission to come in June.

None of the space station work would have been possible without the bravery of the astronauts who flew the STS-121 mission on Discovery, which was the second of two test flights designed to check out the safety techniques developed after the tragic *Columbia* accident in 2003. Commander Steven W. Lindsey, Pilot Mark E. Kelly, and Mission Specialists Michael E. Fossum, Lisa M. Nowak, Piers J. Sellers, and Stephanie D. Wilson lifted off on July 4, 2006, with Reiter aboard as a passenger to reach his

ISS post. They spent almost 13 days testing repair techniques for the heat shield and fixing wear and tear on the station. The flight was billed as the most photographed mission in shuttle history, because engineers wanted to monitor the spacecraft carefully to ensure that no piece of insulating foam would fall off the external propellant tank and damage the heat shield, as had happened on Columbia.

Discovery also delivered some 3,357 kilograms (7,400 pounds) of badly needed supplies to sustain Vinogradov, Williams, and Reiter. Reiter became the first European Space Agency (ESA) astronaut to serve a long-duration mission on the ISS. Discovery returned to a safe landing at Kennedy on July 17, and shuttle managers were able to declare the shuttle ready for normal operations as a result.

Advances in commercial spaceflight. Promoters of private spaceflight made some important advances in 2006 that could one day allow tourists to enjoy the views of Earth from space or perhaps even go to the moon and

SPACE TECHNOLOGY continued

beyond. On July 12, a Ukrainian rocket launched Genesis 1, an unmanned, inflatable test structure paid for by Robert Bigelow, a wealthy businessman in Las Vegas, Nevada. Bigelow hopes to develop private space stations where anyone with the price of admission can spend time in space. The price is expensive—at least $4.5 million a month for a stripped-down half-module—but Bigelow and other private spaceflight developers hope that if enough customers sign up, the cost will come down to affordable rates for many passengers.

Since the space shuttle fleet is retiring in 2010 and Russia charges $25 million for a round-trip flight to the ISS on one of its Soyuz capsules, several people are working to build less expensive rockets for future private space adventurers to use. Among them are Sir Richard Branson, a British businessman who owns Virgin Atlantic Airlines, and Jeff Bezos, who founded Amazon.com. NASA has put up almost $500

million in seed money for private rockets to deliver cargo and perhaps crew to the ISS. The space agency is also offering cash prizes to encourage companies to develop other technology needed for future public and private human space exploration as part of its plan to return to the moon by 2020 in order to use it as a stepping stone to Mars.

Mars missions. Mars continued to receive a lot of attention from Earth's robotic explorers. NASA's Mars Exploration rovers continued to explore on opposite sides of the Red Planet for a third year, far exceeding their planned service life of 90 days. Above the pinkish skies overhead, a fleet of sophisticated orbiters returned more evidence of water on Mars.

The Mars Global Surveyor (MGS) that NASA sent into orbit around Mars in 1997 spotted two places where water has gushed onto the surface since 1999, when the MGS first finished photographing most of the planet. The

MISSION TO MARS

NASA's Mars Reconnaissance Orbiter (above), which reached the Red Planet in March 2006, uses its Shallow Subsurface Radar (SHARAD) to scan below the planet's surface in an artist's rendering. SHARAD seeks out and maps ice, rock, and any liquid water deposits present at depths of up to about 1 kilometer (0.6 mile). An image taken by one of the orbiter's cameras (right) in September reveals a series of sand dunes and buttes (steep, flat-topped hills) in an area where erosion has exposed underlying layers (depicted as dark-toned bands).

orbiter's cameras sent back pictures of ice or mineral deposits taken in 2005 that were not there the first time the area had been photographed. The photos suggest that water is still bursting out from underground reservoirs to the surface, where it quickly freezes and evaporates in the thin, cold atmosphere.

Unfortunately, the MGS fell silent in November 2006 and was never recovered—probably a victim of battery failure caused by a faulty computer command from the ground. But like the rovers Spirit and Opportunity, the MGS far outlived its expected service life. The rovers themselves kept on delivering. Opportunity finally made its way to the Victoria Crater, which is 70 meters (230 feet) deep. Scientists used the robot's eyes to study the layers of rock exposed on the crater's walls, hoping to learn more about a time when the planet was covered with liquid water that might have supported life.

Also delivering important data were NASA's new Mars Reconnaissance Orbiter (MRO), which reached the planet in March 2006, and the ESA's Mars Express orbiter. The MRO delivered images and data on rock layers that added a new dimension to the information returned by the rovers on the surface. Mars Express found there is enough water frozen into ice at the south polar region to cover the entire planet with 11 meters (36 feet) of liquid water. The European orbiter's radar has measured ice layers as thick as 3.7 kilometers (2.3 miles).

Built by Italian industry, the radar on Mars Express, called MARSIS, beams radio waves of very long wavelengths—230 to 980 meters (750 to 3,200 feet). Such long radio waves are designed not to make images, but rather to penetrate the surface of Mars and probe layers down to depths of many kilometers. This type of radar sounder has been employed on Earth but not previously on Mars. It is the most direct way to search for ice beneath the surface of Mars and to measure the thickness of the polar caps. The MARSIS transmits radio waves into the surface and detects changes in the returned waves that indicate the presence of boundaries or layers in the subsurface. At the south pole of Mars, the radio waves were reflected from a boundary as deep as 3.7 kilometers (2.3 miles) below the surface of some parts of the polar cap. The signal that came back to the Mars Express antenna was so strong that apparently little absorption or loss of energy occurred in the intervening depths, suggesting that the radio waves were transmitted through relatively clean water ice—that is, with 10 percent or less dust. While some carbon dioxide ice might be present

below the surface, measurements of the top of the permanent cap by other instruments show that it is mostly water ice.

News from Jupiter and Saturn. A fast-moving space probe took some snapshots of the fifth planet from the sun—massive Jupiter—as the spacecraft zipped past on its way to distant Pluto. NASA's nuclear-powered New Horizons spacecraft turned on its cameras and other sensors to collect new details about Jupiter's turbulent atmosphere and the behavior of some of its many moons. Among spectacular shots New Horizons delivered was one showing volcanic plumes soaring into space over the surface of the moon Io.

Even more distant from the sun, the Cassini orbiter continued its study of the ringed planet Saturn and Saturn's own set of moons. The NASA spacecraft has delivered never-before-seen views of the planet and its rings. Its imaging radar has revealed what may be a huge sea of liquid on the moon Titan—probably liquid methane or ethane—in the northern latitudes where earlier it had found smaller features that appear to be lakes. The Cassini probe carries a variety of instruments designed to penetrate the thick fog of Titan's atmosphere. The radar system, in particular, takes advantage of the transparency of clouds and haze to radio waves, and scientists can construct images of the surface from the radio waves bounced off it as the orbiter passes by.

Titan's newly discovered sea, which is bigger than Lake Superior between the United States and Canada, offers new evidence that the weird moon has weather that produces features like those on Earth, but with different chemistry. Instead of water evaporating to form clouds and falling as rain to create rivers and seas, Titan's weather takes place at such cold temperatures that methane—a gas on Earth—condenses into rain and flows on the surface like water.

News from the inner solar system. ESA's Venus Express entered orbit around that planet in April 2006 and had a very productive first year. Like Titan, Venus is shrouded in clouds, and Venus Express was designed to study those clouds and the terrain beneath them in a systematic way. At the end of the first year in orbit, it had delivered three-dimensional (3-D) data on the sulfuric acid clouds in the atmosphere, temperature readings on the surface at various altitudes, and photos of the swirling atmosphere as seen from space.

Passing by Venus in October 2006 was NASA's Messenger probe, which is following a circuitous route as it makes its way to orbit

SPACE TECHNOLOGY continued

Mercury in 2011. Messenger passed within 3,000 kilometers (1,870 miles) of Venus on its first pass and dipped to an altitude of only 313 kilometers (195 miles) on a second pass on June 5, 2007, to pick up speed for the final leg of its journey with a slingshot gravity assist.

NASA's twin Stereo spacecraft produced their first 3-D images of the sun in March 2007, mimicking human eyes in giving slightly different perspectives of the same scene. The human brain translates those differences into depth perception. Scientists operating the two Stereo spacecraft used powerful computers to generate 3-D pictures that can be seen with special glasses. Launched together in October 2006, the almost identical spacecraft are gradually separating in different solar orbits—one in front of Earth and one trailing it. Researchers will use the high-resolution 3-D images of the sun and the streams of particles it releases into space to learn more about the powerful solar storms that can disrupt communications on Earth and may someday endanger astronauts on the moon or en route to Mars.

Earth probes. While many robotic probes venture away from Earth to advance scientific knowledge about other worlds, many more orbit this planet to track weather and learn more about the changing environment that sustains humankind. Last year, a pair of spacecraft developed jointly by the United States and Germany—known together as the Gravity Recovery and Climate Experiment (GRACE)—took careful measurements of the gravity beneath them. By literally measuring its mass, they found that the ice at both of Earth's poles is melting rapidly as global temperature levels rise.

In Greenland alone, the thick ice is melting at the rate of almost 240 cubic kilometers (58 cubic miles) a year, and the rate of melting is increasing rapidly. The GRACE satellites have detected similar melting in Antarctica. Scientists worry that the large influx of water previously locked in the ice will cause a significant rise in the average sea level around the world, threatening low-lying coastal and island territories.

■ Frank Morring, Jr.

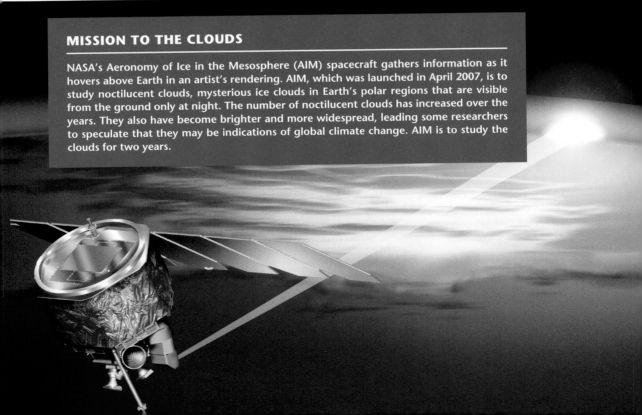

MISSION TO THE CLOUDS

NASA's Aeronomy of Ice in the Mesosphere (AIM) spacecraft gathers information as it hovers above Earth in an artist's rendering. AIM, which was launched in April 2007, is to study noctilucent clouds, mysterious ice clouds in Earth's polar regions that are visible from the ground only at night. The number of noctilucent clouds has increased over the years. They also have become brighter and more widespread, leading some researchers to speculate that they may be indications of global climate change. AIM is to study the clouds for two years.

The Threat of Space Junk

Wherever people go, garbage follows. Space is no exception. Since the 1950's, more than 11,000 artificial objects larger than 10 centimeters (4 inches) have entered Earth orbit, and most of them are junk. The total includes functioning satellites, fragments of rockets that exploded, cameras, and a glove that astronauts accidentally let float away. Space professionals call human-made objects other than working satellites *orbital debris.*

In the ocean of space, even tiny pieces of this debris can threaten the survival of spacecraft and astronauts. The reason is the great speed at which objects in space are traveling. Objects in orbit, such as the space shuttle and the International Space Station (ISS), for example, travel about 28,000 kilometers (17,500 miles) per hour. That is several times faster than a bullet fired by a high-powered rifle. Even a tiny object can have a large impact when it is traveling that fast.

After one early space shuttle mission in the 1980's, technicians noticed a nick in the orbiter's thick glass windshield. They determined that it had been caused by a collision with a speck of dried paint that had flaked off another spacecraft. In 1996, a fragment of an old rocket hit a communications spacecraft at 51,000 kilometers (31,500 miles) per hour and broke off a piece of the satellite.

Not all space junk has been created by accident. Decades ago, Russia and the United States deliberately destroyed spacecraft in tests of anti-satellite weapons. But after scientists and engineers became concerned about the growing threat of space junk, no nation conducted such a test again—until Jan. 11, 2007. China hit one of its own aging weather satellites with a missile. That weapons test increased the number of large pieces of orbiting junk by 10 percent.

"This is by far the worst satellite fragmentation in the history of the space age," Nicholas L. Johnson told *Aviation Week & Space Technology* magazine, which first reported the Chinese test. Even before that explosion, Johnson, the chief scientist specializing in orbital debris at the National Aeronautics and Space Administration (NASA), was worried. He and others said that the amount of debris in orbit had reached the point that a single collision could set off a slow chain reaction of more collisions, more fragments of debris, more collisions, and so on.

Operators of spacecraft have three basic approaches to dealing with the threat of orbital debris. The first strategy is simply to take one's chances. Most space junk is in relatively low orbit, so it doesn't seriously threaten communications satellites, most of which are in high orbits. Because no astronauts are on-board these spacecraft, accepting the risk they face seems reasonable.

The second strategy is to have a plan to get out of the way. The space shuttle, for example, has been maneuvered in orbit to avoid colliding with debris. For that to work, however, the junk has to be detected and tracked. Objects measuring 10-centimeters or more are cataloged and tracked by the United States Space Surveillance Network, using radar and telescopes.

CONTINUED

The third strategy for dealing with the debris threat is to design spacecraft to take a hit without suffering catastrophic damage. The ISS has layers of shielding designed to slow small debris to the point that it cannot puncture the walls of the modules in which astronauts work and live.

Occasionally, space junk presents a hazard on the ground. Objects in Earth orbit enter the atmosphere far more frequently than most people realize—on average, about one cataloged object a day. Sometimes, objects such as satellites decay, eventually, leaving their orbits. The intense heating during reentry through Earth's atmosphere causes most spacecraft to break apart and burn up. In 1979, however, when NASA's Skylab space station plummeted back to Earth, large portions landed in the desert of Australia. Rocket parts and fuel tanks have also survived reentry and struck Earth. Fortunately, there has been only one documented case of a piece of orbital debris hitting someone on the ground, and it was too small to cause injury.

Predicting precisely when and where an uncontrolled object in space will come back to Earth is virtually impossible. But even though the likelihood of a piece of a satellite hitting a person or building is extremely low, most spacefaring nations now consider it irresponsible not to plan for the safe disposal of spacecraft. After the space shuttle reaches orbit with its large external fuel tank still attached, astronauts perform a maneuver so that the discarded tanks can break up safely over the Indian Ocean.

ORBITAL DEBRIS

The locations and concentrations of objects drifting in low-Earth orbit (the region of space within 2,000 kilometers [1,243 miles] of Earth's surface) are depicted in a computer-generated graphic. Space junk, officially known as orbital debris, makes up 95 percent of the objects in this region.

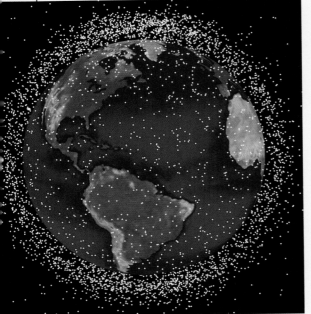

A large zone in the South Pacific Ocean has been established as a safe area in which to dispose of spacecraft in lower orbits. Instead of leaving reentry to chance, the goal is to leave enough fuel on board to de-orbit a satellite so that it is deliberately crashed into the ocean. In 2001, Russia conducted such a controlled destruction of its obsolete Mir space station. At 120 metric tons (132 tons), Mir is the largest object to reenter the atmosphere.

For some aging satellites, a better strategy is to move them higher to get them out of the way. Most communications satellites are in orbits 35,786 kilometers (22,236 miles) high. Those orbits are said to be *geosynchronous,* because a satellite at that distance orbits Earth exactly once a day. That makes it stationary in relation to points on the ground, since Earth turns at the same rate. For these spacecraft, the accepted procedure is to retain enough fuel at the end of their useful life to boost them 300 kilometers (186 miles) higher to a "graveyard" orbit where they will stay for eternity.

Engineers have devised schemes to remove human-made debris from space, but so far the ideas have been deemed too expensive. For that reason, the focus will likely remain on minimizing the chances that new space junk will be created. ■ James R. Asker

SUPPLEMENT

New encyclopedia articles are devoted
to the following topics:

Shrek (2001) is one of the most popular animated motion pictures ever made. The computer-generated comedy tells about a green ogre named Shrek, who falls in love with the Princess Fiona. Other characters are Shrek's wisecracking donkey and the ogre's rival for Fiona, Lord Farquaad.

Animation

Animation is a visual technique that creates the illusion of motion, rather than recording motion through live action. The technique is used mainly for motion pictures and video games. Animation can be created by illustrators, filmmakers, video makers, and computer specialists. Advertisers also employ animation to develop commercials for television. In addition, producers of instructional films may use animation to help explain a difficult idea or one that could not be shown in live action. Animation can also be combined with live action in a movie.

In the past, in making an animated film, a filmmaker would photograph a series of drawings or objects one by one. Each drawing or object takes up one frame of the film. The position of a character or scene changes slightly from frame to frame. When the film is shown through a projector, the pictures appear to move.

Animation can exist with little technology. One simple animation device is the *flip book*, a group of sketches in sequence placed one on top of the other. When a viewer flips the pages rapidly, the images appear to move.

Since the late 1900's, however, *digital technology* has dominated animation. Digital technology includes computers and other types of electronic equipment and applications that use information in the form of numeric code. Digital technology can add to or replace traditional techniques by creating animation partly or entirely using a computer. Computers have become so common in film, video, and animation production that almost every moving image made today is generated on a computer to some extent.

Through the digital revolution, animators have many technical choices available when they create a movie. Digital technology has made possible greater realism, more exciting special effects, and more elaborate fantasy stories. However, technology alone does not attract or entertain audiences. An interesting story and appealing characters will always be necessary.

This article will discuss the preliminary steps in creating an animated film, the different paths followed by traditional hand-drawn animation and by computer animation, and the history of animation.

Preliminary steps in animation

The use of computers has brought great changes to animation production. But several processes remain the same in both traditional and digital methods.

The first step in making any animated film is creating a story. After a story has been established, an artist and writer prepare a *storyboard*, which serves as the film's script. The storyboard resembles a giant comic strip. It consists of rough sketches that portray the action of the story, with the dialogue accompanying each sketch.

After the director and other key personnel approve the storyboard, performers make a recording of the dialogue and any music that must be *synchronized* (matched) with the action. The composer and performers carefully follow the storyboard to make sure the mu-

The contributors of this article, John Canemaker and Peter Weishar, are animators who have both written widely on the art of animation. Canemaker is head of the animation program at New York University's Tisch School of the Arts. Weishar is Dean of Film and Digital Media at the Savannah College of Art and Design.

sic and dialogue match each sequence of the action.

Animators synchronize animation to sound using a guide called an *exposure sheet*. The sheet indicates the number of frames needed to express each movement and each word of the recorded dialogue. In computer animation, the artist "digitizes" the sounds so they can be played back as well as visually graphed on the computer screen. Material is digitized by translating it from its original form into a format that a computer can read, electric charges representing numbers.

Up to this point, both computer-animated and traditionally drawn animated productions follow a similar path. But now traditional animation and computer animation diverge.

Traditional animation

In traditional animation, layout artists work with the director to determine what settings will be drawn, how each character will act and look, and how the action can best be broken down into scenes. After these decisions have been made, the layout artists prepare drawings to guide two other groups of artists, called *background artists* and *animators*.

The background artists draw all the backgrounds for the film—that is, everything that will appear on the screen except the characters. The animators make separate drawings of the characters. Working from the exposure sheet, the animators must create the exact number of drawings required by the action and dialogue. In one episode, for example, a character may answer the telephone by saying "Hello." The exposure sheet shows that the word "Hello" requires eight frames. The animators thus must make eight drawings in which the character's mouth moves in sequence to form the word. They must also include all the character's body movements.

In the past, after the animators completed their drawings, another group of artists traced the drawings onto clear sheets of celluloid acetate called *cels*. Tens of thousands of separate cels in sequence were required for a feature-length animation movie, and a lesser number were needed for many television cartoons.

A painting department applied colors to the reverse

Traditional animation Groups of artists, each with separate responsibilities, develop an animated film through thousands of drawings that create the backgrounds and characters which will make up the completed movie.

An artist called an *animator* makes separate drawings of each character, creating the exact number of drawings required to portray all the movements required by the action and dialogue.

Other artists trace the animator's drawings onto clear sheets of celluloid acetate called *cels*. A painting department then applies the necessary colors to the reverse side of the cels, *shown here*.

The finished cels are placed over backgrounds drawn by background artists, *shown here*. Backgrounds also can be scanned and painted on a computer and combined with the characters.

WORLD BOOK photos by John R. Hamilton, Globe Photos

The completed cels are sent to the camera department, where camera operators photograph the cels frame by frame over the proper background, *shown here*. Then the sound track is added.

side of the cels. The completed cels were then sent to the camera department, where camera operators photographed the cels frame by frame over the proper background. The exposure sheets told the camera operator which cels and backgrounds were needed for each frame. After the camera operators completed the photography, the sound track was added. Finally, the studio made prints of the film and released it.

Today, most hand-drawn animated productions use photoelectric devices called *scanners* to translate the drawings from their original form into a format that a computer can read. Artists can then ink and paint the drawings on the computer. The backgrounds are also scanned and painted on the computer and combined with the characters.

Computer animation

The most popular form of animation is called a *computer-generated image* (CGI) or just c*omputer graphics* (CG). Almost every modern film, video, and animation production uses computers to create at least some images. CGI can create the illusion of entire three-dimensional worlds as models inside a computer. These models can include trees, grass, and even weather that interact with believable, but entirely digital, characters.

Generating animation on a computer can be complex. Since the 1980's, the artists in the computer animation and effects industry have become more specialized. Some artists concentrate on modeling figures on the computer and designing *virtual* sets—that is, artificial sets created on a computer. Others concentrate on special effects, such as fire, rain, smoke, and even hair. A computer animator can create such effects by running *dynamic simulation* software. In a dynamic simulation, software calculates the physics of how objects or characters would move and react in the real world and then turns them into computer animation. For example, in a dynamic simulation of marbles pouring out of a cup, the software would figure out the collisions, bouncing, and rolling of the marbles. Without dynamic simulation, an animator would have to spend many hours determining the movement of each marble.

Modeling. To create a character using CGI animation, most designers start with a series of detailed sketches, often along with a small-scale physical model known as a *maquette.* Animators use these aids to study and refine the character from all angles. A CGI artist will then use computer software to create a digital model of the character. This model is not a photograph. It is a three-dimensional computer "sculpture," made of data, that can be viewed from all sides. The digital modeling process can be relatively quick for simple objects. However, a professional computer modeler can spend three or four months building a single character model for a feature production.

Making the model move. After the digital character model is approved, it goes to the *rigging department.* Just as a boat is "rigged" so a sailor can pull ropes to turn and unfurl the sails, a CGI character is rigged so it will move correctly. An artist called a *rigger* creates a computer model called a *skeleton* with "bones" connecting pivot points, called *joints.* The joints are placed wherever the model is expected to rotate or bend. The rigger also sets up a series of restraints on these pivots so the joints move correctly. For example, the fingers on a hand should curl forward, not backward or sideways. The fingers should also stop when they meet the palm of the hand. The rigger often creates dozens of controls to make it easier for the animators to manipulate the character. The skeletons, restraints, and controls are invisible when the final image is generated.

If the character has a speaking part, a rigger poses the face into many different expressions. The rigger labels the expressions (such as "happy" or "sad") and then saves them on the computer. Various mouth shapes are saved as well. When people speak, they make many distinct mouth shapes, such as a circle for an "oh" sound or closed lips for an "em." These shapes correspond to basic sounds of language called *phonemes*. An animator will then *lip-synch,* using the library of phonemes and expressions to match the digitized dialogue track. The correct shapes and expressions create a realistic speaking character.

A common method of computer animation called *keyframe animation* begins when the animator poses the model at different points along a timeline. These poses are known as "key poses" or "keyframes." Each keyframe pose will take up a single frame in the final animation. The computer then *interpolates* (inserts) directions for how the character will move between the frames. The interpolation will determine the smoothest path between the two poses. To make an animation look lifelike, an animator may rework a sequence of keyframes hundreds of times until the final animation looks right.

Another approach to computer modeling and animation is known as *motion capture.* Typically, small reflective dots (also called *pick ups)* are placed along many of a live actor's joints and other key body parts. The actor then moves within a circle of specialized cameras. These cameras record the actor's motion by tracking the dots through space and send the information, in digital form, to a computer. The animator applies the motion data to a computer-generated character, who will then move in the same general way as the live actor. Many video game makers use motion capture for character movement. Filmmakers often use the technique for humanlike creatures, such as Gollum in *The Lord of the Rings* trilogy (2001-2003). *The Polar Express* (2004) used motion capture for all the characters in the movie.

Lighting and rendering. The next steps in the computer animation production process are lighting and creating texture. An artist assigns a *shader* to every object in a computer-generated image. A shader is software code that determines the properties of a surface, such as color, transparency, or reflectivity, or whether it is shiny or dull, smooth or rough. Once the textures are applied to the objects, the frames are lit and *rendered*. In the rendering process, the computer calculates the effects of light, shadow, and color on each object and generates a digital picture of each frame. Rendering can require a great deal of processing time on the computer. All major CGI animation studios have a network of computers known as *render farms* that can consist of hundreds of processors, all devoted to rendering. Computers also assist in editing the final images and the sound track.

Compositing. Computer-animated characters can be combined with live action or with other computer-

Computer animation   Computer animation is the leading animation technique. The photo sequence from the film *The Lord of the Rings* shown here illustrates some of the steps required to create a single frame.

An actor stands on a partial set in front of a blue wall called a *blue screen*. The computer artist can select the blue in a software application and remove that color from the image, thus removing unwanted parts of the scene.

The actor and the set are *composited* (combined) with a computer-generated background.

The Lord of the Rings: The Return of the King © MMIII, New Line Productions, Inc. The Lord of the Rings characters, names, and places therein. ™ The Saul Zaentz Co. d/b/a Tolkien Enterprises under license to New Line Productions, Inc.

The final composited shot includes a model boat enlarged to look like a real sailing ship. Additional actors have been placed in the scene. Deeper shadows and a golden glow have also been added to make the shot appear outdoors at sunset.

animated characters and sets in a process called *compositing.* In compositing, two or more images are combined on one piece of film by photographic or digital means. Compositing can also be used to combine real actors with computer-generated sets and special effects. To do so, actors perform in front of a solid-color green or blue background called a *green screen* or a *blue screen.* A computer removes that single color around the actor's silhouette. The actor can then be *composited* (placed) onto another background, either a digital set that exists only in a computer or a "real" location.

Other kinds of animation

There are several kinds of animation besides hand-drawn and computer-generated animation. They include (1) stop-motion animation, (2) pixilation, (3) pin screen animation, and (4) drawing on film.

Stop-motion animation, also called *puppet animation,* uses three-dimensional figures or objects. To make puppet animation possible, a special camera is stopped after a single frame is photographed. Each time the camera stops, animators make slight adjustments in the positions of the figures or objects. When the frames are projected in rapid succession, the models appear to move. This type of animation is frequently used in making short animated films and sometimes in making feature-length films. Puppet animation also appears in live-action features, such as *King Kong* (1933) and the *Star Wars* movies (1977-2005).

Clay animation is a type of stop-motion animation that uses figures or objects made of clay or plastic. This technique is often used for commercials and short animated films. The American animator Will Vinton patented a form of the technique under the name Claymation.

Pixilation is a way of animating live action. When the camera is stopped, the actors slightly alter their positions. Pixilation makes people look cartoonlike in films.

Pin screen animation is a seldom-used technique that employs a large screen with about 1 million pinholes. Animators place headless pins into the holes and light the screen from the side so that shadows cast by the pins create images. Animators move the pins to change the images. After each change, they photograph the screen to produce a series of frames.

Drawing on film is an inexpensive technique that requires little equipment. The animator draws, paints, stencils, or scratches the sequence of images directly on the film stock, instead of photographing them.

History

Early animation. The first examples of animation were toys developed in the 1800's. One of the earliest devices was the *phenakistoscope,* invented by the Belgian scientist Joseph Antoine Plateau in 1832. It was a notched wheel attached to a handle. One side of the wheel had a series of drawings. The viewer held the wheel up to a mirror, with the drawings facing the mirror. When the viewer spun the wheel and looked through the notches on the blank side of the wheel, the images appeared to move. The phenakistoscope and similar devices contributed to the invention of motion pictures.

Arthur Melbourne-Cooper of England was one of the first to make motion pictures using animation. In 1899,

Photofest

A gorilla puppet was used in the famous motion-picture thriller *King Kong* (1933). Animators used *stop motion,* creating a small model of a gorilla that appeared as a giant on the screen.

Melbourne-Cooper moved matchsticks in different sequences and photographed them frame by frame to produce an advertisement called *Matches: An Appeal.*

J. Stuart Blackton, a British-born American newspaper cartoonist, was the first person to film drawings frame by frame. In 1906, Blackton made *Humorous Phases of Funny Faces* by filming a series of faces drawn on a blackboard.

Émile Cohl of France was another important early animator. Cohl made about 250 short animated films from 1908 to 1918.

Pioneers of American animation. Winsor McCay exhibited his first animated film, *Little Nemo,* in 1911 in

© John Canemaker Collection

An early animated film by Winsor McCay in 1914 starred Gertie the dinosaur. McCay pioneered in creating cartoon characters with flexible movements and distinct personality traits.

New York City. McCay produced films that featured cartoon characters with graceful movements and distinct personality traits. He established the techniques and visual approaches that set the standard for character animation. McCay's work became influential because of its fluid motion, high-quality draftsmanship, and feeling of weight. McCay's most famous animated short film was called *Gertie the Dinosaur* (1914), a story about a trained dinosaur.

In 1914, the American animator John Randolph Bray began streamlining the production processes involved in animation. Under Bray, studios hired large staffs and operated like assembly lines, making cartoons cheaper and faster to produce. Bray collaborated with the animator Earl Hurd, who had patented the cel technique. Together, Bray and Hurd revolutionized the process of animation. Before cels were used, animators had to completely redraw both the characters and the background for each frame in a scene. With cels, however, animators draw the background only once, which saves work.

About 1915, American movie studios began to create cartoon characters who appeared regularly in series of animated films. The *Felix the Cat* series, which debuted in 1919, was produced by cartoonist Pat Sullivan. Felix was the first internationally popular animated character. Animator Otto Messmer created and directed about 175 short Felix films during the 1920's.

Max Fleischer, a former newspaper cartoonist, and his brother Dave produced animated series featuring Koko the Clown, Betty Boop, and Popeye the Sailor. Other well-known cartoon characters of the early 1900's included Krazy Kat and Mutt and Jeff. Some of the characters first appeared in newspaper comic strips.

Animation in Europe. While animators in the United States concentrated on developing cartoon characters, animators in Europe experimented with creative techniques. From 1910 through the 1920's, for example, the Polish-born artist Ladislas Starevitch (also spelled Władysław Starewicz) used puppet animation. Germany's Lotte Reiniger produced short animated films with black silhouettes and created the first feature-length animated film, *Adventures of Prince Achmed* (1926).

Some European artists experimented with abstract animation. The German artists Walter Ruttmann and Oskar Fischinger created animated short films with abstract geometric shapes. In France, Russian-born Alexandre Alexeieff and American-born Claire Parker developed pin screen animation in the early 1930's.

Walt Disney became the most famous producer of animated films. He created such popular cartoon characters as Mickey Mouse, Donald Duck, Goofy, and Pluto. Disney produced *Steamboat Willie,* starring Mickey Mouse, in 1928. It was the first animated cartoon with a synchronized sound track that creatively integrated music, voices, and sound effects. From 1928 to 1939, Disney perfected the character animation film, mainly through his popular cartoon series called *Silly Symphonies.*

In 1937, Disney issued *Snow White and the Seven Dwarfs,* his first full-length animated film. It became one of the most popular films in movie history. Disney died in 1966, but his influence on animated storytelling, design, and artistic theory continues to be felt throughout the animation industry.

Snow White and the Seven Dwarfs was the first feature-length animated film issued by Walt Disney. This frame shows Snow White, the heroine, and Dopey, one of the seven dwarfs.

Animation in the mid-1900's. Along with Disney, several other major film studios dominated the animation industry from the 1930's to the early 1950's. At Metro-Goldwyn-Mayer (MGM), William Hanna and Joseph Barbera made short animated features starring Tom and Jerry, a cat and mouse team. Walter Lantz of Universal Studios produced animated shorts featuring Oswald the Rabbit and later Woody Woodpecker. At Warner Brothers, Tex Avery, Chuck Jones, Bob Clampett, and Friz Freleng directed animated shorts starring Bugs Bunny, Daffy Duck, Elmer Fudd, and Porky Pig.

In 1945, a group of former Disney animation artists established United Productions of America (UPA). This group broke away from Disney's emphasis on realism. Instead, they stressed a bold, flat, modernist style. Famous UPA cartoon characters included Gerald McBoing Boing and Mr. Magoo. UPA also popularized a technique called *limited animation* that differed from the full-figure animation done by Disney. In limited animation, only certain simple movements of a character are animated, allowing portions of the figure to be reused.

The UPA style proved less expensive than full-figure animation and influenced many other studios. The low cost of limited animation made it popular for children's television cartoons, such as "The Flintstones" and "Yogi Bear" by Hanna-Barbera Productions. In 1960, "The Flintstones" became the first animated series to appear on prime-time television.

Over time, some animators left UPA to form their own production companies. Among the most talented was John Hubley. He and his wife, Faith, created films whose playful images and sense of fantasy expanded the content and style of character animation. The Hubleys produced cartoons for the "Sesame Street" TV series and won three Academy Awards for their animated short films *Moonbird* (1959), *The Hole* (1962), and *Herb Alpert and the Tijuana Brass Double Feature* (1966).

During the mid-1950's, the Scottish-born animator Norman McLaren made acclaimed animated films for the National Film Board of Canada. McLaren became known for his technique of drawing directly on film in such productions as *Blinkity Blank* (1955).

The animation revival. Production of feature-length animated cartoons declined from the mid-1950's through the 1960's, partly because of the rising popularity of television. However, a revival of feature-length cartoons began during the 1970's. The American filmmaker Steven Spielberg released his first animated cartoon feature, *An American Tail,* in 1986. The Disney and Spielberg studios jointly produced *Who Framed Roger Rabbit* (1988), which combined live action and animation. Disney followed with several creative and popular features, including *Beauty and the Beast* (1991), *Aladdin* (1992), and *The Lion King* (1994). In 2001, the Academy of Motion Picture Arts and Sciences created a new category for feature-length animated films to receive an Academy Award.

The computer revolution. Computer scientists and artists had begun to experiment with computer visualization in the 1960's. In the early 1970's, a few academic institutions, such as the University of Utah, animated simple shapes with computers. Disney's *TRON* (1982) was the first feature film to use significant amounts of CGI animation. The film was a major technical achievement which proved that computers could be used to create imagery.

The science-fiction film *Jurassic Park* (1993), directed by Spielberg, expanded the use of computer animation. The film combined actual actors and sets with dinosaurs created by Industrial Light & Magic (ILM), a company that develops special visual effects for motion pictures. The computer-generated dinosaurs moved across the screen as realistically as live animals. *Jurassic Park* was a

© Walt Disney Pictures from Shooting Star

Toy Story, released in 1995, was the first feature-length animated motion picture that was entirely computer generated. The movie follows the adventures of toys living in a boy's bedroom.

breakthrough event in the entertainment industry. It proved that computer animation could help filmmakers achieve almost any effect.

In 1995, John Lasseter and Pixar Animation Studios produced an all-CGI feature film, *Toy Story.* The film became a blockbuster hit and elevated CGI from a tool for creating special effects to a unique artistic medium. Pixar went on to produce many box-office hits, including *A Bug's Life* (1998), *Toy Story 2* (1999), *Monsters, Inc* (2001), *Finding Nemo* (2003), and *The Incredibles* (2004).

New diversity. In the 1990's and 2000's, animators used a great variety of methods and styles of animation. Two-dimensional animation continued to thrive, especially on television. Although earlier animation was aimed mainly at children, new animated TV series proved to be popular with older audiences. Such series as "The Simpsons," which began in 1989, and "King of the Hill," which began in 1997, received high audience ratings.

A Japanese style of two-dimensional animation called *anime* also became popular. Anime uses some of the traditions of limited animation, such as characters who speak by moving only their mouths. Many anime characters have distinctively large, saucerlike eyes. In 2003, the Japanese film *Spirited Away* became the first anime production to win the Academy Award as best animated feature film.

A new studio, DreamWorks SKG, began releasing animated features that employed both traditional methods and CGI. DreamWorks issued such popular films as *Antz* and *The Prince of Egypt* (both 1998), *Shrek* (2001) and its sequel *Shrek 2* (2004), and *Over the Hedge* (2006). Aardman Animations, a British studio, produced feature-length films in the clay puppet animation style, including *Chicken Run* (2000) and *Wallace & Gromit: The Curse of the Were-Rabbit* (2005). The American director Tim Burton

© Warner Bros. Inc.

Bugs Bunny and Daffy Duck are two of the most popular characters in animation history. Like many cartoon characters, they are animals who speak, dress, and behave like human beings.

© DreamWorks Animation from ZUMA Press

Stop-motion animation using clay puppets was used to create the popular English animated motion picture *Wallace & Gromit: The Curse of the Were-Rabbit* (2005). The feature-length film portrays the adventures of an inventor named Wallace and his pet dog, Gromit.

used stop-motion animation in making *Tim Burton's The Nightmare Before Christmas* (1993) and *Tim Burton's Corpse Bride* (2005).

International cooperation increased among animation studios in different countries. An example of such cooperation was *The Spongebob Squarepants Movie* (2004), based on a popular TV series. Filmmakers in the United States created storyboards and layouts for the film. They then sent them to South Korea, where artists animated the characters by hand. The film returned to the United States for digital coloring and compositing.

Animation today. Thousands of artists work in animation houses in such countries as South Korea and Japan. They turn out feature-length films as well as cartoons and commercials for television. Many Canadian, U.S., and Russian animators operate smaller studios.

Many movie theaters today have digital projectors that allow a feature to be shot and screened without using film. Many filmmakers choose to shoot their features using high-end digital cameras. They use all digital production to create a feature without developing any film. This enables them to streamline production and better integrate digital sets and characters.

John Canemaker and Peter Weishar

Outline

I. Preliminary steps in animation
II. Traditional animation

III. Computer animation
    A. Modeling
    B. Making the model move
    C. Lighting and rendering
    D. Compositing
IV. Other kinds of animation
    A. Stop-motion animation
    B. Pixilation
    C. Pin screen animation
    D. Drawing on film
V. History

Questions

What is a *storyboard?*
Who starred in *Steamboat Willie?*
How does a *flip book* work?
What was a *phenakistoscope?*
How does puppet animation work?
What is the role of animators in cel animation?
What is CGI?
How did Winsor McCay influence animation?
What is *rendering* in computer animation?
What animation process was used in *The Polar Express?*

Additional resources

Canemaker, John. *Paper Dreams: The Art and Artists of Disney Storyboards.* Hyperion, 1999.
Grant, John. *Masters of Animation.* Watson-Guptill, 2001.
Kanfer, Stefan. *Serious Business: The Art and Commerce of Animation in America from Betty Boop to Toy Story.* Scribner, 1997.
Laybourne, Kit. *The Animation Book.* Rev. ed. Three Rivers Pr., 1998.
Weishar, Peter. *Digital Space: Designing Virtual Environments.* McGraw, 1998.
Woods, Samuel G. *Computer Animation.* Blackbirch Pr., 2000. Younger readers.

The Pyramid of the Sun rises above the Valley of Mexico in the ancient city of Teotihuacán, near present-day Mexico City. The city was an important religious center for the Aztec, though it was built centuries before by a culture unknown to them. The Aztec believed that Teotihuacán had been built by an ancient race of giants. Later, the gods met there and created the world in which the Aztec lived.

Aztec

Aztec were an American Indian people who ruled a mighty empire in Mexico during the 1400's and early 1500's. The Aztec had one of the most advanced civilizations in the Americas. They built cities as large and complex as any in Europe at that time. They also practiced a remarkable religion that affected every part of their lives. To worship their gods, the Aztec developed a sophisticated ritual system, built towering temples, and created huge sculptures. They held impressive religious ceremonies featuring dancing, musical performances, and the bloody sacrifices of animals and human beings.

The name *Aztec* is also commonly applied to the people who founded the city of Tenochtitlan (pronounced *tay nohch TEE tlahn*). It stood on the site of present-day Mexico City and, according to legend, was established in 1325. Its people referred to themselves by the names *Colhua-Mexica, Mexica,* and *Tenochca.* In the 1400's, the city and its allies conquered many groups in central and southern Mexico, forming the Aztec empire. Tenochtitlan became the capital. The empire was destroyed by the Spaniards, who conquered Tenochtitlan in 1521. But the Aztec left a lasting mark on Mexican culture. *Aztec* also refers to this larger group of Indians who made up the empire. This article uses *Aztec* in that sense.

The Aztec empire

The center of Aztec civilization was the Valley of Mexico, a huge, oval basin about 7,500 feet (2,300 meters) above sea level. Although the valley was in the tropics, its high altitude gave it a mild climate. The surrounding lowlands had a hotter, wetter climate.

The Aztec empire included as many as 20 million people in about 400 cities and towns. Most were concentrated in the Valley of Mexico, but the empire extended well beyond that. The largest city was the capital, Tenochtitlan, which occupied an island in Lake Texcoco. *Causeways* (raised earthen roads) linked the city to the mainland. On a nearby island to the north stood the city of Tlatelolco, a commercial center. Both Tenochtitlan and Tlatelolco lay within the borders of what is now Mexico City. Present-day Mexico City covers much of the bed of Lake Texcoco, which was drained during the 1600's. In 1473, warriors of Tenochtitlan conquered Tlatelolco and united the two cities. When the Spaniards arrived in the 1500's, Tenochtitlan may have had a population of 200,000 to 300,000. The Spaniards were astonished by its complexity and richness when they first saw it. No Spanish city had so many people. They compared it to Constantinople (now Istanbul, Turkey), the capital of the Ottoman Empire, and other great European cities.

The emperor of the Aztec was called the *huey tlatoani* (great speaker). A council of high-ranking nobles chose him from the members of the royal family. The emperor, who was considered to have both human and supernatural abilities, had immense political power. However, he had to consult the council of nobles when making important decisions. Military units were stationed in key locations throughout the empire to keep it secure. Most of these units were commanded by a great noble, who often also served as governor of the territory. An elaborate system of government offices administered the affairs of the empire. Many of the top positions were hereditary, but service to the emperor was another way for a person to obtain high office.

Aztec society had four main classes: (1) nobles, (2) commoners, (3) serfs, and (4) slaves. Among nobles and commoners, closely related families belonged to groups called *calpollis*. The members of a calpolli owned an area of land in common, and each family was allowed to farm a plot large enough for its needs. In addition to their calpolli land, most nobles had their own private land or received government land for use during their term in public office. Commoners made up the

---

David Carrasco, the contributor of this article, is Neil L. Rudenstine Professor of the Study of Latin America at Harvard Divinity School and the coauthor of Moctezuma's Mexico: Visions of the Aztec World.

The Aztec empire had its capital at Tenochtitlan, which stood on the site of present-day Mexico City. The empire was established during the 1400's, when the Aztec and their allies conquered much of central and southern Mexico.

WORLD BOOK maps

majority of the population, and many made a living by farming their calpolli plots. Serfs worked the land held by nobles and remained on the land when a new noble acquired it. Slaves were considered property, but their children were born free. Many slaves had been captured in war, and the Aztec also purchased slaves from other groups. Other slaves were criminals or people who could not pay their debts.

Way of life

Religion was extremely important in Aztec life. The people devoted much of their time to religious practices, such as praying, singing, dancing, pilgrimages, and offerings. They even waged war largely to obtain prisoners to sacrifice to their gods.

The Aztec worshiped many gods and goddesses, each of whom ruled one or more human activities or aspects of nature. The Aztec economy was based largely on farming, and so the people had many agricultural divinities. They included Centéotl, a corn god; Tláloc, a rain and fertility god; and Xipe Totec, associated with springtime and regrowth. Other major gods included Tezcatlipoca, an all-powerful divinity; Tonatiuh, the sun god; Mictlantecuhtli, ruler of the dead; and Xiuhtecuhtli, the fire god. Huitzilopochtli, a war god, was the special guardian of the people of Tenochtitlan. Xochiquetzal was a goddess of fertility, weaving and other women's crafts, flowers, and beauty. The god Quetzalcoatl was associated with civilization and learning. However, he sometimes took the form of Ehécatl, god of the wind.

The Aztec held many religious ceremonies. The most important observed planting, harvesting, and other events in the agricultural year. The purpose of many ceremonies was to motivate people to work together to ensure good crops by winning the favor of the gods.

Human and animal sacrifice played a vital role in the ceremonies. The Aztec regarded the human body and all living things as gifts from the gods. They believed that a divine power resided in three parts of the body—the head, the heart, and the liver. The Aztec thought that the gods required a ritual payment in the form of human hearts and blood to remain strong. Human sacrifices were elaborate, dramatic ceremonies designed to magically transform the human victims into living representatives of the gods before they were sacrificed. Often, priests slashed open the chest of a living victim and tore out the heart. Worshippers sometimes ate portions of a victim's body. They may have thought that the dead person's strength and bravery passed to anyone who ate a portion of the flesh. Most victims were male prisoners of war or slaves. The Aztec also sacrificed women and occasionally, to the god Tláloc, children.

Most religious activities took place inside walled ceremonial centers. The chief structures within the centers were *teocallis.* A typical teocalli consisted of a wide, solid base, upon which rose steep stairsteps. Priests climbed the stairs to reach a temple dedicated to a divinity at the top. The ceremonial centers also included royal palaces, gardens, living quarters for priests, sacred pools for ritual cleansing, and racks holding the skulls of sacrificial victims. In addition, many centers had a *tlatchli* (playing court) for a game called *ullamaliztli* that resembled a mixture of soccer and basketball. The players tried to hit a rubber ball through a ring with their hips and knees. They could not use their hands or feet.

The Aztec had a 260-day religious calendar. Priests used the calendar to determine lucky days for such activities as sowing crops, building houses, and going to war. The Aztec also had a 365-day solar calendar. It consisted of 18 months of 20 days each plus 5 extra days.

Drawing from the *Codex Florentino* (mid-1500's); © American Museum of Natural History, New York City

Human sacrifice played a major role in Aztec religion. This drawing by an Aztec artist shows priests cutting out a victim's heart. Clay flutes broken during the ceremony lie nearby.

Xiuhtecuhtli was the Aztec god of fire. This statue shows Xiuhtecuhtli *(shee oo tay KOO tlee)* seated with his arms folded to receive sacrifices. The Aztec worshiped many gods, each of whom ruled one or more human activities or aspects of nature.

Every 52 years, the Aztec held a great celebration called the Binding of the Years or the New Fire Ceremony. Before the celebration, people throughout the empire let their hearth fires go out and destroyed some of their kitchenware. At the start of the new 52-year cycle, the priests lit a fire on the chest of a sacrificial victim. People pricked themselves to add their blood to the sacrifice. Fire bearers delivered the sacrificial fire to towns and cities throughout the empire. Then the people relit their hearth fires from the new fire and feasted.

Family life. The typical Aztec household consisted of a husband and wife, their unmarried children, and a number of the husband's relatives. All members of this extended family, including the children, helped with the work. The husband's chief responsibility was to support the family, usually by farming or craftwork. The wife's duties included weaving the family's clothing, raising girls in the home, and cooking the family's food.

Boys were educated by their father until about the age of 10. They then attended a school run by their calpolli or—especially if they belonged to the nobility—a school connected with a temple. Calpolli schools provided general education and military training. Temple schools offered a religious education, which prepared boys to become priests or other leaders. Some girls also attended the temple schools, but the majority learned household skills at home. The Aztec married at an early age, women at about 16 and men at about 20.

Food. Many types of corn and squash were staples of the Aztec diet. The principal food was a thin corn-meal pancake called a *tlaxcalli*. In Spanish, it is called a *tortilla*. The Aztec used tlaxcallis to scoop up other foods or wrapped them around bits of meat and vegetables to form tacos. Aztec cooking was rich and spicy. Many dishes had sauces flavored with chili peppers.

Hunting and, to a lesser extent, fishing provided animal protein for the Aztec diet. Game animals included deer, rabbits, and such birds as ducks and geese. The only animals raised for meat were dogs and turkeys.

The Aztec used the juice of maguey plants to make an alcoholic beverage called *octli*. Chocolate drink was also a favorite beverage, but only the wealthy could afford to have it often.

Clothing. Aztec women wore a loose, sleeveless blouse and a wraparound skirt. Men wore a cloth around their hips and a cloak knotted over one shoulder. The poorer people used cloth made from maguey fibers, but richer people had cotton clothing. The amount of decoration on a garment further indicated the wealth and social rank of the wearer. When the Spaniards first arrived in Tenochtitlan, they were amazed by the elaborate and rich clothing of the Aztec nobles.

Shelter. Most houses for Aztec commoners were simple and designed for usefulness rather than beauty. In the highlands, the houses were made of adobe. In the lowlands, they had thatched roofs, and the walls were made of branches or reeds plastered with clay. In addition to the main dwelling, most families had several other buildings, including a storehouse and a small sweat house, where the family took steam baths. Wealthy Aztec families had large adobe or stone houses finely decorated and built around a patio.

Arts and crafts. Aztec sculptures, which decorated temples and other buildings, were among the most elaborate in the Americas. The most famous surviving Aztec sculpture is the large, circular Calendar Stone, which represents the Aztec universe. The stone measures about 12 feet (3.7 meters) in diameter. In its center is the face of the sun god Tonatiuh. Other carvings

12 ft. (3.7 m) in diameter; Instituto Nacional de Antropología e Historia, Mexico City

The Aztec Calendar Stone was used in ceremonies honoring the sun god Tonatiuh. His face is in the center of the stone. Other carvings represent the Aztec universe.

Codex Borbonicus (early 1500's); Bibliothèque du
Palais Bourbon, Paris (Giraudon/Art Resource)

Aztec writing consisted of small pictures called *pictographs.*
This page from an Aztec book shows Xipe Totec, *left,* the god of
spring, and the god Quetzalcoatl, who appears as a snake, *right.*

represent the days of the Aztec month and religious
symbols related to the sun god. Many archaeologists
believe that Aztec priests placed the hearts of human
sacrifices on the stone.

The Aztec produced various forms of oral literature,
including poetry and traditional accounts of their history. When Spanish priests studied this oral tradition, they
were deeply impressed by the elaborate metaphors and
prose used by the Aztec speakers.

Music played a major part in religious services. The
chief instruments were drums, flutes, and rattles.

Aztec craftworkers used feathers to make cloaks,
headdresses, and other garments. Other crafts included
metalworking, pottery, weaving, and woodcarving.

Language. The Aztec spoke a language called *Nahuatl.* It belongs to a large group of Indian languages
known as the Aztec-Tanoan or Uto-Aztecan family. This
language family also includes the languages spoken by
the Comanche, Pima, Shoshone, and other tribes of
western North America.

The Aztec used a form of writing called *pictographic
writing,* which consisted mostly of images, pictures, and
scenes. Some pictures symbolized ideas. Others stood
for the sounds of syllables. For example, the Aztec town
of Coatepec was represented by a snake and a hill. The
Nahuatl words for *snake* and *hill* were *coatl* and *tepetl,*
which together sounded like Coatepec. This system of
writing was not developed enough to provide full expression of ideas, and so the Aztec combined pictorial
images with oral explanation or interpretation. They
used the pictorial system alone for business records,
censuses, and tax lists.

Warfare was considered a religious duty by the
Aztec. They fought not only to enlarge their empire but
also to take prisoners to sacrifice to the gods. The high-

est goal for a young man was to be a successful warrior.
Men who took many captives in battle were rewarded
with land, high social rank, and important government
offices. Warriors wore costumes that symbolized their
accomplishments and rank.

Aztec methods of combat were designed primarily
to capture prisoners rather than to kill. The chief
weapon was a wooden club edged with sharp pieces
of the volcanic glass obsidian. This weapon, called a
macuahuitl, was effective for disabling an opponent
without killing him. The Aztec also used bows and arrows and spears. A spear-throwing device called an
atlatl increased the range and force of their spears. For
protection, warriors carried shields and wore armor of
tightly quilted cotton.

Economy

Agriculture formed the basis of the Aztec economy.
Corn was the most important crop. Farmers also grew
avocados, beans, squashes, sweet potatoes, tomatoes,
and many other crops. The lowlands provided such
tropical products as cotton, papayas, rubber, and cacao
beans, from which chocolate is made.

The basic agricultural tool was a pointed stick for dig-
ging. In the densely forested lowlands, farmers practiced *slash-and-burn agriculture.* They chopped down
and burned a section of forest, then planted crops in the
clearing. The ashes fertilized the soil. In the highlands,
the Aztec cut terraces into the hillsides to increase the
amount of level farmland. They also dug irrigation systems to water their crops. In addition, farmers turned areas of shallow lakes into cropland by scooping up mud
from the lake bottoms to form islands. These islands
were called *chinampas.* The farmers regularly added
fresh mud, which was extremely fertile. As a result, the
chinampas yielded huge crops. Lake Xochimilco in Mexico City still has many chinampas. Although they do not
float, they are often called *floating gardens.*

Trade and transportation. The marketplace was a
major center of Aztec life. The market at Tlatelolco was
the largest in the Americas. It displayed nearly every
kind of merchandise available in the Aztec world. The
Spanish explorer Hernán Cortés reported that more
than 60,000 people visited it daily. There were also many
smaller markets throughout the empire. Government officials supervised the trading.

Merchants called *pochteca* traveled throughout the
empire on trading expeditions and also served as spies.
The merchants employed many bearers, who marched
in long caravans with heavy loads on their backs. People
of the lowlands traded such products as cacao beans,
cotton, jaguar pelts, rubber, and the feathers of tropical
birds. In return, they received goods from the highlands,
including obsidian, which was used for knives and
weapons, and a variety of manufactured products.

The Aztec had no system of money as we know it.
They usually traded goods and services for other goods
and services. But the Aztec used cacao beans and other
widely acceptable goods somewhat as we use money.

The Aztec used the wheel only in toys, and they had
no beasts of burden. As a result, the people themselves
carried all their goods on land. Dugout canoes were an
important means of transportation in the Valley of Mexico, which had many lakes, canals, and other waterways.

History

The Aztec migration. According to legend, the ancestors of the Aztec came to the Valley of Mexico from a place in the north called *Aztlan* or *Chicomoztoc* (Place of Seven Caves). Their supreme deity inspired them to leave their homeland and travel until they found a new home, which would be marked by an eagle eating a serpent on a blooming cactus. The name *Aztec* comes from *Aztlan*. The Aztec wandered for many years before settling in the valley in the 1200's. At first, they were subjects of people who lived in the area. But in 1325, the legend says, they founded their own city, Tenochtitlan.

Middle American growth of the Aztec empire. By the early 1400's, Tenochtitlan had become a powerful city that controlled the region around it, forming a city-state. Tenochtitlan joined with Texcoco and Tlacopan, two other city-states in the Valley of Mexico, to form an alliance. Tenochtitlan became the most powerful member of the alliance and began to build the Aztec empire. Under Montezuma I, who ruled from 1440 to 1469, the alliance conquered large areas to the east and south. Montezuma's name is also spelled *Moctezuma* or *Motecuhzoma*. His successors expanded the empire until it extended between what are now Guatemala and the Mexican state of San Luis Potosi. Hundreds of conquered towns paid heavy taxes in goods to the empire. When Montezuma II became emperor in 1502, the Aztec empire was at the height of its power.

The Spanish conquest. In 1519, the Spanish explorer Hernán Cortés landed on the east coast of Mexico. After several skirmishes and setbacks, he began a march inland to the Aztec capital. He and his troops were eventually joined by many Indians who had been conquered by the Aztec and resented their heavy taxes and brutality. For reasons that are still mysterious, Montezuma II did not oppose the advancing Spaniards with military force. Instead, he tried to use religious magic to discourage them from coming to the capital. Some scholars think he believed Cortés represented the creator god, Quetzalcoatl, and his Toltec incarnation, *Topiltzin Quetzalcoatl*, who had ruled centuries before. An Aztec legend said that Quetzalcoatl had sailed away to the east, the direction from which the Spaniards came. Cortés eventually entered Tenochtitlan and made Montezuma a prisoner in his own palace.

In 1520, the Spaniards massacred Aztec dancers, priests, and musicians at a sacred ceremony. The Aztec rebelled and drove the invaders from their city. Montezuma died that year, probably from wounds received early in the rebellion. Cortés and the Spaniards retreated, but soon reorganized their army and attacked Tenochtitlan in May 1521. Montezuma's successor, Cuauhtemoc, surrendered in August of the same year.

The Aztec heritage. Little Aztec architecture remains. The Spaniards considered it their duty as Christians to wipe out the temples, idols, sacrifices, and all other traces of the Aztec religion. They destroyed Tenochtitlan and built Mexico City on the ruins. However, archaeologists have excavated the site of the Great Temple in downtown Mexico City. They have uncovered all four sides of the building and recovered thousands

Drawing by an unknown Aztec artist from *History of the Indies of New Spain* (late 1500's) by Diego Durán; Biblioteca Nacional, Madrid, Spain (Ampliaciones y Reproducciones MAS)

The Spanish conquest in 1521 destroyed the Aztec empire. This drawing shows Aztec warriors, *right,* fighting to recapture a palace from the Spaniards, *left.* One Aztec wears an eagle costume, and one a jaguar suit. Warriors earned the right to wear such costumes by taking many prisoners.

Detail of *Great City of Tenochtitlan* (1929-1945), a fresco mural by Diego Rivera; National Palace, Mexico City (Granger Collection)

The marketplace was a center of Aztec life. It displayed nearly every kind of merchandise available in the Aztec world. Merchants employed many bearers, who marched in long caravans with heavy loads on their backs. This painting from the mid-1900's depicts the market at Tlatelolco in the Aztec capital. The Spanish explorer Hernán Cortés reported that more than 60,000 people visited it daily. There were also many smaller markets throughout the Aztec empire.

of objects, including jewelry, pottery, statues, wall carvings, and remains of animal and human sacrifices. Archaeologists have restored some other Aztec buildings, including temples at Tenayuca and Tepoztlan near Mexico City. The National Museum of Anthropology in Mexico City has a large collection of Aztec art.

Thousands of people in Mexico have Aztec ancestors, and many speak a modern form of Nahuatl. Many Mexican place names, including Acapulco and Mexico itself, come from Nahuatl, as do the English words *avocado, chocolate,* and *tomato.* Such Mexican painters as José Orozco, Diego Rivera, and David Siqueiros have used Aztec themes in their work. Foods of Aztec origin, including chili, chocolate, and tacos, have become popular in many countries. Descendants of the Aztec also live in the United States, especially in California and Texas. Many Mexican Americans take pride in the creative aspects of Aztec culture.   David Carrasco

Outline

I. **The Aztec empire**
II. **Way of life**
    A. Religion
    B. Family life
    C. Food
    D. Clothing
    E. Shelter
    F. Arts and crafts
    G. Language
    H. Warfare
III. **Economy**
    A. Agriculture
    B. Trade and transportation
IV. **History**

Questions

Why did Montezuma II fail to oppose Cortés?
How many days are in a month in the Aztec solar calendar?
Why did the Aztec want prisoners of war?
When was the Aztec empire at its height?
What were *chinampas?*
How did the Aztec move their goods on land?
Why did the Aztec perform human sacrifices?
What are two popular foods of Aztec origin?
Where was the Aztec capital of Tenochtitlan?
Why are so few Aztec buildings left?

Additional resources

Aguilar-Moreno, Manuel. *Handbook to Life in the Aztec World.* Facts on File, 2006.
Carrasco, David, and Matos Moctezuma, Eduardo. *Moctezuma's Mexico: Visions of the Aztec World.* Rev. ed. Univ. Pr. of Colo., 2003.
Matos Moctezuma, Eduardo, and Solís Olguín, Felipe R. *Aztecs.* Royal Academy of Arts, 2002.
Saunders, Nicholas J., and Allan, Tony. *The Aztec Empire.* Heinemann Lib., 2005. Younger readers.
Smith, Michael E. *The Aztecs.* 1996. Reprint. Blackwell, 1998.
Van Tuerenhout, Dirk R. *The Aztecs: New Perspectives.* ABC-CLIO, 2005.

Andean condor
Vultur gryphus
Found in South America
Body length: Up to about
52 inches (132 centimeters)

Little sparrowhawk
Accipiter minullus
Found in Africa
Body length: 8 to 11 inches
(20 to 28 centimeters)

Eurasian eagle-owl
Bubo bubo
Found in Europe, Asia, and
northern Africa
Body length: 23 to 30 inches
(60 to 75 centimeters)

Plumbeous forest-falcon
Micrastur plumbeus
Found in South America
Body length: 12 to 14 ½ inches
(30 to 37 centimeters)

WORLD BOOK Illustrations by Myke Taylor, Wildlife Art Ltd.

Birds of prey vary in appearance. The Eurasian eagle-owl, *left,* has a broad head with forward-facing eyes, and the Andean condor, *second from left,* has a featherless head. The plumbeous forest-falcon, *second from right,* and the little sparrowhawk, *right,* have smaller, more delicate bodies.

Bird of prey, or *raptor,* is any of over 300 birds that typically eat flesh. Birds of prey rank among the world's most effective hunters. They include eagles, falcons, hawks, and vultures. Many people also consider owls to be birds of prey, even though owls are distantly related to the other raptors. Birds of prey frequently search for food during the day. Owls and a few other raptors are active at night. Raptors consume a wide variety of animals, including reptiles, small mammals, fish, insects, and other birds.

There are over 300 *species* (kinds) of raptors. Scientists arrange birds of prey into several groups called *families. Accipiters* make up the largest and most widespread raptor family. They include eagles, hawks, kites, and Old World vultures. The *falcon* family contains some of the world's fastest fliers. This group also includes caracaras, which live in warm regions of North and South America. Another family, the *New World vultures,* includes the rare California condor. The African *secretary-bird,* a ground-dwelling raptor, makes up its own family. Owls form two separate families. The *barn owl* and its relatives make up one group, and all other owls belong to the *typical owl* family.

The bodies of birds of prey

Physical appearance. Birds of prey vary widely in size. One of the smallest species, the black-thighed falconet of Asia, measures only 5 ½ to 7 inches (14 to 18

centimeters) long and weighs 1 to 2 ounces (28 to 56 grams). The largest raptor, the Andean condor of South America, grows nearly 52 inches (132 centimeters) long and weighs up to 33 pounds (15 kilograms). Most female raptors grow larger than males.

Most birds of prey share certain basic features. They typically possess broad, powerful wings that enable them to fly quickly. Raptors also have hooked beaks and strong feet with hooked *talons* (claws). These features assist them in capturing, tearing apart, and eating prey. To blend into their environments, most raptors have primarily brownish, grayish, or blackish coloring.

Some body features vary according to where raptors live and what kinds of prey they consume. Many eagles, for example, live in open areas. They possess broad wings that enable them to soar over long distances. Forest-dwelling hawks, however, have shorter, rounded wings that enable them to maneuver easily through trees when chasing prey. Many caracaras search for food on the ground and need longer legs and feet for walking. Bird-eating falcons must fly fast to capture their prey. Peregrine falcons, for example, catch prey by making *stoops* (steep descents) of more than 200 miles (320 kilometers) per hour. Such rapid flights require streamlined bodies.

Senses. Raptors typically have better vision than do human beings or many other animals. Like people, most raptors possess *binocular vision*—the ability to see an object with both eyes at the same time. But raptors detect colors in their environment more clearly than human beings can. These visual abilities help raptors spot prey from great distances.

Owls have a better sense of hearing than other raptors. They can detect prey by sound alone, even at night. Some species of vultures and caracaras scavenge for food by using smell. However, most raptors have a relatively poor sense of smell.

Ways of life of birds of prey

Reproduction and growth. Birds of prey generally mate with different partners each breeding season. But some individuals pair for several years, especially if they return to the same breeding area. During the breeding season, raptors may fiercely defend their territories against others of their own species or against different birds.

Most raptors build a nest, though some species lay their eggs on the ground, on cliffs, or in abandoned nests of other birds. Females typically select the nest site. Some species build a new nest annually, but others keep and repair old nests for several years. Many raptors that mate in northern regions may have various alternate nests in the breeding area.

After mating, females stay close to the nest site until the young are hatched and become well developed. Males provide food for their families during this time. Raptor eggs typically have white, light green, or light blue coloring, sometimes with dark flecks. Females typically lay a *clutch* (set) of two to three eggs, but some species can produce five or more. Eggs normally hatch from 22 to 50 days after being laid. Smaller raptors often produce larger clutches, but the eggs of larger raptors usually take longer to hatch.

Newborn chicks have a thin coat of downy feathers. Most young raptors leave the nest from 25 to 100 days after they hatch. However, the young remain dependent on their parents for a period after leaving the nest. In large eagle species, young birds may remain with their parents for almost a year.

Overall, larger birds of prey live longer than smaller species. Adult raptors can survive from about 8 to 20 years in the wild. Certain captive individuals have lived for more than 50 years.

Food. Many birds of prey seek food from the air while soaring over large distances or hovering over smaller areas. Others look for prey from a perch. Most raptors catch prey with their feet using one of two methods. In the first method, the bird squeezes its prey and sends its talons into the animal's body. In the second technique, the raptor stuns its prey by striking it with its feet. A few species use their beak during a kill, though most raptor beaks serve to rip apart and eat food.

Many small raptors spend most of each day feeding on insects and other small animals. Large hunting species often wait from one to several days between feedings.

Roosting. Most raptors roost alone or in small family groups. A few species roost in groups. The birds roost in trees, cliffs, buildings, or sometimes on the ground. Birds of prey that are active during the day often produce calls or songs in the morning. Raptors generally *preen* (clean and smooth) their feathers at the roosts before hunting.

© Anthony Mercieca, Photo Researchers
A bird of prey can capture food with its strong feet and claws. The bird shown here, an American kestrel, is about to catch a mouse. This kestrel has mostly grayish-blue wings, a largely reddish-brown tail, and bright yellow feet.

Migration. Birds of prey that live in colder climates migrate to warmer regions in the winter. Some birds migrate alone, while others travel in groups of thousands. A few species migrate at night and rest during the day. Others rely on fat reserves during migrations and forgo regular feeding. At times, different sexes or different age groups follow different routes. The Swainson's hawk has one of the longest migrations of any raptor. Each year, it flies from southern Alaska to Argentina.

Birds of prey and people

People have admired birds of prey for centuries, often as symbols of beauty and courage. Images of raptors decorate flags, coins, artwork, and even the uniforms of sports teams. People have long trained birds of prey to hunt game. This sport, called *falconry,* first developed more than 3,000 years ago in ancient China.

Human beings also threaten the survival of raptors. Because birds of prey kill livestock, farmers and ranchers often shoot them. But the biggest threat to raptor survival is the destruction by people of the birds' natural environments. To prevent the extinction of raptor species, parks have been set aside as protected habitats for raptors and other wildlife.   Thomas G. Balgooyen

Scientific classification. Birds of prey belong to several families. Eagles, hawks, kites, and Old World vultures belong to the family Accipitridae; falcons and caracaras belong to the family Falconidae; New World vultures are in the family Cathartidae; and the secretary-bird makes up the family Sagittariidae. Owls belong to either the barn owl family, Tytonidae, or the typical owl family, Strigidae.

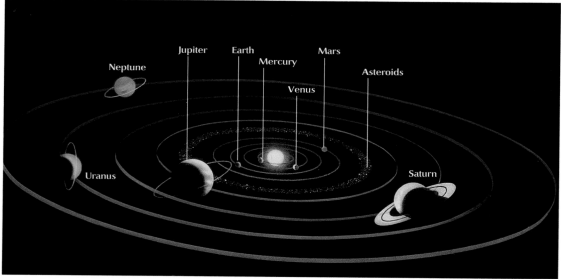

WORLD BOOK illustration by Rob Wood

The solar system includes many different objects that travel around the sun. These objects vary from planets much larger than Earth to tiny meteoroids and dust particles.

Solar system is a group of heavenly bodies consisting of a star and the planets and other objects orbiting around it. We are most familiar with our own solar system, which includes Earth and the other objects that orbit the sun. Besides the sun, Earth, and Earth's moon, many objects in our solar system are visible to the unaided eye. These objects include the planets Mercury, Venus, Mars, Jupiter, and Saturn; the brightest asteroids; and occasional comets and meteors. Many more objects in the solar system can be seen with telescopes.

Since the 1990's, astronomers have discovered many planets orbiting distant stars, though the planets cannot be seen directly. By studying the masses and orbits of these planets, astronomers hope to learn more about solar systems in general. For example, our own solar system contains four small, rocky planets near the sun—Mercury, Venus, Earth, and Mars—and four giant, gaseous planets farther out—Jupiter, Saturn, Uranus, and Neptune. Astronomers were surprised to find that other stars have giant, gaseous planets in close orbits.

Our solar system

Our solar system includes the sun and all the objects that revolve around it. Astronomers have different ideas about how to classify these objects. The International Astronomical Union, the recognized authority in naming heavenly bodies, divides them into three major classes: (1) planets, (2) dwarf planets, and (3) small solar system bodies. Small solar system bodies include comets, asteroids, and meteoroids. The solar system also includes all the satellites or moons of these objects and a thin cloud of gas and dust known as the *interplanetary medium*.

The sun is the largest and most important object in our solar system. It contains 99.8 percent of the solar system's *mass* (quantity of matter). It provides most of the heat, light, and other energy that makes life possible.

The sun's outer layers are hot and stormy. The hot gases and electrically charged particles in those layers continually stream into space and often burst out in solar eruptions. This flow of gases and particles forms the *solar wind*, which bathes everything in the solar system.

Planets orbit the sun in oval-shaped paths called *ellipses,* according to a law of planetary motion discovered by the German astronomer Johannes Kepler in the early 1600's. The sun is slightly off to the side of the center of each ellipse at a point called a *focus.* The focus is actually a point inside the sun—but off its center—called the *barycenter* of the solar system.

The inner four planets consist chiefly of iron and rock. They are known as the *terrestrial* (Earthlike) planets because they are somewhat similar in size and composition. The four outer planets are giant worlds with thick, gaseous outer layers. Almost all their mass consists of hydrogen and helium, giving them compositions more like that of the sun than that of Earth. Beneath their outer layers, the giant planets have no solid surfaces. The pressure of their thick atmospheres turns their insides liquid, though they may have rocky cores.

Dwarf planets are round objects smaller than planets that also orbit the sun. Unlike a planet, a dwarf planet lacks the gravitational pull to sweep other objects from the area of its orbit. As a result, dwarf planets are found among populations of smaller bodies. The dwarf planet Ceres, for example, orbits in a region of space called the *Main Belt* between the orbits of Mars and Jupiter. Ceres shares the Main Belt with millions of smaller asteroids.

Other dwarf planets orbit mainly beyond Neptune in a region known as the Kuiper belt. They share this region with many smaller icy bodies. Together, these objects are known as the *Kuiper belt objects* (KBO's). Compared to the planets, KBO's tend to follow irregular, elongated orbits. Dwarf planets of the Kuiper belt include Pluto and Eris, originally known by the designation 2003 UB_{313}.

Moons orbit all the planets except Mercury and Venus. The inner planets have few moons. Earth has one, and Mars has two tiny satellites. The giant outer planets, however, resemble small solar systems, with many moons orbiting each planet. Jupiter has at least 63 moons. Jupiter's four largest moons are known as the Galilean satellites because the Italian astronomer Galileo discovered them in 1610 with one of the first telescopes. The largest Galilean satellite—and the largest satellite in the solar system—is Ganymede, which is even bigger than Mercury. Saturn has at least 56 moons. The largest of Saturn's moons, Titan, has an atmosphere thicker than Earth's and a diameter larger than that of Mercury. Uranus has at least 27 moons, and Neptune has at least 13. The giant planets probably have more small moons not yet discovered.

Many dwarf planets, asteroids, and other bodies also have smaller moons. Pluto's moon Charon measures half Pluto's diameter. Eris's moon Dysnomia measures around ⅛ Eris's diameter.

Rings of dust, rock, and ice chunks encircle all the giant planets. Saturn's rings are the most familiar, but thin rings also surround Jupiter, Uranus, and Neptune.

Comets are snowballs composed mainly of ice and rock. When a comet approaches the sun, some of the ice in its *nucleus* (center) turns into gas. The gas shoots out of the sunlit side of the comet. The solar wind then carries the gas outward, forming it into a long tail.

Astronomers divide comets into two main types, *long-period comets*, which take 200 years or more to orbit the sun, and *short-period comets*, which complete their orbits in fewer than 200 years. The two types come from two regions at the edges of the solar system. Long-period comets originate in the *Oort* (pronounced *oort* or *ohrt) cloud*, a cluster of comets far beyond the orbit of Pluto. The Oort cloud was named for the Dutch astronomer Jan H. Oort, who first suggested its existence. Short-period comets come from the Kuiper belt. Many of the objects in the Oort cloud and the Kuiper belt may be chunks of rock and ice known as *planetesimals* left over from the formation of the solar system.

Asteroids are rocky or metallic objects smaller than planets. Some have elliptical orbits that pass inside the orbit of Earth or even that of Mercury. Others travel on a circular path among the outer planets. Most asteroids circle the sun in the Main Belt. The belt contains over 200 asteroids larger than 60 miles (100 kilometers) in diameter. Scientists estimate that there are over 750,000 asteroids in the belt with diameters larger than ⅗ mile (1 kilometer). There are millions of smaller asteroids.

Meteoroids are chunks of metal or rock smaller than asteroids. When meteoroids plunge into Earth's atmosphere, they form bright streaks of light called *meteors* as they disintegrate. Some meteoroids reach the ground, and then they become known as *meteorites*. Most meteoroids are broken chunks of asteroids that resulted from collisions in the Main Belt. During the 1990's, astronomers discovered a number of meteoroids that came from Mars and from the moon. Many tiny meteoroids are dust from the tails of comets.

Heliosphere is a vast, teardrop-shaped region of space containing electrically charged particles given off by the sun. Scientists do not know the exact distance to the *heliopause,* the limit of the heliosphere. Many astronomers think that the heliopause is about 9 billion miles (15 billion kilometers) from the sun at the blunt end of the "teardrop."

Formation of our solar system

Many scientists believe that our solar system formed from a giant, rotating cloud of gas and dust known as the *solar nebula.* According to this theory, the solar nebula began to collapse because of its own gravity. Some astronomers speculate that a nearby *supernova* (exploding star) triggered the collapse. As the nebula contracted, it spun faster and flattened into a disk.

The nebular theory indicates that particles within the flattened disk then collided and stuck together to form asteroid-sized objects called planetesimals. Some of these planetesimals combined to become the eight large planets. Other planetesimals formed moons, asteroids, and comets. The planets and asteroids all revolve around the sun in the same direction, and in more or less the same plane, because they originally formed from this flattened disk.

Most of the material in the solar nebula, however, was pulled toward the center and formed the sun. According to the theory, the pressure at the center became great enough to trigger the nuclear reactions that power the sun.

Eventually, solar eruptions occurred, producing a solar wind. In the inner solar system, the wind was so powerful that it swept away most of the lighter elements—hydrogen and helium. In the outer regions of the solar system, however, the solar wind was much weaker. As a result, much more hydrogen and helium remained on the outer planets. This process explains why the inner planets are small, rocky worlds and the outer planets are giant balls composed almost entirely of hydrogen and helium.

Other solar systems

Several other stars have disk-shaped clouds around them that seem to be developing solar systems. In 1983, an infrared telescope in space photographed such a disk around Vega, the brightest star in the constellation Lyra. This discovery represented the first direct evidence of such material around any star except the sun. In 1984, astronomers photographed a similar disk around Beta Pictoris, a star in the southern constellation Pictor.

By the early 2000's, astronomers had discovered that more than 50 stars like our sun have planets orbiting them. In almost all cases, they found only one planet per star. Most of the planets found are probably gaseous with no solid surface.   Jay M. Pasachoff

Additional resources

Level I
Ride, Sally, and O'Shaughnessy, T. E. *Exploring Our Solar System.* Crown, 2003.
World Book's Solar System & Space Exploration Library. 10 vols. World Book, 2006.
Level II
Lang, Kenneth R. *The Cambridge Guide to the Solar System.* Cambridge, 2003.

Black and yellow garden spider *(Argiope aurantia);* © Mark Gibson, Index Stock

A beautiful spider web consists of silk spun from the spider's own body. The silk threads on this web resemble beaded necklaces. Spiders use webs to catch insects.

Spider

Spider is an eight-legged animal that spins silk. About half of all known *species* (kinds) of spiders make silk webs. These webs range in appearance from simple jumbles of threads to complex, often beautiful designs. Spiders use their webs to catch insects for food.

All spiders have fangs, and all except a few have poison glands. Spiders use their fangs and poison glands to kill prey. A spider's bite can paralyze or kill insects and other small animals. Although spiders feed mostly on insects, larger spiders may occasionally capture and eat tadpoles, small frogs, fish, birds, or even mice. Spiders frequently eat each other. Most female spiders are larger and stronger than male spiders, and they may attack males or young of their own species.

Spiders live anywhere they can find food. They thrive in fields, woods, swamps, caves, and deserts. One species, the *European water spider,* spends most of life underwater. Other species live on beaches between high and low tides so that they lie under salt water for part of each day. Some spiders thrive in houses, barns, or other buildings. Others prefer the outsides of buildings—on walls, on window screens, or in the corners of doors and windows. Spiders often live near lights that attract insects at night.

Many people think spiders are insects. However, spiders differ from insects in a number of ways. Ants, bees, beetles, and other insects have six legs. Spiders have eight. Most insects also have wings and *antennae* (feelers), but spiders do not. Biologists classify spiders as *arachnids.* Other arachnids include scorpions, ticks, and the spiderlike daddy longlegs (also called *harvestmen).* Both arachnids and insects belong to a large group of animals called *arthropods,* which have jointed legs and a stiff outside shell or skin.

Scientists arrange the thousands of spider species into more than 100 classifications called *families.* One family, the *liphistiids,* consists of primitive burrowing spiders. Liphistiids have abdomens that are visibly divided into segments. In all other kinds of spiders, the abdomens do not show segmentation. Scientists divide nonsegmented spiders into *araneomorphs,* or *true spiders,* and *mygalomorphs.* More than 90 percent of all spider species belong to the true spider group. Mygalomorphs include tarantulas.

Another way to group spiders divides them into *web-building spiders,* which make webs to trap insects; and *hunting spiders,* which catch prey without webs. Hunting spiders catch food in a variety of ways. *Jumping spiders,* for example, sneak up and jump on prey. *Crab spiders* ambush their victims.

This article will describe the body of a spider, how a spider makes and uses its silk, and the life of a spider. It

Jonathan A. Coddington, the contributor of this article, is Senior Scientist in the Department of Entomology at the Smithsonian Institution's National Museum of Natural History.

will then discuss different spider families and the ways spiders and people have interacted.

The spider's body

Some spiders are smaller than the head of a pin. Others grow as large as a person's hand. One South American tarantula can measure more than 10 inches (25 centimeters) long with its legs extended.

Spiders may be short and fat, long and thin, round, oblong, or flat. Their legs range from short and stubby to long and thin. Most spiders have brown, gray, or black coloring. But some types are as colorful as the loveliest butterflies. For many tiny spiders, people must use a microscope to clearly see the color patterns.

A spider has no bones. Its tough, mostly rigid skin serves as a protective outer skeleton. Fine hairs sprout from a spider's skin. Many spiders also have bumps and *spines* (outgrowths of skin) on their bodies.

A spider's body has two main sections, the *cephalo-thorax,* which consists of the fused head and *thorax*

Interesting facts about spiders

The goliath birdeater tarantula ranks as one of the world's largest spiders. With its legs extended, it can measure more than 10 inches (25 centimeters) long. The tarantula shown here has captured a baby bird.

Goliath birdeater tarantula *(Theraphosa blondi);* © John Mitchell, Photo Researchers

An ogre-faced spider traps insects in a small web of sticky silk. The spider stretches the web to several times its normal size and sweeps it over the insect.

Ogre-faced spider *(Deinopis spinosus);*
WORLD BOOK illustration by Jack Kunz

European water spider *(Argyroneta aquatica);* © O.S.F./Animals Animals

The European water spider lives mostly underwater. This animal "breathes" by carrying air bubbles on its abdomen. The water spider also encloses its underwater web in air bubbles.

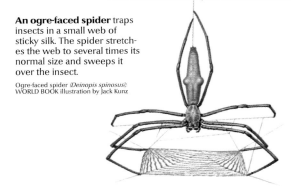

Jumping spider *(Phidippus clarus);* © Kim Taylor, Nature Picture Library

A jumping spider catches prey by pouncing on it. Jumping spiders can leap more than 40 times the length of their bodies. The spider shown here is attacking a beelike insect called a hoverfly.

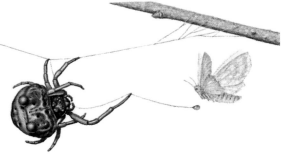

Bolas spider *(Mastophora cornigera);* WORLD BOOK illustration by Jack Kunz

A bolas spider does not trap its insects in a web. Instead, it spins a line of silk with a ball of sticky silk at the end. The spider swings the line at an insect and traps it on the sticky ball.

(middle section), and the abdomen. A thin waist called the *pedicel* connects the cephalothorax and abdomen.

Eyes. A spider's eyes lie on top and near the front of its head. The size, number, and position of the eyes vary among different species. Most species have eight eyes, arranged in two rows of four each. Other kinds have six, four, or two eyes. Some spiders have better vision than others. For example, hunting spiders have good eyesight at short distances, which enables them to see prey and mates. Web-building spiders generally have poor eyesight. They use their eyes to detect changes in light. Some species of spiders that live in caves or other dark places have no eyes at all.

Mouth. A spider's mouth opening lies below its eyes. Spiders do not have chewing mouthparts, and they swallow only liquids. Extensions around the mouth form a short "straw" through which the spider sucks the body fluid of its victim.

A spider eats the solid tissue of its prey by predigesting it. First, the spider vomits digestive juices on its prey to dissolve the tissue. Then the spider drinks the liquid and repeats the process.

Chelicerae *(kuh LIHS uh ree)* are a pair of mouthparts that the spider uses to seize, crush, and kill its prey. The chelicerae are above the spider's mouth opening and just below its eyes. Each chelicera ends in a sharp, hard, hollow fang. An opening at the tip of the fang connects to the poison glands. When a spider stabs an insect with its chelicerae, poison squirts through the fang into the wound to paralyze or kill the victim. Some spiders use their chelicerae to dig burrows in the ground.

The fangs of true spiders point crosswise and move toward each other. True spiders have poison glands in their cephalothorax. The fangs of tarantulas and other mygalomorphs point straight down from the head and move parallel to each other. Mygalomorphs have poison glands in their chelicerae.

Pedipalpi *(PEHD uh PAL py),* also called *palps,* are a pair of projecting parts that look like small legs attached to each side of the spider's mouth. Each pedipalp has six *segments* (parts). The segment on each palp closest to the body forms one side of the mouth. In most spiders, the mouth segment bears a sharp plate with toothed edges. The spider uses this plate to cut and crush food.

Wolf spider *(Lycosa punctulata);* WORLD BOOK illustrations by Jack Kunz

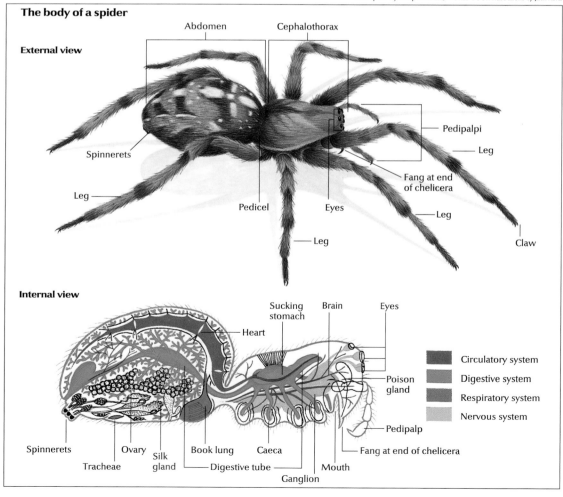

The body of a spider

In adult male spiders, the last segment of each pedipalp bears a reproductive organ.

Legs. A spider has four pairs of legs, which are attached to its cephalothorax. Each leg has seven segments. The tip of the last segment has two or three claws. A brush of hairs called a *scopula* may surround the claws. The scopula sticks even to smooth surfaces and helps the spider walk on ceilings and walls.

Each leg is also covered with various kinds of sensitive hairs that serve as organs of touch and smell. Some hairs pick up vibrations from the ground or air. Others detect chemicals in the environment.

When a spider walks, the first and third leg on one side of its body move with the second and fourth leg on the other side. Spiders lack muscles in one leg joint and squirt blood into their legs to make them extend while walking. If a spider's body does not contain enough fluids, its blood pressure drops. The legs then curl up under its body, and the animal cannot walk.

Respiratory system. Spiders have two kinds of breathing organs—*tracheae (TRAY kee ee)* and *book*

WORLD BOOK illustrations by Jack Kunz

Spider faces

Eyes

Chelicera

Fang

Carolina wolf spider
Lycosa carolinensis

Tarantula
Lasiodora

Eyes

Chelicera

Fang

Jumping spider
Phidippus variegatus

Ogre-faced spider
Deinopis spinosus

Spider feet

Claws

Last leg segment

Comb

Foot

Garden spider
Argiope

Common house spider
Achaearanea tepidariorum

lungs. Tracheae, small tubes found in almost all kinds of true spiders, carry air to the body tissues. Air enters the tubes through one or, rarely, two openings called *spiracles* on the abdomen.

Book lungs are cavities in the spider's abdomen. Air enters the cavities through a tiny slit on each side and near the front of the abdomen. The wall of each cavity consists of 15 or more thin, flat sheets of tissue arranged like the pages of a book. Blood covers the inner sides of the sheets, and air covers the outer sides. Oxygen passes through the sheets into the blood, while carbon dioxide passes out of the sheets. Most true spiders have one pair of book lungs. Mygalomorphs have two pairs.

The *European water spider* lives mostly underwater. This animal "breathes" in water by carrying air bubbles on its abdomen. It fills its underwater web with air bubbles, which gradually push all the water out of the web. The spider can survive on air from these bubbles for up to several months, if necessary. It then has to return to the surface to gather more bubbles.

Circulatory system. Spider blood contains many pale blood cells and has a slightly bluish color. The heart consists of a long, slender tube in the abdomen that pumps blood to the body. The blood drains back to the heart through open passages instead of veins, as in the human body. If a spider's skin is broken, it may quickly bleed to death.

Digestive system. A digestive tube extends the length of the spider's body. In the cephalothorax, the tube is larger and is surrounded by an organ called the *sucking stomach*. Powerful muscles attached to the stomach alternately squeeze and expand it, causing a strong sucking action. The sucking pulls the liquid food through the stomach into the intestine. Digestive juices break the food into molecules small enough to pass through the walls of the intestine into the blood. The blood then distributes the food to all parts of the body. Food is also pulled through the stomach into fingerlike storage cavities called *ceca,* also spelled *caeca (SEE kuh)*. The ability to store food in the caeca helps enable spiders to go for months without eating.

Nervous system. The spider's central nervous system lies in the cephalothorax. It includes the brain, which is linked to a large group of nerve cells called the *ganglion*. Nerve fibers from the brain and ganglion run throughout the body. These fibers carry information to the brain from sense organs on the head, legs, and other body parts. The brain can also send signals through the nerve fibers to control the body's activities.

The spider's silk

Spider silk consists of protein. The silk cannot be dissolved in water, and it ranks as the strongest natural fiber known.

How spiders make silk. Silk glands in the spider's abdomen make silk. As a group, spiders have eight kinds of silk glands, each of which produces a different type of silk. However, no species of spider has all eight kinds. Every spider has at least two kinds of silk glands, and most species have five. Some silk glands produce a liquid silk that dries outside the body. Other glands create a silk that stays sticky.

The spider spins silk with short, fingerlike structures called *spinnerets* on the rear of the abdomen. Most

Spider silk

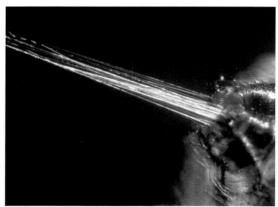

© Hans Pfletschinger from Peter Arnold, Inc.

A spider spins silk with fingerlike spinnerets on the rear of its abdomen. Liquid silk made in the silk glands flows through the spinnerets to the outside, where it hardens into threads.

© M. A. Chappell, Animals Animals

Threads of sticky spider silk look like beaded necklaces. The threads trap insects, which stick to the silk. Oil on the spider's body prevents the silk from sticking to the spider.

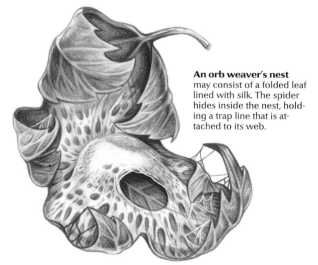

An orb weaver's nest may consist of a folded leaf lined with silk. The spider hides inside the nest, holding a trap line that is attached to its web.

WORLD BOOK illustration by Carol A. Brozman

kinds of spiders have six spinnerets, but some have four or two. The tip of a spinneret contains the *spinning field.* As many as 100 tubelike *spinning spigots* cover the surface of each spinning field. Each spigot serves one silk gland. Liquid silk flows from the silk glands through these spigots to the outside. As the liquid silk comes out, it hardens. Using different spinnerets and spigots, a spider may combine silk from different silk glands and produce a thin thread or a thick, wide band.

In addition, some spiders can make a sticky thread that looks like a beaded necklace. To do this, the spider spins a dry thread and coats it with sticky silk. The sticky silk then contracts into a series of tiny beads along the thread.

Some kinds of spiders have another spinning organ called the *cribellum.* It lies almost flat against the abdomen, just in front of the spinnerets. Hundreds or thousands of spigots cover the cribellum, producing extremely thin fibers of silk. Spiders with a cribellum also have a special row of curved hairs called a *calamistrum* on their hind legs. Spiders use the calamistrum to comb sticky silk from the cribellum onto dry silk from the spinnerets. This combination of threads forms a flat or tubular mesh of microscopic fibers called a *hackled band.* The mesh entangles the bristles, spines, and claws of insects and other small prey.

How spiders use silk. Spiders, including those that do not build webs, depend on silk in so many ways that they could not live without it. Wherever a spider goes, it spins a silk thread behind itself. This thread is called a *dragline.* The dragline is also called a "lifeline" because it can help the spider to escape from enemies. Spiders use their draglines to lower themselves to the ground from high places. When in danger, a spider can drop on its dragline and hide in the grass. Or the spider can simply hang in the air until the danger has passed, then climb back up the dragline.

Spiders also can use a special kind of fine silk to spin tiny bundles of sticky threads called *attachment disks.* Attachment disks cement the spiders' draglines and webs to various surfaces.

Each kind of web-building spider makes a different type of silk *retreat* (nest) as its home. Some *wandering spiders* rest each day in a leaf that they fold around themselves and line with silk. Other spiders dig burrows in the ground and line them with silk. Still others build retreats in the center or at the sides of their webs.

Many web-building spiders wrap silk lines or sticky bands around their prey as they capture them. Some *orb weavers* wrap their victims with wide sheets like mummy wrappings so the victims cannot escape.

The life of a spider

Most spiders live less than one year. But large species can live longer. Some female tarantulas have survived more than 20 years in captivity. Spiders become adults at different times of the year. Some mature and mate in the fall and then die during the winter. Their eggs do not hatch until spring. Others live through the winter, mate and lay eggs in the spring, and then die.

Except during mating, most spiders are loners. But some species live in social groups. Certain kinds of spiders live together on a communal web. In one tropical species, for example, tens of thousands of spiders may share a web 25 feet (7.6 meters) long and 6 to 8 feet

(1.8 to 2.4 meters) wide. Other spiders live close to one another in large groups, but each individual has its own web.

Courtship and mating. As soon as a male spider matures, he seeks a mate. Most male spiders perform courtship activities to identify themselves and to woo females. In web-building spiders, the males usually pluck and vibrate the female's web. Some male hunting spiders wave their legs or vibrate the ground in a courtship dance. Male jumping spiders use the colored hairs on their legs to attract females. In certain spiders, the male presents the female with a captured fly before mating.

Before he mates, the male spider spins a silk platform called a *sperm web.* He deposits a drop of sperm from his abdomen on the platform. Then he fills the organs at the tips of his pedipalpi with sperm. He uses the pedipalpi to transfer the sperm to a female during mating. After mating, the female stores the sperm in her body. When she lays her eggs, weeks or even months later, the sperm fertilize the eggs. Female spiders do not usually eat the males after mating, as some people believe.

Eggs. The number of eggs that a female spider lays at one time varies with her size. Females of many species lay about 100 eggs. But some of the smallest spiders lay just 1 egg, while some of the largest lay more than 2,000.

In most species, the mother spider encloses the eggs in a silken egg sac. This sac consists of several kinds of silk, including one type used only for egg sacs. Egg sacs can

have a complex structure with an outer papery layer, an inner threadlike layer, and a soft core to support the eggs.

In many species, the mother dies soon after making the egg sac. In other species, mothers remain with the eggs until they hatch. Some spiders keep the sac in their web. Others attach the sac to leaves or plants. Still others carry it with them. A female *wolf spider* attaches the sac to her spinnerets and drags it behind her. *Fishing spiders* carry the sac with their fangs.

Spiderlings hatch inside the egg sac. They do not leave the sac immediately because they are not yet able to walk or spin silk. After *molting* (shedding their skin) once inside the egg sac, the spiderlings are developed enough to leave. But they remain in the sac until warm weather arrives. If the eggs are laid in autumn, the spiderlings stay inside their egg sac until spring. After leaving the sac, most spiderlings begin spinning draglines. In a few species, the spiderlings remain for a time in the mother's web and share the food she captures.

Many spiderlings move far away from their birthplace. To do this, a spiderling climbs to the top of a twig or some other high perch and tilts its abdomen up into the air. It then pulls silk threads out of its spinnerets. The wind catches the threads and carries the spiderling into the air. This method of traveling is called *ballooning.* A spiderling may travel a great distance by ballooning. Sailors more than 200 miles (320 kilometers) from land

Spider reproduction

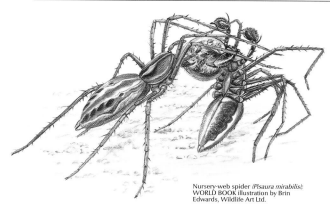

Nursery-web spider *(Pisaura mirabilis);* WORLD BOOK illustration by Brin Edwards, Wildlife Art Ltd.

Spider courtship sometimes includes an elaborate ritual. This illustration shows a male nursery-web spider, *right,* presenting a female, *left,* with a captured fly that he has wrapped in silk. The two spiders will mate after completing the ritual.

Thinlegged wolf spiders *(Pardosa milvina);* WORLD BOOK illustrations by Jack J. Kunz

A mother wolf spider carries her spiderlings on her back for a short time after they hatch. Wolf spiders take more care of their young than do most other kinds of spiders.

WORLD BOOK illustration by John F. Eggert

Spiderlings hatch from eggs inside the egg sac. One by one, they leave the sac through a tiny hole that they tear in its side. Most spiderlings immediately begin spinning draglines. Many then move to other areas, often by *ballooning,* a method of traveling along air currents.

Kite spider *(Gasteracantha sanguinolenta);* © Anthony Bannister, Corbis

A kite spider belongs to a group of orb weavers with distinctive spines on the abdomen. This African spider has a largely yellow abdomen with reddish spines and dark markings.

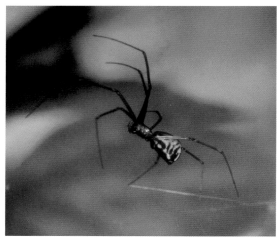

Bowl-and-doily spider *(Frontinella pyramitela);* © John Anderson, Animals Animals

A bowl-and-doily spider has bright yellow markings on its abdomen. This sheet-web weaver spins an unusual web that consists of a bowl-shaped sheet above a flat sheet.

have seen ballooning spiders. But most ballooners travel less than a mile or kilometer.

Spiderlings must molt to grow larger. First they make a new, larger skin just beneath their old skin. The tight old skin splits. The animal then wriggles out of the old skin and plumps up the new skin until it hardens. Most kinds of spiders molt from four to twelve times before becoming adults. When mature, most spiders stop molting. Female tarantulas and a few others continue to molt even after they become adults.

Enemies of spiders consist mainly of birds, insects, and other spiders. *Pirate spiders* eat only other spiders. Wasps rank among the spider's worst enemies. Predators also include lizards, snakes, frogs, toads, fish, or any other animals that eat insects. In addition, spiders suffer from fungal infections and from flies and wasps that live as parasites inside the spiders' bodies.

Web-building spiders

Web-building spiders catch food by spinning webs to trap insects. A web-building spider does not usually become caught in its own web. When walking across the web, it grasps the silk lines with a special hooked claw on each foot.

Tangled-web weavers spin the simplest type of web. It consists of a jumble of threads attached to supports, such as the corner of a ceiling. *Cobwebs* are old tangled webs that have collected dust and dirt.

Cellar spiders spin tangled webs in dark, empty parts of buildings. One cellar spider that looks like a daddy longlegs has thin legs more than 2 inches (5 centimeters) long.

Cobweb weavers spin a tangled web with a tightly woven sheet of silk in the middle. The sheet serves as an insect trap and as the spider's hideout. Also called *comb-footed spiders,* these spiders have a comb of hairs on their fourth pair of legs. They use the comb to throw liquid silk over an insect and trap it. The *black widow* spiders belong to the cobweb weaver group.

Ogre-faced spiders, also called *net-casting spiders,* make webs that consist of a small, sticky mesh support-

Mexican redknee tarantula *(Brachypelma smithi);* © William Ervin, Photo Researchers

A Mexican redknee tarantula rests on a leaf. Its legs have black, red, and yellow bands. Tarantulas rank as the largest spiders. The creature shown here lives in a forest in Costa Rica.

ed by a structure of dry silk. The sticky mesh consists mostly of hackled bands. The spider hangs upside down from the dry silk and holds the sticky mesh with its four front legs. When an insect crawls or flies near, the spider stretches the mesh to several times its normal size and sweeps it over the insect.

Funnel weavers live in large webs that they spin in tall grass, under rocks or logs, or in water. The bottom of the web, in which the spider hides, is shaped like a funnel. The top part of the spider's web forms a large sheet of silk spread out over the grass, soil, or other surface.

When an insect lands on the sheet, the spider runs out of the funnel and pounces on the victim.

Linyphiids, sometimes called *money spiders,* weave flat sheets of silk between blades of grass or branches of shrubs or trees. Many of these spiders also spin a mesh of crisscrossed threads above the sheet web. When a flying insect hits the mesh, it falls onto the sheet. Often, an insect will fly into the sheet web. The spider, which hangs beneath the web, quickly runs to the insect and pulls it through the webbing. Sheet webs last a long time because the spider repairs any damaged parts.

Scientists typically divide linyphiids into two basic groups, *dwarf weavers* and *sheet-web weavers.* The tiny

Redback spider *(Latrodectus hasselti);* © Carol Buchanan, Alamy Images

A redback spider has a striking red mark on both the top and bottom of its abdomen. This poisonous spider lives in Australia. It belongs to the group of spiders called tangled-web weavers.

Carolina wolf spider *(Lycosa carolinensis);* © Paul & Joyce Berquist, Animals Animals

A Carolina wolf spider has a large, hairy body. The creature shown here, in Arizona, is feeding on an insect. Wolf spiders are excellent hunters and can run swiftly in search of food.

dwarf weavers usually measure less than $\frac{1}{10}$ inch (2.5 millimeters) long. Sheet-web weavers generally grow larger and often have patterns on their abdomens.

Orb weavers build the most beautifully patterned webs of all. They weave their round webs in open areas, often between tree branches or flower stems. Threads of dry silk extend from an orb web's center like the spokes of a wheel. Coiling lines of sticky silk connect the spokes and serve as an insect trap.

Some orb weavers lie in wait for their prey in the center of the web. Others attach a signal line to the center. These spiders hide in a retreat near the web and hold on to the signal line. When an insect lands in the web, the line vibrates. The spider then darts out and captures the insect. Most orb weavers spin a new web every night. It takes about 30 minutes. Such spiders often eat their old webs to reuse the silk and to consume any tiny insects stuck in the web. Other orb weavers repair or replace damaged parts of their webs.

The *bolas spiders* spin a single line of silk with a ball of sticky silk at the end. This ball attracts certain kinds of male moths. When the moth flies near, a bolas spider will whirl the line and trap the moth on the sticky ball.

Hunting spiders

Hunting spiders typically creep up on their prey or lie in wait and pounce on it. The strong chelicerae of hunting spiders help them overpower victims. Most seem to locate prey using vibrations transmitted through the ground. A few hunters have large eyes and can see their prey from a distance. Tarantulas have poor vision. They use a system of silk lines radiating from their retreats to both alert them of passing prey and to trip up prey. Some hunting spiders spin simple web nets that stretch out along the ground and stop insects.

Jumping spiders sneak up and pounce on their prey. These spiders have short legs, but they can jump more than 40 times the length of their bodies. Male jumping spiders rank among the most colorful of all spiders. Thick, colored hairs cover their bodies, especially on their first pair of legs. Jumping spiders possess excellent vision, and the males use their colors to attract females.

Tarantulas rank as the world's largest spiders. The biggest ones live in South American jungles. Great numbers of tarantulas also inhabit dry regions of Mexico and the southwestern United States. Many tarantula species dig burrows. A California tarantula builds a *turret* (small tower) of grass and twigs at the entrance to its burrow. This spider then sits just below the rim and waits for insects to pass within striking distance. A few kinds of tarantulas live in trees.

Nursery-web spiders, sometimes called *fishing spiders,* live near water and hunt aquatic insects, small fish, and tadpoles. These spiders have large bodies and long, thin legs. Because of their light weight, many can walk on water without sinking. They also can dive underwater for short periods. Many females in this group build special webs for their young.

Wolf spiders thrive in a variety of environments and are excellent hunters. Many kinds have large, hairy bodies, and run swiftly in search of food. Other kinds live near water and resemble fishing spiders in appearance and habits. Still others live in burrows, while some spin funnel-shaped webs.

Artificial spider silk may provide manufacturers with an extremely strong and durable industrial fiber. The artificial spider silk shown here was produced by scientists in Munich, Germany.

© Matthias Schrader, Landov

Spiders and people

How spiders help people. Spiders have helped people for thousands of years by eating harmful insects, including flies, mosquitoes, and such crop pests as aphids and grasshoppers. Spiders rank among the most important predators of these insects.

Scientists believe spider silk and venom will also prove useful to human beings. Spider silk, though extremely fine, has great strength and durability. Biologists study the microscopic structure of this silk to understand its unusual properties. They also study how spiders make the silk by using only a few kinds of proteins dissolved in water. Such studies may help manufacturers develop new ways of producing extremely strong industrial fibers.

Spider venom can affect the human nervous system in many ways, and scientists have learned much about the nervous system by studying the effects of spider venom. Knowledge gained from these studies may lead to cures for illnesses of the nervous system, including Parkinson disease.

Manufacturers also hope to use spider venoms to make new kinds of insecticides. Collectively, the many different spider venoms may contain thousands of compounds that are highly poisonous to insects but harmless to people or other animals.

Dangerous spiders. Only a few kinds of spiders can inflict bites severe enough to endanger people. The most dangerous spider groups include the *recluses* and the *widows* of North America, the *redbacks* and *funnel-web spiders* of Australia, and the *button spiders* of Africa. The bites of these spiders can cause severe pain, but they rarely prove fatal. Moreover, spiders rarely bite people unless seriously threatened.

Spiders in the home. Many people have a fear of spiders, known as *arachnophobia,* and do not want spiders in their homes. Web-building spiders often live well hidden indoors and rarely touch floors or walls. As a result, pesticides may not prove effective. A good way to control spiders indoors is to eliminate insects from the home. Spiders will not infest houses in which they can find no food.   Jonathan A. Coddington

Scientific classification. Spiders belong to the phylum Arthropoda and the class Arachnida. They make up the spider order, Araneae. Liphistiids make up their own family, Liphistiidae. True spiders include the cobweb weaver family, Theridiidae; the crab spider family, Thomisidae; the dwarf and sheet-web weaver family, Linyphiidae; the funnel weaver family, Agelenidae; the hackled orb weaver family, Uloboridae; the jumping spider family, Salticidae; the nursery-web spider family, Pisauridae; the ogre-faced spider family, Deinopidae; the orb weaver family, Araneidae; and the wolf spider family, Lycosidae. Mygalomorphs include the purse-web spider family, Atypidae, and the tarantula family, Theraphosidae.

Outline

I. The spider's body
  A. Eyes
  B. Mouth
  C. Chelicerae
  D. Pedipalpi
  E. Legs
  F. Respiratory system
  G. Circulatory system
  H. Digestive system
  I. Nervous system

II. The spider's silk
  A. How spiders make silk
  B. How spiders use silk

III. The life of a spider
  A. Courtship and mating
  B. Eggs
  C. Spiderlings
  D. Enemies

IV. Web-building spiders
  A. Tangled-web weavers
  B. Ogre-faced spiders
  C. Funnel weavers
  D. Linyphiids
  E. Orb weavers

V. Hunting spiders
  A. Jumping spiders
  B. Tarantulas
  C. Nursery-web spiders
  D. Wolf spiders

VI. Spiders and people
  A. How spiders help people
  B. Dangerous spiders
  C. Spiders in the home

Questions

What is ballooning?
What are some of the ways in which spiders use silk?
How do tarantulas differ from true spiders?
How does an orb weaver know an insect has landed in its web?
How do spiders differ from insects?
Which kinds of spiders are dangerous to people?
How does a female wolf spider carry her egg sac?
What is the only food of pirate spiders?
Why are spiders valuable to people?
Why is a dragline often called a spider's "lifeline"?

Additional resources

Foelix, Rainer F. *Biology of Spiders.* 2nd ed. Oxford, 1996.
Mason, Adrienne. *The World of the Spider.* Sierra Club, 1999.
O'Toole, Christopher, ed. *Firefly Encyclopedia of Insects and Spiders.* Firefly Bks., 2002.
Simon, Seymour. *Spiders.* HarperCollins, 2003. Younger readers.

© David R. Frazier

© PhotoDisc, Inc., from Getty Images

AT&T

The telephone is a valuable means of communication. An automatic telephone answering device, *above left,* records messages from callers. A cellular telephone, *top right,* uses radio waves to send and receive telephone calls. A fax machine, *left,* lets people send written words and pictures over telephone lines.

Telephone

Telephone is an instrument that sends and receives voice messages in the form of electrical or radio signals. It is one of our most valuable means of communication. A telephone enables people to talk with each other at distances beyond voice range. In just a few seconds, you can phone a person across the street or on another continent. More sophisticated telephones can send and receive not only voice messages but also written words, songs, drawings, photographs, and video. Alexander Graham Bell, a Scottish-born teacher of the deaf, patented the telephone in 1876. The word *telephone* comes from two Greek words meaning *far* and *sound.*

Telephones are connected through a vast, complex communication network. The network includes large computers, tremendous lengths of copper wire and hair-thin glass fibers, cables buried in the ground and

Arthur R. Brodsky, the contributor of this article, is Communications Director for Public Knowledge, a Washington, D.C., organization that focuses on intellectual property and technology policy. He is a former telecommunications journalist.

laid along the ocean floor, radio transmitters and receivers, and artificial satellites orbiting far above Earth.

Many telephones connect with the communication network by means of wires that run through the walls of buildings. Usually, a small clip connects a telephone to the wiring. Other phones, called *wireless telephones* or *mobile telephones,* are not wired to the network but rather are linked to it via radio signals.

How a telephone works

Telephones come in a wide variety of designs. For much of the 1900's, many of the parts inside phones were mechanical. In contrast, most contemporary telephones are primarily electronic devices.

Types of telephones. Phones with a traditional design consist of a base unit and a handset that is held near the ear and mouth during a call. The handset is connected to the base unit by a cord or by radio signals. When messages travel as radio signals between handset and base, the phone is called a *cordless telephone.*

The mouthpiece of the handset contains a microphone that picks up the user's voice and converts it into outgoing electrical signals. The earpiece of the handset contains a speaker that converts incoming electrical signals into sound that the user can recognize.

Many phones vary from this traditional design. Sometimes, a headset takes the place of a handset, allowing use of the phone without hands. A *speakerphone* also allows hands-free calls. It has a microphone that can pick up all voices in a room and a loudspeaker that can broadcast incoming sound throughout the room. Often, a desktop or laptop computer can be used as a phone. The computer needs special software, a microphone, speakers, a device called a *sound card* to *digitize* the electrical signals, and an Internet connection. Digitizing the signals involves translating them from their original form into tiny impulses that represent numbers. Some phones contain built-in computer hardware and software that allow them to connect directly to the Internet.

A *cellular telephone* is a common type of wireless telephone. Cellular phones communicate via radio antennas arranged in small geographical areas called *cells*. A *satellite telephone* is a wireless telephone that communicates via satellites instead of land-based antennas.

Most cell phones are handheld units small enough to be carried in a pocket, a purse, or a briefcase, or on a belt clip. Many cell phones are equipped with extra communication or computer features. For example, most of them can store phone numbers, calendar events, or other data. The phones may also include such features as Internet access, digital cameras, digital music players, alarm clocks, electronic games, and receivers for Global Positioning System navigation. Cellular phones with a variety of computer features are often called *smartphones.*

Parts of a telephone. All telephones have three basic parts: a dialing mechanism, a microphone, and at least one speaker. Other common parts of modern phones include one or more printed circuit boards with various electronic chips, a display, radio equipment, and a battery or other power source. Usually, a plastic or metal housing surrounds the parts of a phone.

The dialing mechanism enables a caller to enter phone numbers. On most phones, the dialing mechanism is a set of numbered buttons or keys called a *keypad* or *keyboard.* On many phones, the keypad uses *tone dialing.* In tone dialing, each key generates a pair of accurately controlled tones when pressed. Computers in the phone network recognize the sequence of tones as the phone number and direct the call accordingly.

The microphone, also called the *transmitter,* changes sound waves into electrical signals and sends them on their first step into a phone network. In most cases, the microphone is a small *electret condenser microphone,* also called an *electret capacitor microphone.* It has two metallic plates set slightly apart. The plates are electrically charged and serve as a *capacitor,* a device that stores a charge. The flexible front plate—which typically consists of an electrically insulating foil backed by a metal coating—acts as a *diaphragm* (thin, vibrating disk). The back plate is fixed and faces the foil side of the diaphragm. Sound waves make the diaphragm vibrate, causing variations in the capacitor's electric current. These variations are an electric "copy" of the sound.

The speaker, also called the *receiver,* collects electrical signals coming from a phone network and changes them into sound waves. A speaker is like a microphone in reverse. A typical telephone speaker consists of a wire coil called a *voice coil,* a permanent magnet, and a diaphragm. Electrical pulses pass through the voice coil, creating varying magnetic forces around the coil. These forces interact with the forces of the permanent magnet, causing the coil to vibrate rapidly. The diaphragm, which is attached to the coil, vibrates with it. The diaphragm vibrations produce sound waves that duplicate the voice of the caller on the other end of the line.

The printed circuit board contains the "brains" of a modern electronic phone. The circuit board contains tiny chips that control various functions. For example, one chip may generate a sound or vibration when there is an incoming call. This chip has replaced the small bell that served the same function in early phones. Some chips may help the phone interact with the wire or radio antenna that connects the phone to a network. Others may help process the electrical signals into a form that can be sent over a network. Still others supply power to the circuit board or help recharge the phone battery.

An important chip called a *microprocessor* receives inputs from the dialing mechanism and sends outputs to the phone's display. In a cell phone, the microprocessor also communicates through special radio channels with control centers in a cell network. The control centers tell the microprocessor how to send and receive calls through the network. In addition, the microprocessor coordinates the rest of the functions on a circuit board.

Memory chips on the circuit board store instructions and data that are used by the phone's microprocessor. These chips also store inputs from phone users, such as a directory of phone numbers, voice mail messages, text documents, or digital photographs.

The display is usually a *liquid crystal display* (LCD) screen. It may perform only one or two simple functions, such as displaying a clock, or an incoming caller's phone number or name. On more advanced phones, the display may also be used for such functions as viewing a phone directory, playing electronic games, using a calculator, or reading and writing text messages.

The radio equipment. Wireless phones have radio transmitters, receivers, and antennas. An antenna may take different forms, depending on the type of phone and the distance the radio signals need to travel. For example, the antenna may be a small device inside the phone, a short stub or long rod on a handset, or a satellite dish. The transmitter and receiver may be mounted on the phone's circuit board. In a cordless phone, both the handset and the base contain radio equipment.

The power source. Phones that have a traditional copper wire connection to a phone network usually receive their power over the phone line from the central office of the phone company. In most cellular phones and cordless phone handsets, the power source is a small internal battery. Some phones have a cord that is plugged into a regular wall socket.

How a telephone call travels

A caller can connect to a telephone network in a number of ways. The traditional way involves using a phone connected by wires to the worldwide Public Switched Telephone Network (PSTN). A wire connection to the PSTN is often called a *landline.*

The PSTN relies on a technology called *circuit switching.* A circuit-switched network requires a *circuit* (channel) to be opened between two callers before they can talk to each other. The phone signals flow in sequence over this circuit. The circuit is dedicated to that one call and cannot be used by other callers until the call ends. Circuit switching has been the basic technology used to transmit phone calls since the late 1800's.

Today, calls can also be made using a phone connected to the Internet, rather than the PSTN. The Internet relies on a technology called *packet switching.* In a packet-switched network, phone calls are divided into packets of data that are sent individually over many channels. The packets are reassembled when they arrive at their destination. Transmitting calls over the Internet or a similar packet-switched network is called Voice over Internet Protocol (VoIP). Many people believe VoIP will eventually replace phone calls made over the PSTN.

In practice, most traditional long-distance calls already rely partly on packet switching. Even if the phones on both ends of a call have a traditional PSTN connection, phone companies often will route the call through parts of their networks that rely on packet switching.

Most wireless phones rely on circuit switching, which means the call signals travel continuously along single, dedicated radio channels. However, more advanced wireless devices can use packet switching to transmit and receive large amounts of data, including VoIP calls.

Traditional phone calls. On a traditional phone network, a caller first listens for a *dial tone*—that is, a sound indicating that the phone has a connection to a *central office.* The central office is a facility of a local phone company, also known as a *local exchange carrier.* Then, the caller dials a phone number, causing

electrical signals to travel from the phone to a *switch* in the central office. The switch uses the phone number as an "address" to determine where to route the call. At one time, human operators switched phone calls manually by plugging electric cords into a switchboard. Today, electronic switches—actually computers—route calls.

If the call is for someone connected to the same central office, the switch simply creates a loop between the two phones. If the call is for someone farther away, the switch routes the call to another local switch or to a long-distance switch. Long-distance switches are operated by companies known as *long-distance carriers* or *interexchange carriers.* The call may pass through several switches of various carriers before reaching the central office of the local carrier that serves the phone being called. A switch in that office routes electrical signals to that phone, causing it to ring. When that phone is answered, a connection is made between the two phones. All the routing and switching occurs in seconds.

Once the connection is established, the electrical signals that make up the message travel between the two phones. Most traditional phone signals begin and end their journey as *analog* signals transported over copper wires. Analog signals are continuously varying signals that are exact reproductions of the sound. However, for most of the journey, the signals travel as *digital* signals. Digital signals are in *binary code*—the same code that computers use. Binary code consists of sequences of two digits, 0 and 1. Phone signals are digitized by being divided into thousands of tiny impulses that can each be represented by a string of 0's and 1's.

Analog phone signals may travel all the way to the central office switch before they are digitized. Alternatively, a *concentrator*—usually a refrigerator-sized box—

An intercontinental call, such as a call from the United States to the United Kingdom, travels through the sky or under the ocean. In a traditional telephone network, the signals from a caller's home phone pass through wires to a central office of a local phone company, also called a *local exchange carrier.* From there, the signals travel to an office of a *long-distance carrier.* This office directs the call in one of two ways. In one method, the signals go to a *ground station,* which beams them to a communications satellite. The satellite relays the signals to a British ground station. In the other method, the signals are routed to a fiber-optic cable beneath the Atlantic Ocean. With both methods, the signals reach a British long-distance carrier office. The call then travels to a local exchange carrier office and eventually reaches its intended destination.

may digitize the signals before they reach the central office. As the signals move through each switch in a network, the digital sequences are duplicated. This duplication maintains the strength and accuracy of the signals over long distances.

Most digital signals travel through the network over *fiber-optic cables*. These cables consist of bundles of hair-thin glass fibers that carry digital signals as impulses of light. A strand of optical fiber can carry thousands of times as much information as a pair of copper wires. Signals from millions of phones may travel through a single fiber-optic cable at a time. The cables may be buried in the ground or laid on the ocean floor.

The digital signals may also be transmitted on short radio waves called *microwaves*. The network uses a series of relay stations to direct microwaves over vast distances. A dish antenna at a relay station receives a signal, and another dish antenna retransmits the signal to the next station. To direct the signals across oceans, the network uses communications satellites.

Cellular phone calls. Companies that provide cellular phone service maintain one or more cellular networks. In each network, a city or other geographical region is divided into cells. Each cell has an antenna. Most of these antennas are mounted on steel towers. Cables connect the antenna to a radio receiver and transmitter at the base of the tower. This radio equipment site is called a *base transceiver station,* or just a *base station.* A large city may have hundreds of cells and base stations.

In a typical cellular network, a piece of equipment called a *base station controller* (BSC) manages a small group of base stations. A *mobile telephone switching office* (MTSO), also known as a *mobile switching center* (MSC), then manages one or more BSC's. A BSC helps perform some of the more basic tasks of an MTSO. In some networks, BSC's may not be used.

During an outgoing call, a cell phone sends signals to the antenna in the cell where the phone is being used. The base receiver picks up the signals, and the base transmitter routes them to the BSC linked to the base station. The BSC routes the signals to its MTSO. The MTSO switches the signals to another base station (usually via a BSC), to another MTSO, or to an office that is part of the wire-based PSTN. Similarly, an MTSO ensures that an incoming call is routed to the correct base station. The base transmitter sends the call to a phone in the cell. The base stations, BSC's, and MTSO may be connected by ground-based lines or by microwaves.

MTSO's also play other roles. For example, they coordinate the *handoff* or *handover* of calls as a phone moves from one cell to another. An MTSO also keeps track of the location of phones within its network so that calls can be routed properly. If a phone within the network is not linked to that company's cellular service, the MTSO verifies that the phone subscribes to another service. The MTSO relays information about the usage of the phone to the other service provider. When a phone leaves its home network and enters the network of another provider, the phone is said to be *roaming.*

A cellular company is assigned hundreds of radio *frequencies* for transmitting phone signals within a given region in a network. Frequency refers to the number of times an electromagnetic wave, such as a radio wave, vibrates per second. Each cell uses a portion of these ra-

© Kalle Parkkinen, Lehtikuva/Reuters

A smartphone combines the features of a cellular phone and a handheld computer. This smartphone allows the user to take photographs, play video and audio files, and access the Internet.

dio frequencies. The company can use the same frequencies in different cells throughout the network, as long as the same frequencies are not used in two cells that border each other. If the same frequencies were used in adjacent cells, signals from different phone calls would interfere with one another. Because frequencies can be reused across networks, large numbers of people can make calls at the same time.

During calls, signals travel on one or more frequencies within an available *bandwidth* (range of frequencies). The frequencies make up the radio channels over which the calls take place. Most of a company's assigned frequencies are used to transmit phone calls and other data. But some frequencies are used for *control channels.* Cellular phones communicate with an MTSO over a control channel. For example, the MTSO uses a control channel to tell a phone which frequencies it should use to receive an incoming call. When the phone moves into another cell during a call, the MTSO uses a control channel to notify the phone to change frequencies.

If cellular calls are sent as analog signals, each call requires two channels dedicated only to the one call. One caller's voice travels on one channel, and the other voice travels on the other channel. But most cellular signals are transmitted as digital signals. Digital signals can be divided or manipulated so that they travel along channels in different ways. As a result, three or more digital cellular channels can occupy the same bandwidth that would be required for a single analog channel.

VoIP phone calls. Making calls over the Internet or a similar network typically requires a *broadband* connection. The term *broadband* refers to the high-speed transmission of data. The most common broadband services are *cable modem* service and *digital subscriber line* (DSL) service. A cable modem is a device that links a computer to a network via cable TV lines. DSL is a technology that increases the data-carrying capacity of copper phone lines. Broadband data service can also be provided over fiber-optic lines and through the air using satellites or other advanced wireless technologies.

VoIP calls are typically made in one of three ways. One way is by plugging a normal phone into an *analog telephone adapter* (ATA). The ATA changes analog signals into digital signals. When a phone number is dialed, the ATA digitizes the tones from the keypad and sends them to a *call processor* maintained by a VoIP company. The call processor is a device that *maps* (translates) a phone number into an *Internet Protocol* (IP) *address.* An IP address is a number that identifies a specific device connected to the Internet. Mapping is done using a computer program called a *soft switch.* The soft switch connects the two ends of a call.

A caller can also use a special VoIP phone that has a direct connection to a networking device called a *router.* Many VoIP phones have a handset and keypad like a traditional phone. But all the computer equipment and programs needed for VoIP are contained within the phone. A *Wi-Fi phone* is a type of wireless VoIP phone. Wi-Fi is a common wireless packet-switched networking technology. A Wi-Fi device sends data through the air to a base station or router in the network. A number of cities are developing citywide Wi-Fi networks.

A third way to make VoIP calls is by using a desktop or laptop computer. The computer must have VoIP software, a microphone, speakers, and a sound card.

A VoIP call sent out over the Internet travels in much the same way that a Web page or an e-mail message travels. The sending device splits the call up into packets of digital data. Information on each packet indicates the destination of the packet and how it should be reassembled once it arrives. The sending device transmits individual packets to one or more routers. Each packet travels from router to router until it arrives at its destination. After all the packets arrive, the receiving device reassembles them.

Telephone services

Telephone makers and telephone service providers offer a variety of services to callers. These services include operator, business, and residential services.

Operator services use human operators or computers that imitate the human voice to provide various kinds of assistance. For example, in many countries, a person who needs help to complete a call can dial 0 to reach an operator at a local phone company. A service called *directory assistance* provides callers with the phone numbers of parties they wish to call, and can connect calls as well. Many countries have short numbers that can be dialed to reach emergency police, fire, or ambulance service. In the United States and Canada, the standard emergency number is 911. Common emergency numbers elsewhere include 112 and 999.

Business services. Most businesses have more than one phone. A business may set up its phone system in various ways. In one arrangement, provided by the local phone company, each phone has its own number. One name for this service is *Centrex service.* In another arrangement, known as a *private branch exchange* (PBX), several lines owned by the phone company are connected to a switching system owned by the business. In this system, the business has one phone number, and each phone has a separate extension number. Employees can call each other merely by dialing the proper extension. A Centrex or PBX system may use either traditional telephone lines or a business version of VoIP.

Private line service, or *dedicated service,* is designed for businesses that have branch offices with which they communicate frequently. The phone company sets up a line or group of lines that run only between those offices. Private line service eliminates the need to send each of these calls over a public telephone network. Private lines may be equipped to handle large amounts of computer data or fax transmissions.

In many businesses, a system called *voice mail* answers incoming calls. A voice recording stored on a computer chip gives callers instructions to help them reach the desired party. If that party is not available, the caller can leave a message that the system records.

Another common business service is *toll-free service,* also called *Freephone service* or *Freecall service.* A subscriber to the service is issued a special number and pays the charges for all calls received by that number. Many companies that sell goods or services by mail or by telephone use toll-free service. In the United States and Canada, the service is commonly called *800 service,* because the first three digits of toll-free numbers were all originally 800. Today, many toll-free numbers in the United States and Canada begin with 888, 877, or 866.

Residential services. Many home telephone users have access to a variety of services. For example, the phone company can provide voice-mail service similar to that used by businesses. *Call waiting* lets a person put one call on hold to speak with another caller. *Call forwarding* automatically sends all calls to a designated phone number. *Call blocking* automatically rejects calls from phones whose numbers are designated by the subscriber. A service called *automatic caller identification,* or *caller I.D.,* enables a person to see the caller's phone number or name before answering. *Automatic callback* service notifies a caller when a busy number he or she has been dialing becomes free.

Other services. Many companies sell *phone cards* or *calling card*s that can be used to pay for long-distance, international, or cellular calls. They usually resemble credit cards. Many pay phones can read a phone card electronically and automatically deduct the cost of the call. Alternatively, the caller may have to first dial an access number to use the card.

Other telephone services supply information or advice, or enable callers to participate in informal polls or to enter contests. Often, a caller must dial a special number to access such services.

The telephone industry

For many years, telephone companies offered landline voice communication as their primary service. Today, the telecommunications industry includes voice, data, and video transmission over both wire-based and wireless networks. The transmission occurs over the PSTN, the

Internet, and private networks. A single company may offer several types of services. For example, a number of companies that once specialized in distributing cable television programs now also offer high-speed Internet access and telephone service. Similarly, companies that once specialized in landline phone service are beginning to offer television programs as well. Some companies specialize in VoIP service.

In the United States, hundreds of companies provide traditional local telephone service. Some have only a few hundred lines, and others have millions. Four firms provide the majority of local service: AT&T Inc., BellSouth Corporation, Qwest Communications International Inc., and Verizon Communications Inc.

A few hundred U.S. companies offer traditional long-distance service. Some own all of their telephone lines and switches. Others—mostly the smaller companies—buy service from large firms and resell it to their customers. The largest U.S. long-distance carriers include AT&T, Sprint Nextel Corporation, and Verizon.

Another type of U.S. telephone company is the *competitive local exchange carrier*. It provides telephone services in competition with established local telephone companies, most often to businesses.

Companies that have been long-time providers of landline service also operate most of the wireless phone networks in the United States. Major U.S. wireless providers include Cingular Wireless, a joint venture of AT&T and BellSouth; Sprint Nextel; T-Mobile USA, Inc., owned by the German company Deutsche Telekom AG; and Verizon Wireless, a joint venture of Verizon and the British firm Vodafone Group plc.

In other countries. For many years, the government provided telephone service in most countries. But since the 1980's, many countries have sold part ownership—or in some cases, a whole telephone company—to private citizens.

Most of the world's largest telephone companies offer a variety of telecommunication services, including local and long-distance landline, wireless, and Internet services. Major companies based in Europe include Deutsche Telekom AG, in Germany; Vodafone Group plc and BT Group plc, both in the United Kingdom; France Télécom SA and Vivendi, both in France; Telecom Italia S.p.A., in Italy; and Telefónica, S.A., in Spain. In Asia, major companies include Nippon Telegraph & Telephone Corporation and KDDI Corporation, both in Japan; KT Corporation, in South Korea; and four state-owned firms in China. BCE (Bell Canada Enterprises) Inc. is Canada's largest telecommunications firm. Telstra Corporation Limited is Australia's largest.

The wealthiest areas of the world—including most of Europe, most of North America, parts of East Asia, and Australia and New Zealand—have modern, extensive telecommunication systems. In these areas, both wire-based and wireless phone networks link almost all regions with one another and with other continents. These areas also have widespread access to the Internet.

In other areas—including most of Africa and Asia, parts of eastern Europe, and much of Latin America—telecommunication systems are less advanced. Traditional phone equipment and networks are often concentrated in the cities and larger towns. People in rural areas may have little or no phone access. Also, Internet availability is extremely limited. However, many of these less developed areas are experiencing large growth in cellular phone usage. Usually, it is easier and cheaper to develop cellular networks than wire-based networks, especially in sparsely populated regions.

History

Bell's invention. Alexander Graham Bell, a Scotsman who came to the United States in 1871, invented the telephone. Bell was a teacher of the deaf in Boston. At night, he experimented with a *harmonic telegraph,* a device for sending several telegraph messages at once over one wire. Bell developed the idea of the telephone in 1874 but kept working on the harmonic telegraph.

On June 2, 1875, one of the metal reeds of the harmonic telegraph stuck. Bell's assistant, Thomas A. Watson, plucked the reed to loosen it. Bell, who was in another room, heard the sound in his receiver. He realized that the vibrations of the reed had caused variations of electric current. In turn, the electric current had reproduced the same variations in the receiver he was using.

On March 10, 1876, Bell finally succeeded in speaking words over a telephone. He was about to test a new transmitter. In another room, Watson waited for the test message. Suddenly, Bell spilled some acid from a battery on his clothes. He cried out, "Mr. Watson, come here. I want you!" Watson heard every word clearly and rushed into the room. In June 1876, Bell exhibited his telephone at the Centennial Exposition in Philadelphia.

Early telephones. In August 1876, Bell received the first one-way long-distance call. This call came over an 8-mile (13-kilometer) telegraph line between Brantford, Ontario, and Paris, Ontario. In October 1876, Bell and Watson held the first two-way long-distance telephone

Historical Pictures Service

Telephone operators connected almost all calls manually by switchboard until the early 1900's. This photograph shows the central telephone exchange of New York City about 1900.

Popular telephone models of the past

The first telephone was this device, patented in 1876 by Alexander Graham Bell.

An 1882 wall phone had a handheld receiver and a crank to signal the operator.

A 1919 dial telephone required complex switching equipment.

The 1928 desk telephone combined receiver and transmitter in a handset unit.

The "300" model desk phone, introduced in 1937, contained a bell in its base.

The colored telephone of 1954 gained widespread popularity as a decorative item.

The Princess phone of 1959 featured a compact design and an illuminated rotary dial.

AT&T

The "trimline" telephone of 1968 featured push buttons on the handset.

conversation. They spoke between Boston and Cambridgeport, a part of Cambridge, Massachusetts, a distance of about 2 miles (3 kilometers). In 1877, Charles Williams, an electrical workshop owner, installed the first line intended exclusively for telephone use. It extended 3 miles (5 kilometers) between Williams's home in Somerville, Massachusetts, and his shop in Boston.

The first telephones used no switchboards. A pair of iron wires connected each pair of phones. As more telephones came into use, each was connected to all the others. Over 1,000 connections were required to link only 50 phones. Switchboards solved this problem by bringing together the wires from all phones in an area. The first switchboard began operating in 1877 in Boston.

Telephone services soon began operating in other parts of the world. Service began in Australia in 1878 and in the United Kingdom in 1879.

Almon B. Strowger, an American inventor, patented an automatic switching system in 1891. The first commercial switchboard based on his patent opened in La Porte, Indiana, in 1892. The caller pressed buttons to get the number, then turned a crank to ring the phone.

In 1891, the first international phone connection was made, between London and Paris. In 1892, service began between New York City and Chicago. In 1896, the first dial telephones began operating in Milwaukee.

The Bell System. Bell, Watson, Gardiner G. Hubbard, and Thomas Sanders formed the Bell Telephone Company in 1877. Hubbard was Bell's father-in-law, and Sanders was the father of one of Bell's pupils. They had helped pay for Bell's experiments. The Western Union Telegraph Company also entered the telephone

business in 1877. It used transmitters developed by Thomas A. Edison, the great American inventor. Elisha Gray, another American inventor, developed Western Union's receivers. The Bell company met the competition by using the improved transmitters of Emile Berliner, a German immigrant, and Francis J. Blake, an American.

In 1878, the Bell company sued Western Union to protect Bell's patents. Western Union claimed that Gray, not Bell, had invented the telephone. On the same day Bell had applied for his first patent, Feb. 14, 1876, Gray had notified the U.S. Patent Office that he was working on a device to transmit speech. However, Bell submitted his application before Gray gave his notification. Bell's patent was issued on March 7, 1876. In 1879, Western Union recognized Bell's patents and sold its telephone business to the Bell company. This case was the first of about 600 lawsuits over Bell's patents. The Supreme Court of the United States upheld Bell's patents in 1888.

In 1878, the first telephone *exchange* (central office) opened in New Haven, Connecticut. It had 21 customers. Exchanges soon opened throughout the United States and Canada.

In 1878, two companies were formed as successors to the Bell Telephone Company: the New England Telephone Company and a new Bell Telephone Company. The New England Telephone Company licensed phone service in New England, and the Bell Telephone Company licensed service in the rest of the United States. In 1879, the two companies combined to form the National Bell Telephone Company. The American Bell Telephone Company was founded as the successor to National Bell in 1880. In 1885, the American Telephone and Telegraph Company (AT&T) was established to operate the long-distance network. AT&T took over American Bell in 1899 and became the parent company of the Bell System.

Improvements in telephone technology. Transcontinental phone service began between New York City and San Francisco in 1915. Transatlantic radiotelephone service between New York City and London began in 1927. The first long-distance coaxial cable linked New York City and Philadelphia in 1936.

Undersea telephone cables between North America and Europe began operating in 1956. A cable joined the U.S. mainland to Hawaii in 1957. A cable from Japan was joined to this cable in 1964, connecting Japan to the U.S. mainland. The first commercial communications satellite, Early Bird, was launched in 1965.

In 1970, international *direct distance dialing* (DDD) began operating between New York City and London. DDD enables people to make direct long-distance calls without the help of an operator.

In 1980, a fiber-optic system for local calls was installed in Atlanta, Georgia. A fiber-optic system between New York City and Washington, D.C., began operating in 1983. Fiber-optic cables began carrying messages across the Atlantic in 1988 and across the Pacific in 1989.

In the late 1970's and early 1980's, cellular systems began to be developed. The world's first commercial cellular system went into operation in Japan in 1979. The first commercial cellular system in the United States went into operation in 1983. By the late 1980's, cellular service had gained popularity throughout much of the world.

In the early 2000's, broadband Internet service began to become widely available in Australia, Canada, Japan, South Korea, the United States, and most countries in Europe. In the United States, Verizon Communications was the first company to launch a major *fiber-to-the-premises* (FTTP) effort. With FTTP, broadband services are provided on fiber-optic cables that lead directly to people's homes.

Competition in the U.S. telephone industry. In the early 1900's, AT&T began buying small telephone companies. In 1913, the attorney general of the United States warned AT&T that some of its planned purchases could violate antitrust laws designed to protect competition. AT&T promised not to buy any more competing telephone companies and to allow all local phone companies to connect to its long-distance network.

The Federal Communications Commission (FCC) ruled in 1968 that telephone users could buy their own telephones and other equipment to connect to the telephone network. Previously, AT&T and its local companies had leased all phone equipment to users. In 1969, the FCC cleared the way for MCI Telecommunications to offer long-distance service. MCI thus became the first long-distance carrier to compete with AT&T.

In 1974, the U.S. government filed a lawsuit against AT&T, charging it with anticompetitive practices. The case was settled in 1982, and AT&T agreed to give up its local telephone companies on Jan. 1, 1984. The local companies were grouped into seven regional holding companies (RHC's), each of which provided local service in a particular U.S. region. The seven RHC's, also known as the "Baby Bells," were (1) NYNEX, (2) Bell Atlantic, (3)

BellSouth, (4) Ameritech, (5) Southwestern Bell, (6) U S West, and (7) Pacific Telesis. The settlement allowed AT&T to keep its equipment-manufacturing plants, its long-distance business, and its research facilities.

The Telecommunications Act of 1996 loosened many restrictions that had limited competition in the U.S. telephone industry. It allowed local phone companies, long-distance companies, and cable-television companies to enter each other's businesses. The act also allowed the RHC's to compete in local markets outside their own regions. Starting in the mid-1990's, many phone companies and other communications firms merged to form large national or international corporations. Most of the RHC's became parts of large telecommunications corporations through mergers, often with other RHC's.

In 1997, NYNEX and Bell Atlantic merged under the Bell Atlantic name. Between 1997 and 1999, SBC Communications (formerly Southwestern Bell) bought Pacific Telesis and Ameritech, as well as Southern New England Telecommunications, an independent local phone company. In 2000, Bell Atlantic acquired GTE, the country's largest independent local phone company. The new corporation was renamed Verizon. Also in 2000, Qwest Communications International, a major communications company, bought U S West. In 2005, SBC purchased AT&T, its former parent company. SBC then changed its name to AT&T Inc. In 2006, Verizon acquired the long-distance company MCI. That same year, the new AT&T announced it would buy BellSouth.　　　Arthur R. Brodsky

Outline

I. How a telephone works
  A. Types of telephones B. Parts of a telephone
II. How a telephone call travels
  A. Traditional phone calls C. VoIP phone calls
  B. Cellular phone calls
III. Telephone services
  A. Operator services C. Residential services
  B. Business services D. Other services
IV. The telephone industry
  A. In the United States B. In other countries
V. History

Questions

What are the basic parts that all telephones have?
How do circuit switching and packet switching differ?
How does a traditional landline call travel over a network?
What are fiber-optic cables?
What does a mobile telephone switching office (MTSO) do?
How do cellular networks transmit calls? Why can many people in the same cellular network make calls at the same time?
What is Voice over Internet Protocol (VoIP)?
Why are many less developed regions of the world experiencing large growth in cellular phone usage?
Who invented the telephone? How did he do it?
Why was AT&T forced to give up its local telephone companies in 1984?

Additional resources

Gearhart, Sarah. *The Telephone.* Atheneum, 1999. Younger readers.

Nobleman, Marc T. *The Telephone.* Capstone Pr., 2004. Younger readers.

Noll, A. Michael. *Introduction to Telephones and Telephone Systems.* 3rd ed. Artech Hse., 1998.

Stern, Ellen S., and Gwathmey, E. M., eds. *Once upon a Telephone: An Illustrated Social History.* Harcourt, 1994.

The sun's motion across the sky forms the basis of a fundamental timekeeping system called *solar time*. The sun can serve as a standard of time because its movements are fairly regular and predictable, as seen in this composite of photographs taken at even intervals. Even before people developed writing, they probably kept time by observing motions in the heavens.

© Larry Landolfi, SPL/Photo Researchers

Time

Time is both a useful and familiar concept and an enduring mystery. Keeping track of time helps us order our activities and coordinate them with other people. People use watches and clocks to determine when to attend school and work, to arrange meetings and other events, and to keep airline, bus, and train systems running smoothly. Telling time ranks among the most important skills that children learn at an early age.

We can measure time more accurately than any other quantity. In fact, much of modern technology could not function without precise timekeeping and *synchronization* (coordination in time). The worldwide navigation network called the Global Positioning System (GPS), for example, uses time signals broadcast by satellites to precisely determine a unit's location. For GPS units to function reliably, clocks on the satellites must vary from one another by one-billionth of a second or less. Other devices that require precision synchronization include cellular telephone and computer networks, radio and television systems, radar equipment, electric power grids, and many scientific instruments.

The nature of time, on the other hand, remains among the deepest mysteries. Scholars have described time as something that flows or as a way of ordering events in sequence. Both of these ideas, however, only describe our experience of time. They do not explain what time really is. Throughout history, scientists and philosophers have struggled to better understand and define time.

The first two sections of this article, *Measuring time* and *Time in today's world,* describe historical and modern methods for keeping track of time. The last section, *Our understanding of time,* discusses ideas from science and philosophy about the nature of time.

The contributors of this article are Craig A. Callender, Professor of Philosophy at the University of California at San Diego, and Thomas R. O'Brian, Chief of the Time and Frequency Division of the National Institute of Standards and Technology.

Measuring time

Nearly all methods of measuring time involve observing *periodic* (regularly repeating) events. Such events include cycles of motion in the heavens, actions performed by mechanical clocks, and changes in nature.

Astronomical cycles. Even before people developed writing, they probably kept time by observing motions in the heavens. The rising or setting of the sun can serve to mark the passage of a day—that is, one rotation of Earth. The *phase* (apparent shape) of the moon varies in a cycle that lasts about 29 ½ days, the basis of a month. Our view of the stars changes slightly each night, with different constellations becoming visible each season. A full cycle of these constellations marks a single year. Studying heavenly motions enabled early civilizations to properly time agricultural activities and religious rituals.

The use of the day as a basic unit of time gave rise to two slightly different systems of timekeeping. These systems are (1) solar time and (2) sidereal time.

Solar time measures the apparent motion of the sun. In most places, the sun appears to reach its highest point in the sky once each day, an event called *local noon*. One *solar day* equals the time between two consecutive local noons.

Some of the earliest timekeeping devices, called *sun clocks* or *shadow clocks,* used the movement of shadows to measure solar time. More than 5,000 years ago, the ancient Egyptians erected pillarlike monuments called *obelisks*. An obelisk's shadow changed position and length as the sun moved across the sky, enabling people to track the time of day. More advanced sun clocks called *sundials* included markings that revealed the hour of day based on the position of an object's shadow.

Sidereal time measures the apparent motion of the stars. One *sidereal day* is the time it takes a certain star to reach its highest point in the sky two times in a row.

A sidereal day basically measures one complete rotation of Earth. A solar day lasts slightly longer because, in addition to rotating, Earth moves around the sun in its orbit. This motion requires Earth to complete slightly more than a full rotation before the sun appears in the same position in the sky. For this reason, a sidereal day measures about 4 minutes shorter than a solar day.

Artificial clocks. Timekeeping methods based on the sun and stars have several limitations. Sun clocks work only when the sun is shining, and many kinds require regular adjustment for changes in the sun's apparent motion. The sun and stars also move too slowly to be of much use in measuring intervals shorter than an hour. As civilizations began to require more precise and convenient timekeeping, people developed artificial clocks.

Clocks that measure change. The first artificial clocks measured some change that proceeded at a fairly constant rate. The *water clock,* used as early as 3,500 years ago, consisted of a container that water flowed into or out of at a steady rate. People measured time by comparing the changing water level to marks on the container. Simpler clocks for everyday use included candles marked at regular lengths and oil lamps with marked reservoirs. As the candle burned down or the oil burned away, the marks indicated how much time had passed.

Most of these clocks probably remained accurate only to about half an hour per day at best. Some complex water clocks, however, kept more accurate time by using special devices to regulate the flow of water.

Clocks that count repeated actions. The first fully mechanical clocks, probably built in the late 1200's, relied

Standard time zones in the United States and Canada

The United States and Canada each have six standard time zones. This map does not show the Hawaii-Aleutian time zone, which includes Hawaii and the western Aleutian Islands (part of Alaska). The rest of Alaska is in the Alaska time zone. Major zones differ from neighboring zones by one hour. Zone boundaries are irregular so that places near the zone's edge can have the same time.

WORLD BOOK map

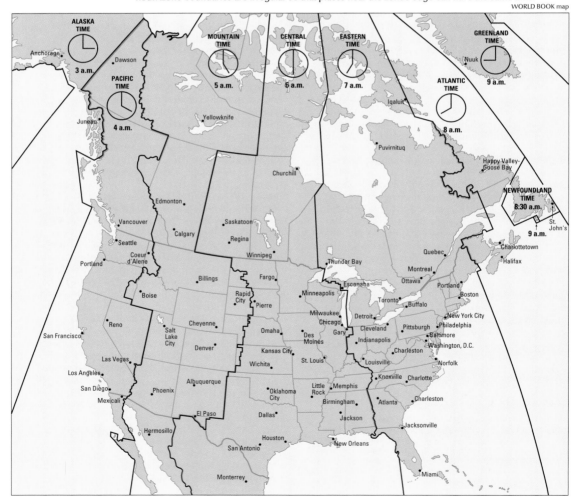

on the periodic motion of weight-driven gears. Because these clocks were complex and costly, most towns had only one. These clocks remained accurate to about 15 minutes per day and were often reset daily to solar noon.

Accuracy increased greatly with the development of pendulum clocks in the late 1600's. These clocks used the swinging of a pendulum, which the Italian scientist Galileo had earlier discovered to be surprisingly regular. Early pendulum clocks remained accurate to about 10 seconds per day, while later, more complex models kept even better time.

Clockmakers continued to design and improve clocks and watches. By the 1800's, most families could afford at least one timepiece, and fairly accurate timekeeping became widespread. In the late 1920's, clockmakers began using natural vibrations of the mineral quartz as a basis for simpler, more accurate timepieces. Still common today, quartz watches and clocks can remain accurate to better than one second per day.

In the late 1940's and 1950's, scientists developed *atomic clocks* that count fundamental vibrations of atoms. The best atomic clocks remain accurate to trillionths of a second per day, not gaining or losing a second in millions of years.

Natural processes. Some natural processes preserve a record of periodic events. These "natural clocks" enable us to measure the timing of events in the past.

Radioactive decay. Atoms of a radioactive element *decay* (break down) into atoms of another element. Because this decay occurs at a known rate, scientists can sometimes determine how old a sample is by measuring the amount of radioactive material it contains.

For example, some of the carbon in living things is a radioactive *isotope* (form) called carbon-14. Carbon-14 decays into nitrogen at a known rate, but living things constantly replenish the carbon-14 in their bodies. When an organism dies, it stops taking in new carbon-14. Thus, by analyzing the amount of carbon-14 left in a sample, scientists can often estimate how long ago an organism died.

The formation of rock. Over billions of years, natural processes, such as the flow of lava and the deposit of *sediment* (tiny bits of solid material), lay down new layers of rock. These layers preserve a record of time in Earth's past often referred to as the *geological record.*

Geologists use various methods to estimate the age of rock layers. By observing lava flows and sediment deposits, they can estimate how long it would take for a certain thickness of rock to develop. They can determine the ages of certain rocks using some kinds of radioactive decay.

Changes in living things. Living things can also preserve a record of time. Many organisms grow in cycles that last a year or even a day. In colder climates, for example, trees often feature prominent growth rings produced by rapid growth during the warm months and slow growth or no growth during winter.

Evolution (the gradual development of living things) also serves as a natural clock. An organism's DNA (deoxyribonucleic acid) includes genetic information encoded in a sequence of chemical units called *base pairs.* Over time, evolutionary processes cause changes in the sequence of base pairs that occur at a predictable rate. By comparing DNA from two related organisms, therefore, biologists can determine how long ago the organisms *diverged* (began to evolve separately) from a common ancestor.

Time in today's world

Advances in communication and transportation have created an increasingly global society. Keeping this society running smoothly requires a standard system of timekeeping that people anywhere can use easily.

Units of time. People once used the day as the fundamental unit of time. They measured this time by Earth's rotation and divided it into hours, minutes, and seconds. Standards changed when atomic clocks provided a more accurate and stable means of keeping time.

In modern society, the second serves as the fundamental unit of time. By international agreement, one second equals exactly 9,192,631,770 cycles of a particular vibration of an atom of cesium-133, an isotope of the element cesium. Atomic clocks count these vibrations to keep the time of day. The second forms the basis for other familiar units of time. Sixty seconds make up a minute. An hour consists of exactly 60 minutes, or 3,600 seconds. Twenty-four hours, or 86,400 seconds, make up one day.

Most nations employ a 24-hour clock, with noon marked as 1200 and midnight as 2400 or 0000. In the United States, the military, the police, airlines, and many other groups use this system. However, most people in the United States favor a 12-hour scale, with the first hour of the day ending at 1:00 a.m. and 11:00 p.m. beginning

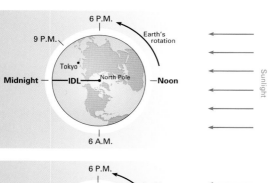
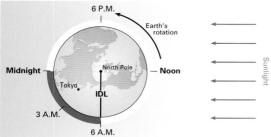

WORLD BOOK diagram

The time and date at any place on Earth change as Earth rotates on its axis in relation to the sun. When the International Date Line (IDL) is on the opposite side of Earth from the sun, *top diagram,* it is midnight there and 9 p.m. in Tokyo. At this instant, every place on Earth has the same date. Six hours later, *bottom diagram,* as Earth continues to rotate, it is 6 a.m. at the IDL. A new day, *shown in red,* has begun in the area between the IDL and midnight. The time in Tokyo is 3 a.m.

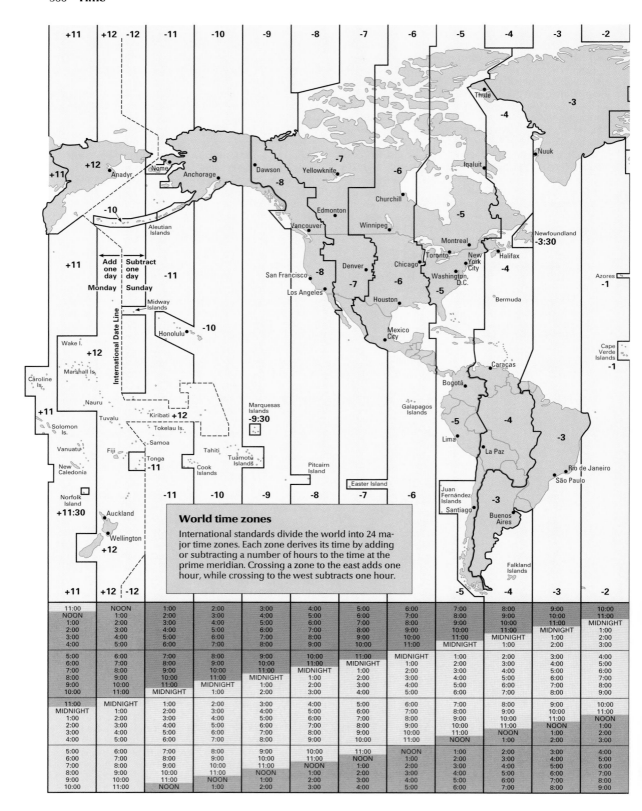

World time zones

International standards divide the world into 24 major time zones. Each zone derives its time by adding or subtracting a number of hours to the time at the prime meridian. Crossing a zone to the east adds one hour, while crossing to the west subtracts one hour.

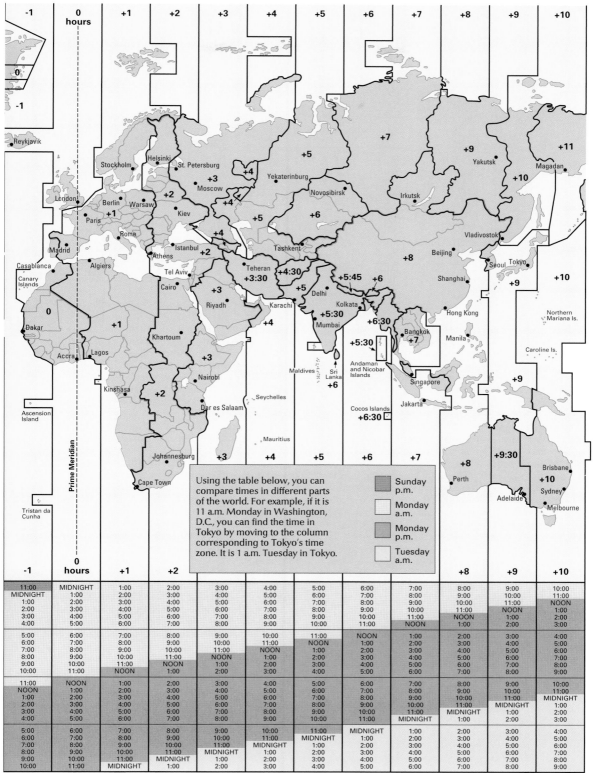

-1	0 hours	+1	+2	+3	+4	+5	+6	+7	+8	+9	+10
11:00	MIDNIGHT	1:00	2:00	3:00	4:00	5:00	6:00	7:00	8:00	9:00	10:00
MIDNIGHT	1:00	2:00	3:00	4:00	5:00	6:00	7:00	8:00	9:00	10:00	11:00
1:00	2:00	3:00	4:00	5:00	6:00	7:00	8:00	9:00	10:00	11:00	NOON
2:00	3:00	4:00	5:00	6:00	7:00	8:00	9:00	10:00	11:00	NOON	1:00
3:00	4:00	5:00	6:00	7:00	8:00	9:00	10:00	11:00	NOON	1:00	2:00
4:00	5:00	6:00	7:00	8:00	9:00	10:00	11:00	NOON	1:00	2:00	3:00
5:00	6:00	7:00	8:00	9:00	10:00	11:00	NOON	1:00	2:00	3:00	4:00
6:00	7:00	8:00	9:00	10:00	11:00	NOON	1:00	2:00	3:00	4:00	5:00
7:00	8:00	9:00	10:00	11:00	NOON	1:00	2:00	3:00	4:00	5:00	6:00
8:00	9:00	10:00	11:00	NOON	1:00	2:00	3:00	4:00	5:00	6:00	7:00
9:00	10:00	11:00	NOON	1:00	2:00	3:00	4:00	5:00	6:00	7:00	8:00
10:00	11:00	NOON	1:00	2:00	3:00	4:00	5:00	6:00	7:00	8:00	9:00
11:00	NOON	1:00	2:00	3:00	4:00	5:00	6:00	7:00	8:00	9:00	10:00
NOON	1:00	2:00	3:00	4:00	5:00	6:00	7:00	8:00	9:00	10:00	11:00
1:00	2:00	3:00	4:00	5:00	6:00	7:00	8:00	9:00	10:00	11:00	MIDNIGHT
2:00	3:00	4:00	5:00	6:00	7:00	8:00	9:00	10:00	11:00	MIDNIGHT	1:00
3:00	4:00	5:00	6:00	7:00	8:00	9:00	10:00	11:00	MIDNIGHT	1:00	2:00
4:00	5:00	6:00	7:00	8:00	9:00	10:00	11:00	MIDNIGHT	1:00	2:00	3:00
5:00	6:00	7:00	8:00	9:00	10:00	11:00	MIDNIGHT	1:00	2:00	3:00	4:00
6:00	7:00	8:00	9:00	10:00	11:00	MIDNIGHT	1:00	2:00	3:00	4:00	5:00
7:00	8:00	9:00	10:00	11:00	MIDNIGHT	1:00	2:00	3:00	4:00	5:00	6:00
8:00	9:00	10:00	11:00	MIDNIGHT	1:00	2:00	3:00	4:00	5:00	6:00	7:00
9:00	10:00	11:00	MIDNIGHT	1:00	2:00	3:00	4:00	5:00	6:00	7:00	8:00
10:00	11:00	MIDNIGHT	1:00	2:00	3:00	4:00	5:00	6:00	7:00	8:00	9:00

Using the table below, you can compare times in different parts of the world. For example, if it is 11 a.m. Monday in Washington, D.C, you can find the time in Tokyo by moving to the column corresponding to Tokyo's time zone. It is 1 a.m. Tuesday in Tokyo.

Sunday p.m.

Monday a.m.

Monday p.m.

Tuesday a.m.

WORLD BOOK map

Time in relativity theory

The experience of time in relativity in some ways resembles slicing a loaf of bread. The "loaf" represents all the events that occur throughout *space-time* (the combination of space and time). Each "slice" contains the events that happen at a single moment. Just as a loaf of bread can be sliced any number of ways, observers can experience space-time differently depending on their states of motion. For an observer in one state of motion, events B and C might occur at the same moment, *left*. An observer in another state of motion would experience the same events differently. For that observer, event B might occur before event C, *right*.

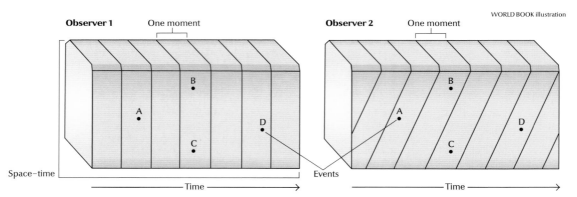

WORLD BOOK illustration

the last hour of the day. To avoid confusion over whether to use a.m. or p.m., people often refer to noon as *12:00 noon* and midnight as *12:00 midnight*.

Local and standard time. Traditionally, people determined time locally, using the sun. Each town set a main clock to noon when the sun reached its highest point overhead. Because of the sun's apparent east-to-west motion, towns separated by a hundred miles could have local times that differed by several minutes.

People relied on local time until after the development of the telegraph and the railroad in the 1800's. Trains could travel between places with noticeably different local times in a couple of hours, and telegraphs crossed these distances nearly instantly. Using a different local time for each place made it nearly impossible to maintain communications and railroad schedules.

In the United States and other countries, the railroad industry promoted the use of *standard time*. In this system, all towns in a certain region, called a *time zone*, share the same time. Further, the time in two adjacent time zones differs by exactly one hour. Time signals sent by telegraph would enable distant places to synchronize their clocks, replacing the practice of setting clocks by the sun. Railroads in the United States adopted this system in the 1880's, and despite objections from a variety of people, it quickly became the informal standard for most of the country. In 1918, the U.S. Congress formally enacted the system of time zones used in the United States today. About the same time, nations around the world began to adopt standard time systems.

International time zones. As standard time became widespread, governments and shipping companies worked to develop a uniform system of international time zones. Encouraged by the development of radio communications and airplane travel, nearly all nations had adopted the current system by 1950.

The international system of time zones takes as its reference point the *prime meridian,* the north-south

line designated as 0° longitude that runs through Greenwich, England. All other places derive their time from the time at the prime meridian. Moving east, each successive zone adds one hour to the time. Traveling west, each zone subtracts one hour. Standard time zones generally span about 15 degrees of longitude each. However, their borders zigzag somewhat to avoid dividing individual communities or regions into different time zones. Some nations deviate from the standard system.

A line called the International Date Line helps the international system of time zones to function properly. Under the system, a traveler flying west subtracts one hour from the clock for each time zone crossed. If the traveler moved fast enough, eventually the clock would return to the previous day. To counteract this problem, travelers add a full day when crossing the International Date Line from east to west. Likewise, they subtract a full day when passing in the opposite direction. The International Date Line runs opposite the prime meridian, roughly following the meridian of 180° longitude.

Coordinated Universal Time, abbreviated UTC, serves as the standard international time. By definition, UTC is the time at the prime meridian as measured by atomic clocks. Other time zones derive their time by adding or subtracting a whole number of hours to UTC.

Although UTC relies on atomic clocks rather than the motion of the sun, scientists work to keep UTC synchronized with solar time. They occasionally add or subtract a leap second to make sure that UTC and solar time never differ by more than 0.9 second.

Our understanding of time

As you read this sentence—right now—you are experiencing the present. Now, the event of reading the last sentence is already fading into the past, and new events are becoming part of the present.

The simple act of reading the previous paragraph

reveals three important features of our experience of time. First, we sense that the present is somehow special. The present moment seems more vivid or even more real than other times. Second, we tend to think of time as moving or flowing, with present events continuously updating themselves. Third, we seem able to remember the past but not the future. As you read the second sentence, you remembered the first sentence but had no memories of the sentences that followed.

A fourth aspect of our experience of time is that time often appears to flow at a varying rate. For example, an hour of a dull class may seem much longer than an hour of playing outside, even if a clock shows that both activities lasted the same amount of time.

These seemingly simple characteristics lead to difficult questions about time. For instance, do moments of time "flow" by, and if so, how? Why does time seem to proceed in only one direction, and is it possible to move backward in time? Are the past, present, and future really different? The search for answers to such questions has helped scholars to refine their ideas about time.

Time in classical physics. To aid in his studies of motion, the English scientist Sir Isaac Newton assigned various precise properties to time. In doing so, Newton became perhaps the first person to propose a detailed formal model of time. Newton considered moments of time to be similar to the numbers on a number line. In such a model, one moment comes after another in sequence. At least one moment exists between any other two moments, and time has no beginning or end. Despite our perceptions, Newton proposed that the "flow" of time is *uniform*—that is, that one hour lasts as long as any other. He warned against confusing our perception or measurement of time with the passage of time itself.

Newton's view relied on two seemingly reasonable assumptions that later proved controversial. First, it assumed that motion did not affect the passing of time. For example, suppose Alice and Bob left school at the same time. Alice went to soccer practice, while Bob visited the library. They met again at dinner. In Newton's view, Alice and Bob would experience the same amount of time between school and dinner despite their separate paths.

Second, Newton's view assumed that all observers could agree on whether two events were *simultaneous*—that is, whether they happened at the same time. If one person observed Alice scoring a goal just as Bob dropped a book, then all other witnesses would agree that the two events were simultaneous.

In some ways, Newton's view of time resembles a deck of cards. Each card represents the universe at one moment and contains all the simultaneous events occurring at that moment. When the cards are placed in order, the deck represents our experience of time. Just as the deck can be divided easily into cards, all observers can agree on the moment at which each event happens.

Time in relativity theory. In the early 1900's, the German-born physicist Albert Einstein developed a new branch of physics called *relativity theory*. His work revised many basic ideas about time. Perhaps most importantly, relativity theory holds that space and time are not fundamentally separate features of reality. Instead, they compose a four-dimensional array of events called *space-time*. In space-time, observers measure space and time differently depending on their state of motion.

Relativity theory overturned Newton's assumptions. First, it showed that the amount of time between events depends on an observer's motion through space. If Alice and Bob leave school, go their separate ways, and meet again for dinner, they will not necessarily experience the same amount of time between school and dinner.

Second, observers can disagree on whether events are simultaneous. Consider Alice's goal and Bob's dropping of the book. A person in one state of motion—perhaps sitting on the sidelines—may witness the two events occurring simultaneously. A person flying overhead in an airplane, on the other hand, might see Alice score the goal before Bob drops the book. A person flying in the opposite direction could see the goal being scored after the book is dropped. In relativity theory, all three observations can be correct. The observers' motion merely causes them to experience time differently.

At relatively low speeds, motion has an extremely small effect on time, so Alice, Bob, and the others probably would not notice the difference. However, experiments have confirmed the predictions of relativity theory. For example, atomic clocks traveling on supersonic jet planes tick more slowly than do clocks on the ground. In a sense, time seems to pass more slowly for a moving object than for an object at rest. This "stretching" of time, called *time dilation,* can result from motion or from the gravitational pull of a massive object.

If time in classical physics is like a deck of cards, the space-time of relativity more closely resembles a freshly baked loaf of bread. Just as the deck can be divided into cards, the loaf can be cut into "slices" representing moments. However, different observers can disagree as to which events happen at each moment, so there is no single correct way to slice the bread.

Time travel. Relativity theory appears to allow for various kinds of time travel. Imagine that Alice left Earth for a round trip in a high-speed rocket. Because of time dilation, Alice would age slower than would Bob, who stayed on Earth. Depending on the rocket's speed, Alice might experience only 10 years of travel but return to find 50 years had passed for Bob. In a sense, Alice would have "traveled" into Bob's future.

According to relativity theory, travel into the past may also be possible. The theory states that gravity represents a curvature in space-time. The mathematics of relativity allows for many kinds of space-time. Some theoretically possible space-times can become so curved that an observer moving into an event's future could eventually arrive at times in the event's past. Other potential space-times offer a traveler even greater freedom. With enough energy, an observer in such a space-time could travel from any event to any other event, regardless of whether the destination lies in the past, present, or future.

Scientists do not know whether travel into the past is possible in our space-time, but the idea poses challenges for our understanding of reality. Suppose, for example, that Bob traveled into the past and killed his grandfather, preventing one of his parents from being born. Bob would not have been born either, but then who would have killed the grandfather? Scientists and philosophers call this famous dilemma the *grandfather paradox*. The paradox does not imply that time travel is impossible, but it does seem to prevent a time traveler from performing certain actions while visiting the past.

Arrows of time. The basic laws of physics do not require that time proceed in a particular direction. If a particle can move from left to right, for example, it can also move right to left. When the first motion is viewed with time reversed, it appears identical to the second motion. In basic physics, these two scenarios cannot be distinguished. The same laws hold true whether time proceeds in one direction or the other.

In our everyday lives, on the other hand, time seems to proceed in a set direction. Imagine watching a film in which a dropped teacup shatters into fragments. This might strike you as a common scene. Now picture the film playing in reverse. You probably would be surprised to see the fragments assemble themselves into a teacup. Although the same basic laws hold true for both actions, experience tells us that the action in the second film violates time's usual progression.

How does time's apparent one-way flow arise from basic laws that do not favor a particular direction? This question ranks as one of the most enduring mysteries of time. In studying this puzzle, scientists and philosophers have identified many processes like the breaking of a teacup that seem to proceed in only one direction. These *arrows of time* indicate the direction in which time proceeds and help explain what distinguishes the past from the future.

Many arrows of time appear in our daily experiences. The *arrow of memory* arises from our ability to remember our past but not our future. The *arrow of knowledge* extends this distinction to facts outside our personal experience. For example, we can know with near certainty that dinosaurs lived 200 million years ago, but we have no idea what creatures will thrive 200 million years from now. The observation that causes precede their effects gives rise to *the arrow of causality*. We tend to believe that we can change the future but not the past. This distinction is sometimes called the *arrow of change*.

Other arrows of time come from the sciences. Perhaps the most important arrow arises from the *second law of thermodynamics*. According to this law, the *entropy* of a closed system will always increase. Entropy is a measure of the amount of a system's energy that is unavailable for work. In a sense, the available energy of a system "runs down" as entropy increases. The system may also appear to grow more disordered.

The arrow of entropy explains why ice water warms to room temperature, gas spreads throughout its container, and cream mixes into coffee. In all of these processes, entropy increases with time. The arrow of entropy can also explain why shattered fragments do not assemble themselves into teacups. Such a scenario would result in an overall decrease in entropy, violating the second law of thermodynamics.

Scientific investigation has revealed other arrows of time. Light and other radiation spread outward from a given source but never come back together, giving rise to the *arrow of radiation*. The *cosmological arrow* arises from the fact that the universe continually expands.

Scientists and philosophers do not know for sure how the various arrows of time relate to one another. Some scholars have suggested that most or all of the other arrows derive from the arrow of entropy.

The past, present, and future. In common experience, the present seems somehow more real than the past or future. The past feels somewhat real in the sense that we can remember it and observe its effect on the present. However, it does not surround us as the present does, and we do not experience it as vividly. To most people, the future seems even less real because we cannot know it and our choices may alter it. These observations have led some scholars to conclude that only the present and perhaps the past can be said to exist.

Relativity theory casts doubt on the distinction between past, present, and future. In relativity theory, observers cannot always agree on which events make up a single moment. Thus, it makes little sense to insist that a unique moment called the present exists. What one observer experiences as the present can include events from another observer's past, present, and future.

In fact, relativity theory appears to imply that the past, present, and future actually exist as an unbroken four-dimensional "block" of space-time. In this view, the future is somewhat like a distant city to which we are traveling—it exists even though we have not reached it yet. Scholars are not quite sure how to reconcile this idea with the widely held notion that our actions and choices can alter the future. Craig A. Callender and Thomas R. O'Brian

Outline

I. **Measuring time**
 A. Astronomical cycles
 B. Artificial clocks
 C. Natural processes
II. **Time in today's world**
 A. Units of time
 B. Local and standard time
 C. International time zones
 D. Coordinated Universal Time
III. **Our understanding of time**
 A. Time in classical physics
 B. Time in relativity theory
 C. Time travel
 D. Arrows of time
 E. The past, present, and future

Questions

What is the fundamental unit of time in modern society?
Does relativity theory imply that only the present moment exists?
What repeated actions do atomic clocks count?
Which measure of time is based on the phases of the moon?
What famous dilemma seems to place limits on the actions a time traveler can perform in the past?
What kind of time do sun clocks measure?
According to the second law of thermodynamics, how does entropy change with time?
Why do the borders of time zones zigzag?
What is *time dilation?*
What time serves as the basis for Coordinated Universal Time?

Additional resources

Adam, Barbara. *Time*. Polity Pr., 2004.
Gardner, Robert. *Experimenting with Time*. Watts, 1995.
Lippincott, Kristen, and others. *The Story of Time*. Merrell Holberton, 1999.
Skurzynski, Gloria. *On Time*. National Geographic Soc., 2000. Younger readers.

INDEX

How to use the index

The "see" and "see also" cross-references refer the reader to other entries in the index. For example, information on **Astronauts** and **Astronomy** will be found under the headings indicated.

A page number in italics means that there is an article on this topic on the page or pages indicated. For example, there is an Update article on **Atmospheric science** on pages 170-176. The page numbers in roman type indicate additional references to this topic in other articles.

When there are several references to a topic, they are grouped alphabetically by clue words under the main topic. For example, the clue words under **Automobile** group the references to that topic under three subtopics.

An entry followed by "reprint" refers to a new or revised article in the supplement section, as in **Aztec.** This means that there is an article on pages 270-275.

The indications (il.) and (ils.) mean that the reference on these pages is to an illustration only, as in **Bangladesh.**

ACKNOWLEDGMENTS

The publishers gratefully acknowledge the courtesy of the following artists, photographers, publishers, institutions, agencies, and corporations for the illustrations in this volume. Credits are listed from top to bottom, left to right, on their respective pages. Entries marked with an asterisk (*) denote illustrations created exclusively for this yearbook. All maps, charts, and diagrams were prepared by our staff unless otherwise noted.

6	Jacques Descloitres, MODIS Land Rapid Response Team, NASA/GSFC	50	Marie Dacke; Rolin Graphics Inc*
7	Dale Debolt*	52	Professor Thomas D. Seeley; © Scott Camazine, Photo Researchers
8	© Landov; © Joerg Carstensen, epa/Corbis	54	Scott Bauer, USDA Agricultural Research Service (www.insectimages.org)
9	© Reuters/Landov	56-58	© OceanStock
10	Chandler Wilkerson, Institute for Molecular Design, University of Houston	59	NOAA; © OceanStock
12	WORLD BOOK illustration by Alton S. Tobey	60-63	© OceanStock
13	© age fotostock/SuperStock	64	AP/Wide World; © OceanStock; AP/Wide World
15	Ortelius Design, Inc.*	65	AP/Wide World; NOAA
16	© S. Claessens, dpa/Landov	66	© OceanStock; NOAA
17-18	AP/Wide World	67	© David Boynton Photography; Na'alehu Anthony
19	© Heather Hurst, National Geographic Society; © Kenneth Garrett, National Geographic Society; © Dan Foley, National Geographic Society	68-69	© OceanStock
		70-71	AP/Wide World
		72	NPS
21	© Della Zuana Pascal, Sygma/Corbis	73	John Good, NPS; AP/Wide World
22	© Kenneth Garrett, National Geographic Society; © John R. Anderson, National Geographic Society	74	Alan Barnett Design*; Yuan, H. and K. Dueker (2005). "P-wave Tomogram of the Yellowstone plume." Geophys. Res. Lett., 32, doi:10.1029/2004GL022056
23	© Kenneth Garrett, National Geographic Society	77	WORLD BOOK illustration by Rob Wood
26	© Mark Garlick, Science Photo Library	78	USGS
27-29	Chicos Project/California Institute of Technology	79	S.R. Brantley, USGS
30	AP/Wide World; © Dana Berry/NASA/The Image Works; © Science Photo Library	81	© Landov; William S. Keller, NPS
		82	AP/Wide World; © Hal Beral, V&W/ The Image Works
32-33	Rolin Graphics Inc*	83-84	AP/Wide World
34	AP/Wide World	86-87	© Landov
36	© Landov; © Tomasz Barszczak, Science Photo Library; © Collaboration/Science Photo Library	89	Alan Barnett Design*
		90	World Health Organization; March of Dimes Defects Foundation
37	Pierre Auger Observatory	91	Library of Congress; March of Dimes Birth Defects Foundation
38-40	Chicos Project/California Institute of Technology	92-96	AP/Wide World
42	AP/Wide World	97	© Jean-Marc Giboux
43	Francis Ratnieks	98	© Michael A. Schwarz, The Image Works
45	WORLD BOOK illustration by James Teason	100	© PhotoDisc/Getty Images; AP/Wide World
46	© PA Photos/Landov	101	AP/Wide World; © Matsushita-Fujifotos/The Image Works
47	© Joe Songer, Newhouse News Service/Landov	103	© Jim West/The Image Works
49	AP/Wide World	104	© Alex Hinds, Shutterstock